M000312275

# A Spacefaring Nation

# A Spacefaring Nation

*Perspectives*

*on American*

*Space History*

*and Policy*

**Edited by Martin J. Collins and Sylvia D. Fries**

*Smithsonian Institution Press   Washington and London*

Copyright © 1991 by Smithsonian Institution
All rights reserved

Edited by Robin A. Gould
Designed by Lisa Buck Vann

Library of Congress Cataloging-in-Publication Data
A Spacefaring nation : perspectives on American space history and policy / edited
by Martin J. Collins, Sylvia Doughty Fries.
p. cm.
Papers from a conference at the Smithsonian Institution's National Air and Space
Museum, spring 1987, sponsored by the museum and the National Aeronautics and
Space Administration.
ISBN 0-87474-907-7
1. Astronautics—United States—History—Congresses.
I. Collins, Martin J.
II. Fries, Sylvia Doughty.
III. National Air and Space Museum.
IV. United States. National Aeronautics and Space Administration.
TL789.8.U5S63   1991
333.9'4'0973—dc20   90—9762

British Library Cataloguing-in-Publication Data available
Manufactured in the United States of America
5 4 3 2 1
98 97 96 95 94 93 92 91

⊗The paper used in this publication meets the minimum requirements of the American National Standard for Permanence of Paper for Printed Library Materials
Z39.48—1984.

By permission of Indiana University Press, portions of "Space Technology and Planetary Science, 1950–1985" are reprinted from Joseph N. Tatarewicz, *Space Technology and Planetary Science* (Bloomington: Indiana University Press, 1990).
By permission of MIT Press, portions of "Research and Development for Whose
Benefit" are reprinted from Pamela E. Mack, *Viewing the Earth: The Social Construction of the Landsat Satellite System* (Cambridge, Mass.: MIT Press, 1990).

# Contents

# Preface

Communication among scholars looking at recent history is complicated by a number of factors—a lack of easily accessible documentation, perspectives issuing from a number of disciplines, and few formal venues for the sharing and comparing of ideas. For these same reasons, however, recent history becomes especially intriguing—the story is not yet codified and different analysts may have sharply contrasting accounts derived from conflicting primary sources. When this recent history involves large institutions—like the government or the military—the sharing of research and ideas from a variety of disciplines becomes even more compelling, but often difficult to achieve among the different spheres of academia, government, and private industry. Occasional seminars and symposia have helped aerospace historians bridge these institutional and disciplinary divides and share perspectives on the American adventure in air and space.

Several years ago the National Aeronautics and Space Administration published *A Spacefaring People: Perspectives on Early Spaceflight,* which shared with a wide readership interested in the history of spaceflight the proceedings of a space history conference held in 1981 at Yale University. That conference (jointly sponsored by NASA and Yale University) and the publication that arose from it illustrated the range of interests and talents brought by historians, writers, journalists and policy scholars to the daunting task of recording and interpreting the first era of human space exploration.

The present volume arises from a conference at the Smithsonian Institution's National Air and Space Museum in Washington, D.C., in the spring of 1987, under the joint sponsorship of the National Air and Space Museum and NASA. Designed to place the U.S. space program in broad historical perspective, the seminar's participants and attendees included NASA historians and contract historians, NASM staff, guest scholars, and others. In general, the meeting was organized to provide flight and space historians with an intimate but structured forum for (1) exchanging and reviewing research results, (2) meeting with scholars from other disciplines and other areas of the history of science and technology, and (3) relating research in aviation and space history to broader concerns in American cultural and social history.

The two-day seminar included four sessions, with two presenters in each session followed by prepared commentary and general discussion. Papers were distributed to participants prior to the seminar, and discussion was often lively and wide-ranging. Coming from a variety of institutional settings and historiographic perspectives, the presenters shared insights, research suggestions, and, sometimes, disagreements. To convey the spirit of the presentations, we have reprinted the formal papers substantially as given.

The presentations and commentary reveal the depth and sophistication of current scholarship in aerospace history. The results of the earlier 1981 conference—while covering broad themes in space science, technology, management, and policy—were clearly preliminary and exploratory. Readers of the present volume will recognize far greater attention to the institutional and political dynamics that, historians now appear to agree, have done as much as technical innovation itself to shape the character of America's ventures into the new frontiers of flight and space travel. The increased attention to nontechnical factors in the evolution of postwar science and technology stems from a heightened appreciation of the dominant role of government in sponsoring, supporting, and directing a broad spectrum of research and development projects. These projects have been implemented through complex and extensive links among government, industry, universities, and other organizations. The changes in the landscape of science and technology resulting from such government policy is emerging as a central and unifying theme of the history of aviation and space.

The editors are indebted to all the conference participants for their insights and for preparing their conference papers for this volume.

Martin J. Collins
National Air and Space Museum

Sylvia Doughty Fries
National Aeronautics and Space Administration

Spring 1990

# Acknowledgments

The editors would like to thank the National Aeronautics and Space Administration, the NASA History Office, and the National Air and Space Museum and its Glennan-Webb-Seamans Project for Research in Space History for their support in sponsoring the seminar and this publication.

# Participants

### *William E. Burrows*

William E. Burrows's most recent book is *Exploring Space: Voyages in the Solar System and Beyond* (1990). His contribution for this volume was based on his research for *Deep Black: Space Espionage and National Security* (1986), a historical and policy study of the United States space reconnaissance activities. He has written about aviation and space flight for more than two decades, reporting for *The New York Times, The Washington Post, The Wall Street Journal,* and *The Richmond Times-Dispatch.* Mr. Burrows's articles have also appeared in *Foreign Affairs, The New York Times Magazine, Harvard Magazine, The Sciences,* and *Harper's.* He holds two degrees in international politics from Columbia University and is presently a professor of journalism and director of the Science and Environmental Reporting Program at New York University.

### *Martin J. Collins*

Martin J. Collins is chief of the Oral History and Research Support Section and co-director of the Glennan-Webb-Seamans Project for Research in Space History in the Department of Space History, National Air and Space Museum, Smithsonian Institution. He is presently a Ph.D. candidate at the University of Maryland. His dissertation research is an institutional history of the RAND Corporation, emphasizing its role in Air Force planning and decision-making and its relation to other scientific and technical advisory and policy bodies in the postwar period. His publications include *Bibliography of the History of Geophysics* [with S. G. Brush and H. Landsberg] (1985) and general editor, *Directory of Sources for Air and Space History*, preliminary edition (1989).

### Virginia P. Dawson

A 1983 recipient of a doctorate in the history of science and technology from Case Western Reserve University, Dr. Dawson has recently completed a history of NASA's Lewis Research Center entitled *Engines and Innovation: Lewis Laboratory and American Propulsion Technology* to be published in NASA's special publication series. In 1988, Dr. Dawson was awarded the Robert H. Goddard Essay Award. Prior to her NASA-sponsored research, Dr. Dawson taught at Case Western Reserve University. Her numerous papers and publications include a book on eighteenth-century biology, *Nature's Enigma* (1987), and a study of technology transfer from Germany to the United States, "From Braunschweig to Ohio: Ernst Eckert and Government Heat Transfer Research," in a special volume published by the American Society of Mechanical Engineers *Journal of Heat Transfer* (1988). She is currently a visiting professor at Oberlin College.

### Sylvia Doughty Fries

Sylvia Doughty Fries was chief historian and director of the History Division at the National Aeronautics and Space Administration from 1983 to 1990, when she was appointed executive secretary of the NASA Advisory Council. She had been a member of the NASA Advisory Council from 1981 to 1983, when she came to NASA to direct the history program, which has been in continuous existence since the agency was first established in 1958.

A native of Germany, Dr. Fries was raised and educated in Washington, D.C. She received her bachelor's degree in English from Hollins College and her doctorate in the history of ideas from The Johns Hopkins University in 1969. She then pursued a typical academic career, teaching European and American cultural history at Vassar College, Southern Methodist University, and the University of Maine at Orono.

Meanwhile, her research and writing evolved from eighteenth-century ideas of urban life to the ideological origins of federal science and technology policy during the late 1960s. Her publications include *The Urban Idea in Colonial America* (1977), *NASA Engineers and the Age of Apollo* (forthcoming), and "2001 to 1994: Political Environment and the Design of NASA's Space Station System," *Technology and Culture* (July 1988), winner of the James Madison Prize of the Society for History in the Federal Government.

### Thomas F. Gieryn

Dr. Gieryn is associate professor of sociology at Indiana University, and director of its program on scientific dimensions of society. He received his doctorate from Columbia University, with a dissertation on career patterns in "problem-choices" by post-World War II American astronomers. Recently, he has investigated a series of episodes where the boundaries of science were contested, and he hopes to gather those studies in a book, *Making Space for Sciences: Volume One, Cultural Cartography.*

### Richard P. Hallion

Dr. Hallion is deputy chief of the Secretary of the Air Force's Action Group, Headquarters United States Air Force, The Pentagon, Washington, D.C. He was appointed the Charles A. Lindbergh Professor of Aerospace History at the National Air and Space Museum, Smithsonian Institution, for the 1990–1991 academic year. After earning his doctorate in history from the University of Maryland, he served as curator of Science and Technology, and subsequently Space Science and Exploration, for the National Air and Space Museum. Since 1981 he has worked in a variety of capacities for the USAF, and has taught on the faculties of the University of Maryland, Chapman College, and the U.S. Army War College. He is the author of thirteen books in aerospace history, the most recent of which is *Strike From the Sky: The History of Battlefield Air Attack,* the inaugural volume of the Smithsonian History of Aviation series.

### James R. Hansen

A member of the history faculty at Auburn University, Dr. Hansen has recently published two major works in the history of American aeronautics, *Engineer in Charge: A History of the Langley Aeronautical Laboratory, 1917–1958* (1987), and *From the Ground Up: The Autobiography of an Aeronautical Engineer* (1988), which he co-authored. Dr. Hansen received his doctorate in the history of science from The Ohio State University. A recipient of the Robert H. Goddard Essay Award and the Air Force Historical Foundation Award, Dr. Hansen is currently working on a history of NASA's Langley Research Center from 1958 through 1975.

### *Karl Hufbauer*

After taking a B.S. in engineering science at Stanford University and a Diploma in history and philosophy of science at Oxford University, Karl Hufbauer earned his Ph.D. in the history of science at the University of California, Berkeley. Since then, he has been a member of the history department at the University of California, Irvine. His special interest has been the history of discipline building and inter-disciplinarity in the physical sciences. Among his publications are *The Formation of the German Chemical Community, 1720–1795* (1982) and *Exploring the Sun: Solar Science Since Galileo* (in press), a book sponsored by the National Aeronautics and Space Administration.

### *W. Henry Lambright*

Dr. Lambright is director of the Science and Technology Policy Center of Syracuse Research Corporation and professor of political science and public administration at The Maxwell School of Syracuse University. His many publications include a book-length study of presidential management of science and technology during the presidency of Lyndon B. Johnson and the now classic *Governing Science and Technology* (1976). He has contributed to numerous collections of essays on the management of research and development in the United States, including a study of former NASA administrator James E. Webb and the role of leadership in federal support for technology innovation.

### Pamela Mack

An associate professor of history at Clemson University, Dr. Mack teaches courses in the history of technology and science. She received her doctorate in history and sociology of science from the University of Pennsylvania. Dr. Mack has published *Viewing the Earth: The Social Construction of the Landsat Satellite Project* (1990) and is presently working on a study of women scientists in nineteenth-century America.

### Howard E. McCurdy

Professor of public affairs at The American University, Dr. McCurdy is the author of a major textbook and two widely used bibliographic guides to the literature of public administration, as well as a popular introduction to congressional politics. His many articles have appeared in such journals as *Psychology Today, Policy Studies Journal,* and *Public Administration Review.* He has recently completed, under NASA sponsorship, a history of NASA's Space Station Task Force and is currently working on a history of NASA's organizational culture.

### Jeffrey Richelson

Dr. Richelson is presently an author and consultant. He has published extensively on the U.S. and foreign intelligence communities. His books include *America's Secret Eyes in Space* (1990), *American Espionage and the Soviet Target* (1987), *The U.S. Intelligence Community* (1985), and, with Desmond Ball, *The Ties That Bind: Intelligence Cooperation Between the UKUSA Countries* (1985).

### Robert W. Smith

Dr. Smith is a historian in the Department of Space History at the National Air and Space Museum, Smithsonian Institution, and an associate professor (part-time) in the Department of the History of Science at The Johns Hopkins University. Trained in the history and philosophy of science at the University of Cambridge, his publications include *The Expanding Universe: Astronomy's 'Great Debate,' 1900–1931* (1982), and *The Space Telescope: A Study of NASA, Science, Technology, and Politics* (1989).

## *Joseph N. Tatarewicz*

Curator in the Department of Space History at the National Air and Space Museum, Smithsonian Institution, Dr. Tatarewicz received his doctorate in history and philosophy of science from Indiana University. His dissertation, *Space Technology and Planetary Astronomy,* will be published by Indiana University Press in 1990. He was also a contributor to *The Space Telescope: A Study of NASA, Science, Technology, and Politics* (1989).

# Space Policy and Decision-Making

# Introduction

If the civilian space program in the United States has ever enjoyed a heyday, it has so far been brief. The measure of popular enthusiasm for any national program that matters is what the Congress — mediating the tug and pull of many constituencies — is willing to spend. In the first decade of the American space program, the 1960s, the percentage of the country's expenses that the Congress was prepared to devote to a civilian space program was nine times larger in 1965 than it had been in 1960. But within a year of the Apollo 11 Moon landing (July 21, 1969), the country sighed in relative disinterest and put its money on more urgent matters; civil space projects received less than half the funding of 1965. By 1985 the percent of federal expenditures represented by the civil space budget was barely above the 1960 level.[1]

The "more urgent matters," of course, were the rising costs of the war in Southeast Asia and fulfilling President Lyndon B. Johnson's vision of a "Great Society" with ambitious programs. And, like an unwelcome visitor stalking the night, the first federal deficit in peacetime began to mount at a rate that alarmed many economy watchers during the administrations of presidents Richard M. Nixon (1969–1974), Gerald R. Ford (1974–1977), and Ronald Reagan (1981–1989).[2] Occupants of the White House could propose what they liked, but the Congress would dispose as it saw fit.

The essays that follow trace how supporters of two ambitious NASA space initiatives — its most technically complex (the Large Space Telescope) and its largest (the Space Station) — struggled to build the constituency backing and political momentum necessary to

**3**

fund their programs. The advocates of each of these programs had
been themselves the creation of the Cold War "space race" between
the two major superpowers that emerged victorious from World War
II.

In the United States, advances in rocketry enabled astronomers
to dream of observing the heavens—the invisible as well as visible
spectra—from above the murky atmosphere that surrounded Earth.
Meanwhile, those who dreamed of extending the romance of human
flight outward into space had found a niche in NASA and, though
momentarily sidetracked into a Moon landing expedition, continued
to hope for a Space Station to serve as an orbiting base for human
space travel.

The Large Space Telescope (renamed Hubble Space Telescope in
1983 after astronomer Edwin P. Hubble) is actually an orbiting observatory. Discussed among astronomers in the 1960s, it was first
seriously proposed by the National Academy of Sciences in 1969.
The initiative thus came from the scientific community and it is the
story of that initiative, as its supporters negotiated their way through
NASA's programmatic concerns and tackled the mixture of preoccu-
pations motivating the Congress, that Robert Smith tells. His emphasis is on the 1974–1977 efforts of the telescope's constituencies to
get a workable level of funding from the Congress to build their
observatory—and the compromises that had to be made before they
could succeed. He places those efforts within the context of the
search by astronomers to find patrons for their enterprise. In this
case, the patrons were NASA, the White House's Office of Management and Budget, and the U.S. Congress.

Howard McCurdy's essay on the "selling" of the Space Station
describes not so much the efforts of an ad hoc coalition as those of
an internal NASA group—the Space Station Task Force—to persuade
the White House to adopt the station as a key feature of its own
program for space exploration. His analysis includes a comparison of
the White House decision to support a space station program with
the decisions to proceed with a manned lunar landing program (the
Apollo Program) and with the Space Transportation System, or
"Space Shuttle."

In the course of his essay, McCurdy points out that in theory,
at least, government agencies (of which NASA is but one) are not intended to advocate new programs. In fact, however, the long-term
exigencies of major technical programs and the expectation of "lead-

ership" by NASA in both the White House and the Congress virtually requires the agency to define and promote new programs. In the case of the Space Station, the initiative came from within NASA, nourished by a vision that predated both the Apollo and the Shuttle programs. A distinctive feature of its advocates' efforts to win White House approval was the degree to which their strategy was shaped by a lesson learned from the two earlier programs: NASA should not, as it sought White House and congressional approval, be willing to negotiate technical design as the price of constituency support. But what could be seen as an important measure of professional accountability made it difficult for NASA to obtain the firm political commitment to the program necessary to proceed.

Engineers and scientists, along with other professionals, hold dear the notion of professional autonomy. It is a notion that has made it difficult for Americans to accept what most see as the growing incursion of politics into technical and scientific choice. Both these essays suggest that as long as any costly scientific or technical program must compete for public funds in a democratic society, politics, not pure professional judgment (if such a thing is even possible), will have much to do with the final character of a technical program. Whenever the allocation of scarce resources is at issue, the rules of politics may be as compelling as the laws of physics.

Large space projects, such as the Hubble Space Telescope or the Space Station, offer special cases in this persistent tension between politics and technology because they typically involve unprecedented operational and managerial, as well as technical challenges. Efforts to anticipate what such programs will cost, much less who they will benefit, will be clumsy at best, making it all the more difficult for friend and foe alike to engage in the sort of rational planning and discourse most of us ostensibly cherish.

If Henry Lambright, in his commentary, does not resolve this dilemma for us, he does help us to focus squarely on the single issue that unites both the historian's and the policy analyst's perspectives on these episodes in the shaping of the civilian space program. Innovation not only complicates the issue, it *is* the issue. An essential social "good" for many, and certainly for engineers, innovation is not an unalloyed social "good" for everybody — witness the shifts in public opinion on nuclear power. Besides, innovation typically costs a lot of money, which Congress and the Office of Management and Budget increasingly find in short supply. Getting technological innovation started, which is mostly what the space program is all about, requires special public force and strategy. These may be orchestrated in the person of individual leadership, through the model of the iron triangle (uniting the interests of congressmen, bureaucrats, and constituencies), or through unstable issue networks, which Lambright calls "ad hocracies." None of them, he suggests, does a very good job of assuring necessarily long-term technological programs the rational consensus necessary to sustain them.

Lambright's commentary and the papers also illustrate the complementarity of the historian's with the policy analyst's work in understanding recent space politics and programming. As Lambright points out, the historian's patient efforts to capture the sense of options as they were perceived at the time by decision makers provide policy analysts with the raw materials from which to build models of contemporary decision-making. The shrinking amount that the public was willing to invest in space activity accompanied, during the late 1960s and early 1970s, increasing skepticism about the real "pay-off" for big space-science projects. At the same time, public concern over the secondary consequences of large-scale technology combined with deficit era cost-consciousness to undermine the foundations of support for major manned space flight programs. The effect was to destroy the equilibrium of consensus behind the nation's civilian space program and thus intensify the politicization of space policy-making.

As the presentations suggest, the disequilibrium of recent space policy has forced us to reassess our models of decision making. The leadership and iron triangle models appear to be giving way to more fluid notions of opinion networks, while the classic policy boundaries that separate the Congress from executive branch agencies have given way to bureaucratic decision-making that is highly sensitive to a changeable political climate.

More fundamentally, the notion that "rational" decision-making and "political" decision-making are somehow at odds with each other may give way to the view that in the policy arena (at least of the 1970s and 1980s) the most rational behavior is perforce the most politically inspired behavior, for politics provides the best barometer of what the American public will or will not support.

Finally, the contributors acknowledged that as policy scholars and historians scrutinize more closely the politics of the nation's space program, they must be alert to the danger of being drawn into the arguments they are examining, thus losing the detachment necessary for objective analysis.


## NOTES

1. The "civil space budget" includes the budget not only for NASA, but the space budgets for the Departments of Energy, Commerce, Interior, Agriculture, and the National Science Foundation. Figures based on real dollars, civil space budget as percent of net federal outlays, 1960 to 1985: 1960 × .5%, 1965 × 4.5%, 1970 × 2%, 1975 × .9%, 1980 × .8%, 1985 × .6%.

2. The federal deficit increased from $1.6 billion in 1965 to $45 billion in 1975, hovered at below $59 billion in 1980, and then soared to $195 billion in 1983. By 1985 it had grown to $202 billion.

*Howard E. McCurdy*

# The Space Station Decision
## Politics, Bureaucracy, and the Making of Public Policy

In 1986, I concluded a paper on NASA's efforts to win approval for its Space Station with the following words: "The moves (that NASA made) were not perfect; they were just good enough to get the job done."[1] Events have since conspired to force a slightly different conclusion. The moves that NASA made were good enough to get the agency through its phase B Space Station studies — the so-called definition and preliminary design phase. The long-term prospects for the Space Station, as NASA officials envisioned it, remain uncertain. NASA will get some sort of Space Station, but it may be different from the 75 kilowatt, permanently manned facility that Administrator James Beggs and the leaders of the Space Station Task Force presented to President Ronald Reagan for his approval in 1983.

Along with the uncertainty generated by the debate about the size and scope of the Space Station, there has been much hand-wringing about NASA's inability to produce a rational long-range plan and any sort of public consensus about America's future role in space. In this paper, I hope to demonstrate once again that bounded rationality (as social scientists use the term)[2] and lack of consensus dominate the conception of major scientific and technological programs. Rather than anomalies, they are the norms in American politics. By comparing the Space Station decision to the decision to build the Space Transportation System and the decision to go to the Moon,

The study described in this paper was supported by The National Aeronautics and Space Administration under Contract NASW-4067. The opinions and findings expressed therein are solely those of the author.

I will in fact suggest that the NASA bureaucracy has learned to avoid the sort of behavior that might be conducive to rational long-range planning and consensus-building. Although this has helped to get new programs approved, it has complicated NASA's ability to actually carry out the technological tasks for which the agency's engineering and scientific talent was assembled.

## ADMINISTRATIVE RATIONALITY

Long-range planning, as a technical exercise, would require administrative officials to analyze new initiatives in a detached, professional way. Agency officials would forward a variety of options for consideration by policy-makers and not become advocates for one particular point of view. They would present technically sound estimates of the total program costs associated with each option. They would engage in extensive planning and program definition before undertaking new programs. And they would insist, in order to reduce the amount of uncertainty with which administrative officials must deal, that members of Congress not approve any long-range technological program unless they were reasonably certain that they wanted to provide the resources necessary to accomplish program goals.

Through its experience with the approval process for the Apollo, Shuttle, and Space Station programs, the NASA bureaucracy seems to have learned the consequences of behaving in this way. While this sort of behavior might seem advisable as a means for strengthening the technical capability of an agency to carry out its programs, it frequently clashes with the political necessities to which members of that agency must also respond. Many government executives have to balance their desire for enhanced technical capability with their desire to get programs approved. In NASA, this seems to have created a demoralizing tension between the need to adjust to the political system as it exists and the need to avoid the technical failures and cost overruns that are the result of weakened professional capability.

### Presenting Options

In public, at least, political leaders discourage bureaucrats from advocating particular public policies. This official posture is based on the traditional separation of powers doctrine and a potently realistic fear of bureaucratic power. The separation of powers doctrine states in principle that the job of the bureaucrat is to execute the law, not to make it. The fear of bureaucratic power arises from the belief that once career executives are unleashed to participate fully in the political process, they will promote policies that further their careers and the status of their organizations at the expense of the national interest, or at least at the expense of the President's agenda. Henry Kissinger often complained that when confronted with an opportunity for action, the bureaucracy tended to present the President with three options: unconditional surrender, nuclear annihilation, and its preferred alternative. Coupled with the realization that career executives in a bureaucratic society probably possess the skill, tenure, and clientele support necessary to achieve their goals, Presidents and their aides have worked hard in recent years to increase their political control over agencies that are independent in either practice or form.

Following the inauguration of Ronald Reagan in 1981, the President's chief of government personnel reaffirmed the traditional doctrine. "The honor of the civil servant," Donald Devine announced, "is vested in his ability to execute conscientiously the order(s) of superior authorities." His successor, Constance Horner, called upon public servants to refrain from the tendency "to serve (their) own private conception of the national interest, whether altruistic or otherwise."[3]

Having listened to voices from the White House expound this doctrine, members of the bureaucracy then learn that neither the President nor the Congress expect them to abide by it. As one writer has observed, "ambiguities in national science and technological policy will invariably have to be resolved at the level of the agencies." Opportunities to resolve those ambiguities through the creation of major new initiatives occur infrequently in the lives of the agencies. When they do, Presidents and lawmakers expect administrative agencies to act as advocates for new programs during those brief periods of public attention. In all three cases under examination here, the NASA bureaucracy was expected to play a major role in formulating national policy. Indeed, NASA executives have been criticized when they have failed to produce a national agenda for space.[4]

In analyzing the Space Station decision, science writer Mitchell Waldrop said that "it happened for one simple reason: Ronald Reagan thought it was a great idea." While true, this interpretation oversimplifies the situation to a certain extent. President Reagan, as President John Kennedy before him, came into office committed to a more aggressive space program. In neither case did those executives bring to the presidency a specific conception of what that posture entailed. Instead, they turned to NASA with the expectation that the agency would frame a specific program to meet their general needs.[5]

NASA's vision of the steps necessary to conquer outer space has remained essentially unchanged since the founding of the agency. The vision was set down by the Goett Committee in May of 1959, with specific deadlines placed in the agency's long-range plan by the end of that year. Essentially, the plan embraced the classic European school of space exploration: attainment of manned space flight, establishment of an experimental orbiting laboratory to be followed by the construction of a Space Station in low earth orbit, and flights to the Moon and nearby planets.[6]

NASA's situation when it set down its goals in 1959 was in one important respect like the situation that the agency faced in 1981. The functions of the National Advisory Committee for Aeronautics (NACA), on whose foundation NASA had been raised in 1958, had expanded rapidly some twenty years earlier. NACA operations then went into a period of decline. In the first five years of the decade following expansion, NACA budgets rose hardly at all and employment actually declined. During that same period, spending for military activities in the same area increased rapidly as most of the glamour programs moved to the Department of Defense. In both 1961 and 1981, the arrival of a space enthusiast in the White House provided NASA employees with a brief window of opportunity to implement the key goals in their long-range plan.[7]

The Shuttle program arose under quite different circumstances. In the euphoria of the lunar landing, NASA and its advocates on the Space Task Group presented President Richard Nixon with all of the elements in their long-range plan plus some. "Plus some" included the Space Transportation System, which had figured prominently in Werhner von Braun's 1952 *Collier's* article but not in NASA's original long-range plan. Confronted with what constituted a set of options for top-level review, Nixon performed a typically presidential maneuver. He returned the options to NASA with instructions to study their feasibility in greater detail. In essence, Nixon communicated the message that NASA could expect only one major new initiative and asked NASA executives to recommend their preferred alternative.[8] Although obviously ambitious, the Space Task Group report contained a large number of distinct options—both manned and unmanned—from which the President could have made selections. This would have been in keeping with the technical approach to planning in which bureaucrats present options instead of single program preferences. While Nixon professed his desire for bureaucratic subservience in public, he rejected this approach in practice, passing the buck back to NASA for a specific proposal without any major alternatives. NASA executives responded with their proposal to build the Space Shuttle, which they pursued aggressively through White House channels until its approval nearly two years later.[9]

Through experiences such as these, career civil servants learn to become advocates for specific objectives in their long-range plans. In the process, they form alliances with groups in what has been characterized as their "issue network": contractors, clientele, congressional committees, advisory groups, and other government agencies. To a certain extent, this strengthens the political accountability of the agency and reduces the potential for the abuse of bureaucratic discretion. It also, however, introduces a source of political necessity that may at times conflict with the agency's professional responsibilities. Nowhere is this more obvious than in the estimation of program costs.

### Total Program Costs

Next to the actual success or failure of a mission, the ability of NASA to meet predicted cost goals is the most important measure of agency performance used by elected officials and a generally inattentive public. NASA's ability to meet its cost goals on the Apollo program established a standard of mythical proportions to which other NASA programs and the performance of neighboring agencies are often compared. A close examination of the process for selecting total program costs reveals how political necessities shape technical estimates.

Prior to President Kennedy's decision, NASA Administrator James Webb and Deputy Administrator Hugh Dryden gave a rough estimate of $20 to $40 billion as the cost of taking an American to the Moon. "Some people use a number as high as $40 billion to land a man on the moon," said Webb. "Others say half that amount." Dryden later announced that "it is much closer to $20 billion than $40 billion." At the conclusion of the mission, actual costs were set at $21.4 billion.[10]

Following extensive negotiations with officials in the Office of Management and Budget, NASA agreed to develop the Space Transportation System and build two orbiters for $5.5 billion. Three months later, in March of 1972, that figure was revised to $5.15 billion after deciding to push the orbiter into space with the assistance of two solid fuel rather than liquid fuel boosters. The actual cost of development, as the first orbiter flew into space nine years later, turned out to be $6.7 billion—a 30 percent cost overrun.[11]

NASA officials originally refused to state the total program cost of the Space Station, insisting that the facility was something that the government could buy "by the yard." Under pressure from opponents of the program, agency officials issued an $8 billion cost estimate on the initial facility. Three years later, having established a "baseline configuration" for the station, NASA officials were forced to admit that the cost had soared to $14.5 billion, an 81 percent cost overrun incurred prior to the construction of any major piece of the facility. In early 1987, NASA Administrator James Fletcher announced that the agency would scale back the Space Station to a "revised baseline configuration" priced out at $12.2 billion.[12]

In the eyes of the public, events such as these suggest a loss of NASA's technical ability to estimate costs. Public impressions account for a great deal in American politics. Upon closer inspection, however, the evidence does not reveal much technical degradation. Instead, it suggests a degradation of the agency's political situation which reduced its capacity to issue realistic cost estimates.[13]

When the Space Station Task Force began its work in 1982, its leaders suggested to the officials whose support they sought that a permanently manned Space Station could be built for between $4 and $6 billion. Brought to Washington to refine the cost estimates in 1983, NASA engineer Luther Powell announced that NASA could build a habitable station for between $4 and $6 billion, but the agency "would not be able to do anything on it." This was patently obvious to anyone familiar with Space Station costs. NASA had spent $2.5 billion in 1973 (over $5 billion in 1984 dollars) just to launch Skylab. Powell suggested that the Task Force work in the $7.5 to $12 billion range.[14]

NASA Administrator James Beggs, working with the leaders of the Task Force and officials in the Administrator's office, made a political decision to set the cost of the initially occupied station at $8 billion. This was based on Beggs's assumption that a Space Station could be built "by the yard" and on what Task Force Director John Hodge called "the scream level." People outside NASA, Hodge recalled, started screaming "at about $9 billion." Supporters of the initiative believed that any price estimate above the $8 to $9 billion range would provide opponents of the program with the "show stopper" they needed to slay the proposal.[15]

Powell and the leaders of the Space Station Task Force were left with the problem of fitting a big foot into a small shoe. They had two choices. They could scale back the Space Station "by the yard" to fit the $8 billion estimate (which due to a dispute in transmitting the figures to the President's budget examiners had turned into $7.4 billion). Alternatively, they could change the base, altering the definition of what NASA would include in the $8 billion figure. Establishing the base for new space flight programs is a slippery business at best. The cost estimate for the Space Station was derived by estimating the development costs of those elements, such as the habitat module and the orbiting platforms, which were obviously part of the initial facility. These technical estimates never varied by more than $1.0 billion, no matter what assumptions NASA officials used, and were always below $7.4 billion. Disagreements arose over the extras. The cost estimators had to decide how much support equipment, most of which would not fly in space, belonged in the base. To this they had to add a reserve fund to cover cost growth and uncertainty. Finally, they had to decide how much overhead to allow the field centers to charge off against the project, what Task Force Director John Hodge called the "institutional tariff."[16]

To preserve the multimodular, 75-kilowatt Space Station the task force wanted, Hodge and his associates shaved the base, reduced the reserve, and eliminated the tariff. They removed from the estimate some $3.6 billion in facilities and overhead and $2.5 billion in reserves that other NASA officials wanted to spend. The latter reduced NASA's margin for cost growth and technological surprises to only $1.3 billion in an area where the agency typically added at least 40 percent. They also omitted from the $8 billion estimate the money needed to transport the station to orbit, the $1 to $2 billion needed to provide the crew with a "lifeboat" to return safely to earth in an emergency, and the funds needed to run the station and conduct experiments on it in the initial years. Such funds might be spent, but they would be charged against other agency accounts, not the Space Station development budget. (These items were also omitted from the base for the revised $14.5 billion estimate.)[17]

NASA officials working to win approval for the Space Station took a risk in shaving their cost estimate so low. In refusing to sacrifice their vision of an ambitious Space Station to meet a politically mandated cost ceiling, they took the risk that Congress might reconsider the program if the costs began to grow. They guessed that Congress would not terminate the program, although the lawmakers could stretch it out or reduce its goals. NASA officials also took the risk that any damage to their reputation for making accurate cost estimates would be compensated by the value of an approved program.

Lessons from the Shuttle program suggest why NASA chose to shave the base rather than issue a realistic cost estimate. The original technical estimates for NASA's dreamboat, the fully reusable two-stage Shuttle, ranged from $10 to $13 billion. Rather than raise this estimate, as they had done with the Apollo program, NASA executives established a self-imposed cost goal of $8.3 billion. Officials in the Office of Management and Budget insisted that the program be conducted at a lower cost and pressured NASA to revise their proposal to fit a $4.7 to $5.5 billion range. To gain the support of the President's budget officers, NASA officials altered the configuration of the Space Shuttle to meet the lower cost goals. The first casualty was the bottom half of the fully reusable two-stage Shuttle. White House budget officials then tried to get NASA officials to accept a smaller Space Shuttle. Serious negotiations took place over the size of the orbiter spacecraft and its cargo bay.[18]

NASA Administrator James Fletcher accepted a $5.0 billion configuration for the Space Shuttle in December 1971, assuming that this compromise was necessary to eliminate areas of disagreement before taking the program to President Nixon. This figure would have produced a Space Shuttle with a 45-foot payload bay. Ironically, NASA found itself in the position of having guessed too low when President Nixon reversed the compromise and approved the $5.5 billion Space Shuttle with a 60-foot cargo bay. That figure got revised down to $5.15 billion with the selection of the solid-fuel boosters.

NASA executives learned two painful lessons during the Space Shuttle decision. First, they learned to live with the illusions that guide the budget process, to buy in for a piece of the program rather than risk losing the whole show. Second, they learned never to negotiate engineering details during the budget process. That second lesson guided one of the most important moves that the leaders of the Space Station Task Force made as they attempted to get the program approved.

### Missions Before Configurations

During the negotiations that led to the approval of the Space Transportation System, the actual design of the Space Shuttle became an item for negotiation. It happened innocently enough. NASA proposed a technologically sophisticated, fully reusable Shuttle to the President's staff. When it became clear that the fully reusable configuration would not meet the cost goals set for the program, the parties began to experiment with designs that would. Everyone became a Shuttle designer: NASA, its contractors, even economists in the Office of Management and Budget. It is trying enough when NASA engineers have to pick up their pencils and design spacecraft before anyone really knows what the vessels will be used for. The situation becomes even more complicated when nonengineers start drawing pictures.

In 1981, the director of the Langley Research Center, Donald P. Hearth, submitted a management study warning of an association between premature design and cost overruns. Hearth found that inadequate definition of project goals prior to program implementation tended to be associated with cost and schedule growth down the line. Space Station Task Force Director John Hodge held a similar belief. He felt that the Space Station would better fit the needs of users if missions for the station were clearly defined before design work began. He thus refused to issue a baseline configuration and insisted instead that NASA spend $600 million and up to three years defining the requirements for the Space Station (phase B) before designing and building the hardware (phases C and D). This was a professionally responsible decision. It was also politically smart in the short run because it did not give opponents of the program a design to redraw when NASA issued its $8 billion estimate. Like other moves that the Task Force made, however, it proved politically risky in the long run.

In both the Shuttle and Apollo programs, early design decisions locked the government into a specific configuration or mode while enthusiasm for the program was still high. NASA scientists and engineers took fourteen months following President Kennedy's speech to

Congress to design a method for the expedition to the Moon. During the second week of July 1962, Administrator James Webb announced that NASA had accepted lunar rendezvous and would add the lunar excursion vehicle to the projects already under development. Less than three months after President Nixon approved the Shuttle program, NASA officials announced the basic configuration for the new transportation system. In March of 1972 Administrator James Fletcher announced that the Shuttle would consist of the already familiar orbiter spacecraft and its external fuel tank and two solid (rather than liquid) fuel rocket boosters. Once the keels were laid — in the sense of having a fixed design or mode — neither the Congress nor the President could reconsider their commitment to either program without stopping work on an engineering project already underway. A specific design helped to lock in the political commitment to the entire program, even when public support began to wane. Public enthusiasm for the space program dropped off in the years following both the lunar and the Shuttle decisions.[19]

As the agency slogged through its phase B definition work on the Space Station, NASA executives announced a number of different designs to meet the goal of a permanently manned capability. These included the power tower (1984), the dual keel (1985), and a baseline configuration based on the dual keel design (1986). Additionally, NASA submitted to Congress a required study on a man-tended Space Station (1986). Recommendations from user groups as well as technical considerations played a large role in the decision to move from the power tower to the dual keel design, as would be appropriate in an organization with strong professional standards.

The phase B definition and preliminary design work lasted up to 1987. NASA was prepared to issue contracts for its dual keel baseline configuration at that time. More than three years had passed since President Reagan had directed NASA to start work on the Space Station. Public confidence in NASA had been shaken by the loss of the *Challenger,* cost growth had become a major consideration with the passage of Gramm-Rudman-Hollings deficit reduction act, and control of the U.S. Senate had passed to the opposition party. House and Senate committees prepared to hold hearings on the status of the Space Station and members of the White House staff pressured NASA Administrator James Fletcher to scale back his design. Fletcher found that he did not have sufficient political support to call for contracts for his preferred baseline configuration. Instead the agency told its contractors to submit proposals for a Space Station built along a single boom, but to also submit proposals for what NASA now called the enhanced capability configuration, which it would phase in if funds became available.[20]

Politically speaking, NASA would have been much wiser to nail down the configuration for the Space Station and sign the contracts for the development of the facility in the wake of the President's decision before the opponents of the program had time to reorganize. By allowing such a long-term definition and preliminary design phase, NASA officials took the chance that nothing major would happen that would call the initial decision into question. It was a professionally responsible thing to do, but it was politically risky.

### Approval Without Commitment

Having stated this, it must now be said that NASA officials were not in a very good position in 1983 and 1984 to insist on the sort of commitment they had received for the Apollo program and get the Space Station of their dreams. The political circumstances in which NASA found itself created a situation in which it was much easier for agency officials to win approval to start planning the program without getting a firm commitment to actually build it. Congress rarely provides any long-term guarantees. In gaining approval for the Space Station, however, NASA obtained the weakest commitment that it had ever received for a major manned space flight initiative.

When President Kennedy proposed that Americans travel to the Moon, he specifically asked Congress and the American public "to accept a firm commitment" to this course of action. "It is a heavy burden," he said. "If we are to go only halfway, or reduce our sights in the face of difficulty, in my judgment it would be better not to go at all." He urged every citizen of this country as well as the members of Congress to consider the matter carefully. "There is no sense in agreeing or desiring," he said, "unless we are prepared to do the work and bear the burdens to make it successful."[21] Kennedy framed the issue in such a way that made a total commitment much easier. "Is there any other space program," he asked Vice President Johnson in his famous memorandum of April 20, 1961, "which promises dramatic results *in which we could win?*" It is often said that the power to define an issue is equivalent to the power to decide the issue. By asking for a program in which "we have a chance of beating the

Soviets" he made a public commitment to the lunar goal politically feasible.[22]

NASA officials got a reasonably firm commitment to build the Space Transportation System, even with its cost overruns, but they arranged it in a very different way. They got it by agreeing to put the decision into the White House staff system and framing a compromise with the opponents of the program. The opponents of the program then proceeded to trap NASA representatives in a debate on the high pillar of rationality. Prove to us, the opponents demanded, that the Space Transportation System you have proposed is cost effective. This NASA could not do, not even with the economists in the consulting firm it had hired, Mathematica, Inc. To receive the commitment they wanted, NASA executives had to give up the Space Shuttle that they found technologically superior.

The Shuttle decision rumbled around in the offices of the White House staff for nearly three years. President Nixon set up the Space Task Group on February 13, 1969 and announced the Shuttle program on January 5, 1972. President Kennedy, by contrast, took less than four weeks to make the decision to go to the Moon. The last of the paperwork from Vice President Johnson's study group reached Kennedy's hands on May 8, 1961, twenty-six days after Yuri Gagarin started the process by orbiting the earth in a Soviet spacecraft. Inclined to make a quick decision, President Kennedy simply did not give his aides enough time to conduct the detailed staff studies that bogged down the Shuttle decision. As a result, NASA officials escaped from the Apollo decision without having to compromise their technological goals.

Initially, NASA executives tried to get President Reagan to make the Space Station decision without extensive White House review by simply announcing it in his speech at the landing of the Space Shuttle *Columbia* at Edwards Air Force Base on July 4, 1982. This the President failed to do, plunging the proposal into the White House staff system. Opponents of the Space Station involved in the staff exercise wanted to debate the initiative on two grounds. Some wanted to debate the cost effectiveness of using a high technology Space Station to accomplish the thirty-three missions that NASA had identified for the initial facility. Representatives from the Department of Defense, for example, took the position that the same missions could be accomplished much less expensively by extending the duration time of the Shuttle in orbit.

Others, such as science adviser George Keyworth, wanted to debate NASA's vision of the steps in the exploration of space. For twenty-five years NASA had clung to its orbital equivalent of the Himalayan school of climbing. Master the techniques of ascent. Establish a base camp. Use the base camp to mount expeditions to higher altitudes. This vision had remained essentially unchanged since first proposed during the Lebensraum movement in the early 1900s, the German-based drive for political and economic expansion. Opponents of this vision wanted to debate whether an elaborate base camp was necessary given American advances in automation technology and robotics. Why not go right for the summit—science adviser George Keyworth argued—using lightweight, high-technology equipment.

NASA officials refused to debate their vision of space exploration, viewing any such debate as a diversionary tactic. It was not part of the "terms of reference" for the White House staff study, NASA representatives insisted. The National Commission on Space could debate the grand vision of future exploration after NASA got approval for the Space Station. Experience with the Space Task Group, which had undertaken a similar analysis of America's future in 1969, suggested that no concrete program was likely to emerge from a comprehensive analysis.[23]

As for the cost-effectiveness of the Space Station, NASA officials took a different tack. That issue definitely sat within the scope of the White House "terms of reference" for debating the Space Station initiative. During the White House staff study on the Space Shuttle, the debate over cost-effectiveness had turned into negotiations over Shuttle design. Unwilling to compromise their vision of a high-technology, multimodule Space Station, NASA official and their allies simply refused to negotiate program details that might make the Space Station more cost effective. Instead, they kept shifting the forum in which the negotiations were taking place. They waited until they were in a forum where they could demonstrate Space Station support, sensing that President Reagan would approve the Space Station if they could just keep from losing their vision in the White House staff maze.

No extensive debate over the future of the American space program took place during the 1984 congressional deliberations of the Space Station either. NASA officials were too busy trying to gather enough votes to fend off an attempt to water down the permanently manned Space Station with a man-tended or highly automated facility.

As a result, NASA officials never came to terms with the opponents of the program. They did not want to come to terms with their opponents, as had been done during the Shuttle debate. Such an undertaking would have been much more likely to produce a compromise than a commitment to NASA's vision. Sensing that they had the President's support, NASA officials and their allies thought that they did not need to compromise their proposal to get the program approved.

It is in the nature of the American political system, in situations where administrative agencies have to deal with opposing groups, for members of the Congress to approve a short-term course of action and leave the door open for future changes in direction. The situation in which NASA found itself in 1984 allowed the Congress to tilt toward the vision of the Space Station that NASA officials and their allies were advocating. The situation in 1987 favored a tilt back in the opposing direction. In the long run, political scientists believe, this tends to create a sort of equilibrium based on the relative power of the opposing parties. In the short run, it creates a situation in which members of Congress remain unwilling to make any long-term commitments because this would reduce their discretion for changing direction down the road. NASA's unwillingness to come to terms with the opponents of the program meant that it could preserve its vision of a large, permanently occupied Space Station, which NASA executives viewed as technologically superior. In exchange, the agency had to settle for a weak political commitment to the program.

## POLITICAL RISKS AND PROFESSIONAL ACCOUNTABILITY

Administrative officials often become advocates for particular points of view in the American system. When they do, they learn to deal with two types of reality. The first reality is the existence of what has been called their "issue network," a universe of groups with diverse interests in a general area such as space policy. The old theory that somehow an agency like NASA can insulate itself from this issue network by constructing a tight alliance with its contractor clientele and its authorizing subcommittees on Capitol Hill simply denies reality. The network is far too complex—and competition for budgets far too intense—to allow agencies like NASA to escape into little subgovernments. Within the White House, NASA officials were obliged to fight for their points of view on interagency councils such as the Senior Interagency Group for Space. On Capitol Hill, they must carry their request for funds before subcommittees that are concerned not only with science policy in general but with programs as diverse as housing subsidies and sewers. NASA has to scratch for feed with many other chickens in a town where it is not the biggest rooster.[24]

No group of administrative officials in a political system this complicated can understand everything that is going on or anticipate the effects of all of their decisions. To use the standard social science term, administrative agencies must learn to live with a great deal of uncertainty. In initiating new programs, agency officials typically deal with that uncertainty in a number of ways. To the maximum extent possible, they reduce the number of initiatives with which they must deal at any one time and try to establish formal procedures for policy review. They rely heavily on past experience in making decisions about the future. They confine their attention to a few problems at a time, building incrementally on the base of established practice. The Space Station decision shows NASA to be similar to other administrative agencies in this regard.

People familiar with such things will recognize that the behavior described above conforms to the model of organizational decision-making developed by Herbert Simon and Charles Lindblom. Simon describes a model of organization decision-making that is incremental, myopic, often random, based on familiar behavior patterns, characterized by a great deal of searching and probing, and above all *not* characteristically rational in the sense that the organization sets a specific goal and traces out a detailed, optimal course of action to achieve it. In both Simon's and Lindblom's view, individuals in organizations are limited by the amount of information they possess and the computational skills they can bring to bear on the type of problems that top managers have to solve. They do not engage in the type of premeditated decision-making that economists or game theorists like to describe.[25]

This description suggests, accurately I believe, that officials from NASA and its Space Station Task Force made a series of moves that made it possible for the President to direct the agency to start work on the program and for Congress to approve the initial funds. The moves were successive, in the sense that one followed upon another and were not all plotted out in advance. The moves evolved as the play developed and experience continued to accumulate. The moves carried risks, dangers that could threaten the success of the program as events moved in different ways. The moves were myopic, in the sense that officials could visualize the general goal toward which they were proceeding but only dimly perceive the exact consequences of their actions. The moves took on the characteristics of decisions, to use Simon's words, in the sense of the "conscious or unconscious selection of particular actions" by which individuals follow one course of action and thereby forgo others.[26] The decision by the Space Station Task Force leaders to stop drawing pictures and focus on missions removed design as an issue from the initial debate, although it also allowed the design issue to pop up three years after the President's decision. The decision to estimate the cost of the Space Station at $8 billion placed the value of program approval over the value of a realistic estimate. The decision—hardly a carefully deliberated one—to deliver the Space Station into orbit in the cargo bay of the Space Shuttle meant that the future of the program rode on the success of each flight of the *Challenger* and her sister ships. (The Space Shuttle was originally viewed as a ferry to and from the Space Station and not as the primary means for pushing the facility into orbit. That work was to be done by heavy-lift, expendable boosters.) Finally, the decision to build such an ambitious and early international component into the program helped to win Presidential and congressional support for the program. In the Oval Office, it made the Space Station look like the vehicle for U.S. technological leadership, which Reagan so desired. In Congress, it made Reagan's directive to NASA to start work on the Space Station easier to stick. Congress has consistently refused to undercut the power of the President once he has invited American allies to participate with the United States in a joint enterprise.

The decision to promote international cooperation prior to program approval shows once again how political reality conditions administrative behavior in an agency where people might otherwise want to take the professionally responsible course of action. In seeking international participation on the Space Station program, NASA officials adopted a "join now, fight later" strategy. It might have been more professionally responsible to resolve the wide areas of disagreement over the terms of that cooperation before inviting the Europeans, Canadians, and Japanese in. Tough issues like equal access to the Space Station and technology transfer could not be resolved, however, without making some of the players angry. NASA officials found it easier to incrementally involve their international partners in the initiative and put off the hard bargaining until the partners were more fully committed. As in any incremental game, it is easier to let each side construct its own vision of the program and get the enterprise underway than to try to resolve potentially divisive issues at the start.

So long as NASA remains an agency within the government, its officials will struggle to learn how to balance professional accountability with political reality. Based on the experience of the Apollo, Shuttle, and Space Station decisions, it would appear that forces of political necessity increase as the relative availability of funds for agency programs shrinks. Officials in an administrative agency can afford to stand up to political pressures that might compromise their professional standards when new programs start up and budgets rapidly rise. Under conditions such as those, politicians tend to defer to the professional judgment of experts at the working level of the agency.

The more common situation is represented by the sort of scarcity that has plagued NASA through the development of the Space Shuttle and the initial stages of the Space Station program. Agency officials have no choice but to try to become more politically adept in order to promote their programs. A great deal less professional autonomy is tolerable under those circumstances. Agency leaders seeking to construct politically shaky alliances cannot tolerate extensive professional criticism from employees who call into question the technical flaws in politically driven decisions.

This cycling between long periods of political compromise and short bursts of professional accountability make it difficult in the long run for agencies like NASA to achieve their technical goals. This might prove less troublesome in an agency where technical failures were not so visible and potentially catastrophic. As members of a technical bureaucracy engage in the policy making process, agency executives walk a fine line between the moves necessary to get their programs approved and the technical independence necessary to make them work.

## NOTES

1. Howard E. McCurdy, "Space Station Task Force History," a paper presented at the NASA History Seminar, Goddard Space Flight Center, February 25, 1986, p. 18.

2. The concept of bounded rationality is most frequently associated with the works of Herbert Simon. See, for example, Herbert Simon, *Administrative Behavior* (New York: The Free Press, 1945). For a discussion of the concept of professional accountability, see Barbara S. Romzek and Melvin J. Dubnick, "Accountability in the Public Sector: Lessons from the Challenger Tragedy," *Public Administration Review* 47 (May/June, 1987): 227–238.

3. Constance Horner, director, U.S. Office of Personnel Management, an address to the conference of the National Association of Schools of Public Affairs and Administration, November 1, 1985, Miami, Florida, pp. 5–6.

4. W. Henry Lambright, *Governing Science and Technology* (New York: Oxford University Press, 1976). In his chapter on "Launching Technology," Lambright discusses in some detail the strategies that administrative agencies utilize to shape national science and technology policy.

5. M. Mitchell Waldrop, "The Selling of the Space Station," *Science* 223 (February 24, 1984): 793.

6. For more detail and sources on the facts cited in this paper, see Howard E. McCurdy, *The Space Station Decision: Incremental Politics and Technical Choice* (Baltimore: The Johns Hopkins University Press, 1990).

7. Figures on the NACA budget and personnel levels, along with spending for defense-based aeronautical R&D, can be found in Alex Roland, *Model Research: The National Advisory Committee for Aeronautics, 1915–1958*, vol. 2, SP 4103 (Washington, D.C.: NASA, 1985), 475–476, 481, 489. Walter A. McDougall describes the decline of the NACA in . . . *The Heavens and the Earth: A Political History of the Space Age* (New York: Basic Books, 1985), 164–169. Due to the military claims on space and the lack of powerful allies, "by the mid-1950s the venerable NACA was slumping," ibid., 164.

8. In his response to the report of the Space Task Group, Nixon embraced continued exploration of the Moon, bold exploration of the planets and the universe (including an eventual manned mission to Mars), feasibility studies on a Space Transportation System, an experimental Space Station (Skylab), and future decisions on "how to develop longer-lived space stations." He did this without approving a single new manned space flight program, as a careful reading of his "six specific objectives" will reveal. Statement by the President, "The Future of the United States Space Program," *Weekly Compilation of Presidential Documents,* March 7, 1970.

9. Among the options presented in the Space Task Group report to the President were a Space Station, a space base, a Space Transportation System, a lunar orbiting station, a lunar surface base, an initial Mars expedition, a space telescope, a "grand tour," a Mars mapper, and Venus atmospheric probes. In the euphoria of the lunar landing, NASA sought approval for all of these programs.

Space Task Group, Report to the President, *The Post-Apollo Space Program: Directions for the Future* (Washington, D.C.: Executive Office of the President, September 1969).

10. Webb made his prediction before the U.S. House Committee on Science and Astronautics, *Discussion of Soviet Man-In-Space Shot,* 87th Congress, 1st session, April 13, 1961, p. 31, the day after the Gagarin flight. Dryden's statement can be found in U.S. House Committee on Science and Astronautics, *1962 NASA Authorization,* 87th Congress, 1st session, July 11, 12, and 13, 1961, p. 1043. The final cost estimate of $21.4 billion (the actual cost accrued through the first manned landing and return) can be found in T. O. Paine, NASA Administrator, letter to the Honorable Clinton P. Anderson, Chairman, Senate Committee on Aeronautical and Space Sciences, November 21, 1969 and Response to NBC Inquiry on Shuttle and Other Manned Space Flight Program Costs, March 10, 1981, a memorandum available in the NASA History Office files under Shuttle Costs.

11. "Response to NBC Inquiry," p. 1.

12. NASA, "NASA Proceeding Toward Space Station Development," *NASA News,* release 87-50, April 3, 1987. Those costs are stated in 1984 dollars (the year in which the Space Station was originally approved), so that the actual costs on a current dollar basis are in fact higher.

13. Lambright agrees. Because of the priority placed on the Apollo program, NASA "was able to avoid a cost overrun by estimating *realistically.*" Lambright suggests that "good management, in this case, was merely cost realism in an environment in which costs were not a very important consideration." Lambright, *Governing Science and Technology,* p. 55.

14. Luther Powell, interview conducted by Howard McCurdy, November 18, 1985.

15. John Hodge, interview conducted by Howard McCurdy, July 10, 1985.

16. Space Station Task Force Roundtable Discussion: John Hodge, Captain Robert Freitag, Terence Finn, and Daniel Herman, interviewed by Howard McCurdy, Sylvia Fries, and Adam Gruen, August 4, 1987. What Hodge referred to as an institutional tariff other agency officials called the basic engineering and technical support that needed to be augmented. See NASA, "NASA Proceeding Toward Space Station Development," *NASA News,* release 87-50, April 3, 1987, p. 1.

17. James C. Miller, director, Office of Management and Budget, Memorandum for the President, Revised Cost Estimates for the Space Station, February 10, 1987.

18. For confirmation of the $13 billion estimate, see the Program Development Memorandum from W. R. Lucas to Dr. Rees dated June 16, 1970. NASA established a cost goal of $8.3 billion in the fall of 1970. See "NASA to Seek $415–465 Million for Shuttle in FY '73," *Space Daily,* July 1, 1971, p. 3. The cost goal is also confirmed in the Lucas memorandum. John Logsdon reviews these developments in "The Space Shuttle Decision: Technology and Political Choice," *Journal of Contemporary Business* 7 (Number 3): 13–30.

19. Webb publicly announced the decision on July 11, 1962. Courtney G. Brooks, James M. Grimwood, and Loyd S. Swenson Jr., *Chariots for Apollo: A History of Manned Lunar Spacecraft,* SP 4205 (Washington: NASA, 1979), 85.

Fletcher announced the Shuttle configuration on March 15, 1972. NASA, "News Conference on Space Shuttle," *NASA News,* March 15, 1972, p. 2. Public support for "doing more" in space dropped off sharply in 1966, a trend reversed after the fatal fire on Launch Complex 34. Public enthusiasm for the space program peaked again following the Shuttle decision and the final two missions to the Moon in 1972, then dropped during 1973. Herbert E. Krugman, "Public Attitudes Toward the Apollo Space Program, 1965–1975," *Journal of Communication* 27 (Autumn 1977): 87–93.

20. The call for the two options can be found in NASA, "NASA Issues Requests for Proposals for Space Station Development," *NASA News,* release 87-65, April 24, 1987. Also see NASA, "NASA Proceeding Toward Space Station Development," *NASA News,* release 87-50, April 3, 1987.

21. John F. Kennedy, "Freedom's Cause," delivered to joint session of Congress, Washington, D.C., May 25, 1961, *Vital Speeches of the Day,* vol. 27, no. 17, June 15, 1961, p. 519.

22. John F. Kennedy, memorandum for Vice President, April 20, 1961, emphasis added. E. E. Schattschneider explained why "the definition of alternatives is the supreme instrument of power" in *The Semisovereign People* (New York: Holt, Rinehart and Winston, 1960), 68. Even the Apollo program was not immune from congressional reconsideration. In 1964, with Kennedy out of the White House, NASA came within four votes of losing 10 percent of its funding for the Apollo program. *Congressional Quarterly, 1964 CQ Almanac,* p. 452.

23. The National Commission on Space was established by President Ronald Reagan by Executive Order on October 12, 1984.

24. The classic explanation of issue network can be found in Hugh Heclo, "Issue Networks and the Executive Establishment," in *The New Political System,* ed. Anthony King (Washington: American Enterprise Institute for Public Policy Research, 1978), 87–124. For a discussion of the erosion of subgovernment power in the face of issue networks, see Randall B. Ripley and Grace A. Franklin, *Congress, the Bureaucracy, and Public Policy,* 4th edition (Chicago: The Dorsey Press, 1987), 6–10, 96–123.

25. Simon, *Administrative Behavior.* For a discussion of the workings of incrementalism, see Charles E. Lindblom, "The Science of 'Muddling Through,'" *Public Administration Review* 19 (Spring 1959): 79–88.

26. Simon, *Administrative Behavior,* 3rd edition, p. 3.

*Robert W. Smith*

# Selling the Space Telescope
## The Interpenetration of Science, Technology, and Politics

*Socrates: Shall we make astronomy the next study? What do you say?*

*Glaucon: Certainly. A working knowledge of the seasons, months, and years is beneficial to everyone, to commanders as well as to farmers and sailors.*

*Socrates: You make me smile, Glaucon. You are so afraid that the public will accuse you of recommending unprofitable studies.*

PLATO, REPUBLIC VII, CIRCA 370 B.C.

*You know, someone said, what good is it going to do when you get it out there? What does it do? What does it find? And somebody says, 'More of the same.' Is that correct?*

CONGRESSMAN EDWARD P. BOLAND, 1976

*. . . we are talking about the salvation of the world.*

NASA ADMINISTRATOR JAMES C. FLETCHER, 1975

In 1969, James Webb, NASA's second administrator, wrote in his *Space Age Management* that in "our pluralistic society any major

**29**

public undertaking requires for success a working consensus among diverse individuals, groups, and interests. A decision to do a large, complex job cannot simply be reached at the top and then carried through. Only through an intricate process can a major undertaking be gotten underway, and only through a continuation of that process can it be kept going."[1] The major undertaking I want to discuss here and examine in the light of Webb's words is the Space Telescope, a telescope designed by NASA, its contractors, and the astronomical community, and placed in orbit by the Space Shuttle in April 1990.

The construction of the Telescope began in 1977, and it was designed to be the most powerful optical telescope ever built. It is certainly the most expensive. By the time of its launch, around $2 billion has been spent on the Telescope and its ground system.

Even in the 1960s, when the Space Telescope program was first seriously discussed, the cost estimates for a program much more extensive than the existing one were around $1 billion (1965 dollars). This was a price that all of its advocates accepted and put it well beyond the reach of private patronage. It was inevitable that if the Telescope was to be built at all it would have to be with the support of the federal government and, given the funding structure for space science in the United States, therefore NASA.

As a costly and highly visible project, the road to executive and legislative approval for the Telescope was, as Webb indicates, an intricate process. Certainly it involved far more than NASA, the contractors, and astronomers presenting a design and a cost to the White House and Congress and getting a "Yes" or "No" decision to proceed. Instead, during the lengthy business of initiating the Telescope program, the demands of coalition building, and the negotiations and resulting compromises that the Telescope's builders and designers had to make, strongly shaped the Telescope's design as well as the program to build it. This was because NASA, the astronomers, and the contractors were compelled to adjust the plans for, and designs of the Telescope to what the market—the White House and Congress— would bear. Elsewhere, I have argued that the political and social differences in the broadly based coalition favoring the Telescope were reflected by hardware choices.[2] In this paper, the focus will instead be on the politics of initiating the Space Telescope program, and the manner in which the coalition, or working consensus in Webb's terms, for the Telescope was assembled, in particular the role played by NASA's clients, the astronomers. In consequence, we are presented with a case study in the influence of government patronage on a large-scale scientific and technological program.

Gaining approval for the Space Telescope program can be divided into four main, although often overlapping and intermingled, stages: selling the Telescope to the astronomers, selling the Telescope to NASA, selling the Telescope to the executive branch, and selling the Telescope to the Congress. It is this last stage, selling to the Congress, that I shall concentrate upon here, and although the efforts to win congressional approval lasted from 1974 to 1977, for brevity the emphasis here will be on the failed attempt to secure a new start in 1976. Although a failure, it would be crucial in the overall process of securing support. But to start and to provide a context for the 1976 activities, I shall turn very briefly to the first three of these stages.

## THE ASTRONOMERS

Astronomers have long dreamt of placing telescopes above the obscuring layers of Earth's atmosphere. Writing in 1933, a Princeton astrophysicist looked longingly to the time when astronomers would be able to make such observations. He even joked that when astronomers died, they might be "permitted to go . . . instruments and all, and set up an observatory on the moon."[3]

Matters took a more serious turn after the Second World War. The advances in rocketry during the war, particularly the German V-2s, provided emphatic evidence that the enormous and complex engineering problems posed by the development of rockets powerful and reliable enough to lift astronomical instruments above the atmosphere had, to a large degree, been solved. One of the astronomers impressed by the new possibilities was Lyman Spitzer, then a 33-year-old professor at Yale. In 1946, through already established contacts with people working for Project RAND, Spitzer described the "Astronomical Advantages of an Extra-Terrestrial Observatory."[4] Spitzer was now set on a course that would lead him to champion the cause of a large telescope in space, and to persistent efforts to persuade his astronomer colleagues that building a large telescope in space was an exciting and worthwhile endeavor, one that was promising enough to consume large parts of their careers.

It did not prove easy. In 1953, for example, a leading astronomer wrote to a colleague on Spitzer's proposal for an astronomical satellite. He was "greatly surprised that the project should be regarded as astronomical. I would place it with rocket research in a class of very expensive technological developments that are bound to benefit astronomy in the end, but which should be carried out primarily for other reasons if at all."[5]

Even during the 1960s, at the same time as astronomical satellites, rockets, and balloons were being regularly flown, many astronomers were hostile to space astronomy. While the scientific advantages of an efficiently functioning large space telescope were obvious to astronomers, many nevertheless thought such a telescope should not be built. The issue was not so much one of the scientific results to be achieved as one of timing and priorities; when and how much money should be expended on such instruments? By the standards of ground-based astronomy, space astronomy was hugely expensive. Ground-based astronomers felt themselves to be short of telescopes and funds, so why not use the money being "wasted" on space astronomy for ground-based activities?[6]

But for the relatively small group of astronomers who advocated building a large space telescope, the scientific prizes to be won by such an instrument were so great that they deemed it essential to lay plans as soon as possible. In fact, their pressure for a space telescope embodied an act of faith, the belief that the construction of an optical telescope more powerful in many ways than any ever built would, as the path-breaking telescopes have often done in the past, make possible major new discoveries and that around these, new theories would be woven. Although small in number, the advocates were politically influential and were able to get their voices heard in NASA, as well as prestigious scientific circles.

Indeed, by the mid-1960s, the advocates had persuaded the National Academy of Sciences to establish a committee to investigate the scientific usefulness of a Large Space Telescope. The chairman was Lyman Spitzer. Because the committee was composed of firm supporters of the Telescope, the outcome was a foregone conclusion. Indeed, the aim of Spitzer's committee was not so much to study scientific problems that might be tackled by the Telescope, but rather to carry the advocates' message directly to institutions and individuals that had so far tended to be the least enthusiastic about space astronomy. The Spitzer committee's report, enthusiastically endorsing the idea of a telescope with a primary mirror 3 meters in diameter, was published in 1969. It was a significant event because it meant that the influential backing of the National Academy of Sciences had been secured for the Large Space Telescope, as the planned instrument was now officially called.[7] The publication of the report was an essential step in winning support for the Telescope, both from astronomers and from NASA.

## NASA

During the early 1960s a few NASA field centers had funded studies of large telescopes in space, usually in connection with possible space station programs. The agency had nevertheless shied away from a firm commitment to build such a telescope. Rather, NASA was, in the terminology of phased project planning, in a kind of pre-phase A, in which some studies were conducted, key technical problems were investigated at a low level, and the interest in the program of potential contractors was being fostered. However, as Homer Newell, the head of NASA's Office of Space Science, told the American Astronomical Society in 1966:

> In the past we have built our program around interested key scientists, with the concurrence and endorsement of their peers. However, for anything so large as a telescope comparable in size to our largest ground-based instruments . . . the cost to the nation would be so great that the enthusiastic support and willing participation of an interested scientific community will be essential. An enlarged participation is essential not merely in the design, development, and operation of space facilities, but also in the pursuit of theoretical and laboratory research and of ground-based astronomical observations necessary to support the space program.[8]

Notice here that Newell, by emphasizing the needs of ground-based astronomy, was paying attention to those ground-based astronomers who were worried by the prospect of space astronomy denuding their activities of funds. More importantly, Newell was also stressing that a Large Space Telescope would not be built until there was very substantial support within the astronomical community for the idea, and by implication, far more interest than was being shown in 1966.

By about 1970, groups at the Marshall Space Flight Center and the Goddard Space Flight Center who, together with their contractors, were studying and developing possible telescope designs, were reporting that the Telescope was looking increasingly more feasible technically. Indeed, in 1971 the Telescope entered its official phase A. There were, nevertheless, still serious doubts in NASA headquarters about building the Telescope, doubts fueled largely by the estimated cost of several hundred million dollars together with the Telescope's relatively flimsy support among astronomers.

The concerns of headquarters had again been expressed by Homer Newell in late 1971. Writing to the recently appointed NASA Administrator James Fletcher, Newell described how the agency had often run into major problems with scientists and how, in part, this was because NASA had pushed projects before the appropriate scientific community had a full appreciation of what the project involved. Newell even suggested that when the time came to consider seriously the building of the Large Space Telescope, the agency should wait until the pressure for it "is so great that we can hardly fail to accede to it." In his marginal comments, Fletcher had written "good point."[9]

Headquarters' anxiety about cost also drove the agency to make some very important changes to the planned program to build the Telescope.[10] The most far-reaching of these was the decision to avoid building what had become known as the "precursor" Telescope. For years a precursor Telescope, or perhaps precursor telescopes, had been widely viewed as an essential step on the road to the Large Space Telescope, a step that would provide a scientific and engineering testbed for the more sophisticated instrument. Such a concept was now dead. The precursor Telescope had not met this fate solely, or even largely, because of scientific or technical reasons. While everyone recognized and accepted that the precursor was to lead to the 3-meter Large Space Telescope, there was never widespread agreement on exactly what the precursor itself was to be, and no one concept had developed a strong base of support among the astronomers, NASA, or the contractors. The precursor was therefore politically vulnerable. Also, by 1972, what were later claimed to be, in certain respects, a kind of precursor to the Large Space Telescope, the Big Bird photoreconnaissance satellites, had already been orbited. Perhaps the Big Bird flights meant that for those NASA managers and engineers, contractors, and astronomers in-the-know, a precursor of sorts to the Telescope had already been launched, and so there was no need for NASA to fund the building of another precursor. Once Marshall, selected in 1972 as the lead center for the project to build the Telescope, had decided that there were no compelling technical reasons to build one, and that by cancelling it, money could be saved, even if it meant a harder task in building the 120-inch Telescope, the precursor's fate was sealed.

## OFFICE OF MANAGEMENT AND BUDGET

If NASA's upper management was sometimes ambivalent about the Large Space Telescope, the Office of Management and Budget was generally supportive of, and in later years enthusiastic about, the Telescope. This would be especially true of OMB in the Ford Administration. Certainly the Space Telescope meshed well with an initiative launched during Ford's presidency to increase spending on research and development in science and technology. Ford's OMB director and close advisor, James T. Lynn, was also a strong supporter of federal funding of science and technology. As Ford was to argue in his fiscal year 1978 budget message, "In spite of the financial pressure on the Federal Budget . . . I am again proposing real growth for basic research and development programs this year because I am convinced that we must maintain our world leadership in science and technology in order to increase our national productivity and attain the better life we want for our people and the rest of the world."[11] Indeed, it was during the Ford Administration that a decline in federal research and development spending was reversed, a policy initiative originating in the Office of Management and Budget.[12] The Ford OMB also sought appropriate ways to cash in on the major investment that the nation had made in funding the Space Shuttle. The Large Space Telescope, being shaped by Marshall to be carried aloft by the Shuttle and serviced by Shuttle astronauts, was seen as an ideal means of doing that.

The Office of Management and Budget's support for the Telescope was not matched by the Congress.

## THE CONGRESS

During James Fletcher's first period as NASA administrator from 1971 to 1977, the agency, unable to grasp or accept that the levels of political and financial support that it had enjoyed in the heyday of the Apollo program were not to be quickly recovered, viewed most of its financial problems as originating in the Executive Branch. As a highly placed White House official put it in April 1975, after a meeting with Fletcher and Deputy Administrator George Low, "Dr. Fletcher tends to feel (a) that his best friends are in the Congress and (b) that questions asked and justifications required for [the] NASA program indicates he has little support within the administration."[13] But, with Large Space Telescope, these positions were reversed.

In 1974, the Telescope had appeared as a line item in the NASA budget. This was not for new start money; rather, it was for $6.2 million in planning funds. The House Appropriations Subcommittee deleted the entire amount, and it was only after a vigorous lobbying campaign by contractors and a small number of astronomers that about half of this amount was reinstated. In a House-Senate conference, the compromise reached was that NASA would receive $3 million for planning funds, "provided that consideration is given to substantial participation by other nations in a less expensive project to be launched at a later date."[14]

The 1974 campaign has been examined elsewhere.[15] Here I shall briefly note the three chief outcomes. First, following the direction of Congress, NASA actively sought the participation of the European Space Agency in the project to build the Telescope. Congress also instructed NASA to cut costs, in part by downgrading its planned scientific performance. Most significantly, the size of the main mirror was reduced to 2.4 meters from the originally planned 3 meters, a reduction of over a third in light-gathering power. And third, the congressional criticisms had served to bolster the Telescope's support among astronomers by making it better known and the goals that had been defined for it better understood. Also, those astronomers who now criticized the Telescope would hardly be able to count on the support of the Telescope's advocates when they in turn argued for their own pet projects. The division between the ground-based astronomers and the space astronomers now began to shrink, at least in public.

The switch to the 2.4-meter Telescope, nevertheless, did not prevent concerted efforts by headquarters to produce a still cheaper program. In June 1975, Deputy Administrator George Low pressed for dramatic savings. He had spoken with highly placed officials in Boeing, Lockheed, and Martin-Marietta, all potential major contractors. The message he had conveyed was that "Fletcher and I were concerned that a large space telescope at the costs now being projected would be impossible to include in any NASA budget in the foreseea-

ble future and the project therefore might well be cancelled." Low
had urged the three contractors to see if, by reducing the Telescope's
requirements, the cost could be cut by about half. "I reminded them
of the situation with the Space Shuttle in the 1971 time period and
that it was industry and not NASA which came up with the clearer
designs which essentially cut the development costs of the Shuttle by
a factor of two. I urged the same kind of innovative thinking by industry on the LST."[16] The issue of whether the Telescope was feasible
in an engineering sense had already been decided. Now it was a
question for NASA to present a Telescope program that was politically feasible. This meant walking a thin line indeed: cut costs too
much and the loss of scientific performance might persuade the astronomers to drop their support, but go to Congress with too expensive a program and the Telescope might never get off the ground.

Certainly the project's participants realized that despite the reductions in cost and the design changes made in the Large Space Telescope program, as well as the alteration in approach underpinning
its planned building, Congress was not guaranteed to fund the building of the Telescope in fiscal year 1977. The congressional hearings
during early 1975 had demonstrated that this would take some hard
selling.

The House Appropriations Subcommittee in particular had
taken a tough line. Of the subcommittee's members, George Shipley
(as in 1974) was again the most aggressive questioner. The NASA
manager to bear the brunt of the questioning was Noel Hinners, the
head of the Office of Space Science in NASA headquarters since the
summer of 1974. The focus of the hearings held firm. Shipley chis-
eled away trying to get a total cost estimate. "I am very hesitant,"
Hinners repeated, "to give an estimate, since it would not be meaningful until the study efforts are completed. . . . I have insisted in
the LST studies that there be no possibility of a 'buy-in'. . . . I am
new enough on the job that I want no problems like that." It was
too much for Shipley: "I am old enough on the job to know . . .
that estimates invariably are low and you run into cost overruns.
Will you know when you complete Phase B what this project will
cost?"[17] That is, Shipley did not want to allow a so-called buy-in, in
which Congress would approve the Large Space Telescope at some
cost figure, but, a few years later, be told that the actual cost would
be much higher. Yet, because so much money had been invested,
there would be great reluctance to cancel the project.

Other space science projects had overrun. The most recent example was the Viking Mission to Mars, and such testimony has to be put in the context of other programs that had appeared before the Appropriations Subcommittee. As Subcommittee Chairman Edward P. Boland pointed out earlier in the hearings, Viking had been projected to cost $364 million, but would reach $1 billion, high for an automated space science project, although very small by the standards of manned spaceflight (to use NASA's term). Hinner's assurance of no buy-in was his promise that it would not happen again. The NASA comptroller also contended that the Viking cost overruns were smaller than they appeared because the earlier estimate had been very preliminary. Hinners emphasized that it should not have been released to Congress because it was unreliable. He did not want to make the same mistake again.

These arguments on the Telescope and criticisms of Viking were, however, a small part of a much larger body of congressional discontent. During fiscal year 1975 and fiscal year 1976 NASA hearings, the views of the House Subcommittee and NASA were not meshing well. At the root of this discord was a widespread opinion in Congress that the agency should do more to apply NASA-developed technology to urgent problems on Earth, such as energy and Earth resources. In fiscal year 1975, for example, the House Subcommittee had urged NASA to build a third Earth Resources Satellite (ERTS), later to be renamed Landsat.[18] To do so, the subcommittee had pressed the agency to take funds from other approved programs. The subcommittee's questioning, then, often turned to what the Telescope could do to solve practical problems on the earth. The NASA witnesses were thereby driven to invoke the lessons of history. At one point, for example, Administrator Fletcher contended:

> The benefits of astronomy are generally longer term than some of the others we talked about. On the other hand, they are far-reaching in their impact. The benefit from Galileo's experiments was literally the Industrial Revolution. How can you put a value on that? We are on the edge of extremely important discoveries in astronomy. It [astronomy] is starting to blossom much in the same way as in the days of Galileo and Copernicus. If you ask the two areas the astronomers are most interested in, one would be the quasars, enormous energy sources coming out of those objects, and second, the nature of our universe . . . is it expanding without end? How did it begin? It is going to contract again? Understanding those processes will contribute to our fundamental knowledge

of science. There could be brand new energy sources downstream, just
as nuclear energy came out of Einstein's investigation's. By the way, that
was astronomy, too. The whole idea of relativity came out of astronomy.

The historical arguments presented by Fletcher, while often repeated by others in various forms, would make even a novice student
in the history of science and technology blush. Representative Max
Bacus of Montana, moreover, was not interested in vague promises.
He wanted Fletcher to do the impossible, to give solid estimates of
the practical benefits to be won by the Telescope. Fletcher responded:
"Even though you try to put probabilities on realizing benefits, even
if it is only 5 to 10 per cent, we are not talking about billions or
trillions of dollars, we are talking about the salvation of the world.
It is worth a 10 percent chance to seize the opportunity."[19]

While this reply is surely hyperbole, Fletcher was nevertheless
striving to make a serious point: scientific advances *can* lead in un-
predictable ways to technological breakthroughs. Indeed, this has
been a central justification of the federal support of science since
World War II. The image it conjures up is of a pool of scientific
knowledge from which those who thirst after technological innova-
tions can drink. Adding new knowledge to the pool increases the
chances of additional technological advances.

Such arguments have of course been made for a long time.[20] Essentially, they can be reduced to a type of "trickle down" argument.
Classical economists identified the market place as the hidden hand
that transformed the pursuit of individual self-interest into the advance of the common good. As David Noble has written, this sort
of argument has been delivered by scientists but without any clear
mechanism, such as the market place, to translate individual self-
interest into the common good. Instead, the claim was that "if scientists remained free to pursue their calling as they saw fit, to satisfy
their scientific curiosity about Nature, their effort would inevitably—
and without the need for conscious intent on their part—contribute
to the general good." Hence, "What was good for scientists was
good for science, and what was good for science was good for society."[21]

The astronomer-lobbyists often invoked the practical benefits
that might "trickle down" from the basic researches to be conducted
with the Telescope. A favorite example frequently cited by them was
how nuclear fusion, discovered in the 1930s, was the power source

that keeps the stars shining. Fusion produces prodigious amounts of energy and since the early 1950s has been widely viewed as a long-term, but likely, source of heat and light for use on Earth. This was a particularly relevant example in the mid-1970s, a period in which America had awakened to an energy crisis.[22] Here was a vivid illustration of how research in astronomy offered chances of solving very practical problems.[23]

A decade earlier, in a very different time and when funds had flowed somewhat more readily, scientists had usually not had to make such direct claims about the technological benefits of scientific research. Defending increased funding of the multihundred million dollar Stanford Linear Accelerator before the Congress in 1964, its director had stated, "I am not of the school who tries to defend this kind of work through its byproducts. I believe if you want the by-product, you should develop the byproduct. I think you would do it more economically and do it more effectively. If you want to push high powered radio tubes, then the best way to do so is to push the development of high powered radio tubes and not to build accelerators which require high powered radio tubes."[24]

Big Science for the sake of Big Science was hardly enough to win congressional support by the mid-1970s. This was reflected in the congressional hearings on the Telescope as well as in private conversations between scientists and lawmakers. "There was," Princeton astronomer and one of the leading astronomer-lobbyists John Bahcall recalls, "excitement and interest among Congressmen and Senators about the science itself . . . but that did not imply this was something that ought necessarily be done." While there were a few exceptions, "It was more often the connection with industrial development in general or in their particular district or state or defense related activities. It was under these sorts of ideas that it was possible to get an immediate sympathetic hearing, so that got you over the question of why, and then only discussed the question of what to do." Only rarely was there the response "science is good, we want to help you with that."[25]

Congressional tussles and the need for NASA to repackage the Telescope also prompted a name change. After a small committee had considered about thirty possible names for the Telescope, in October 1975, quietly and without a stated reason, Deputy Administrator George Low directed the switch to "Space Telescope."[26]

Some of the astronomers were alarmed. They saw the renaming as a portent of yet more cuts to come. Margaret Burbidge, who had worked closely on planning the Telescope and who was soon to be president of the American Astronomical Society, sent a vigorous protest to Low.[27] Low assured Burbidge that the change of name was not driven by any possible further reduction in aperture size from 2.4 meters. Rather, he felt that "in these days of stringent science funding, we should not use titles such as 'Large' or 'Very Large' which suggest an opulence which neither NASA, science nor astronomy are enjoying these days and which tend to invite reductions in the budgets."[28]

The central task facing the advocates of the Telescope was therefore to win approval from a skeptical, and at times hostile, Congress, and the name change was one tactic to reach this goal. But before going to Congress again the program would have to be approved by the White House for inclusion in the President's fiscal 1977 budget.

## LEFT AT THE POST

NASA had begun its detailed discussions with the Office of Management and Budget on the upcoming fiscal year 1977 budget in the spring of 1975. Out of these exchanges had emerged the planning target for the agency's overall budget. This had been sent from OMB to NASA in July 1975, and had been used by the agency to prepare its detailed submission to OMB in late September.[29]

In his letter accompanying the draft budget, Administrator Fletcher told James T. Lynn, the director of OMB, that for a balanced program in aeronautics and space, a number of new programs should be initiated each year. He stressed that for NASA, new program starts "are simply *replacements* for other projects as they are completed. . . . The need for NASA to initiate a number of new programs in FY 1977 is especially acute because of the general moratorium on new program starts in the FY 1976 budget."

Number one on NASA's list of new starts was the Space Telescope. Fletcher explained that it was projected to cost about $400 million (FY 1977 dollars) to design and develop, a cut of $100 million compared to the earlier estimates for the 3-meter Telescope.[30] The other flight project proposed as a new start was the Solar Maximum Mission, a satellite designed to make detailed observations of the Sun during the 1979–1980 period of peak solar flare activity. Its total cost was estimated at $75–90 million.

In their planning ceiling sent to NASA in July, OMB had made a specific provision of $20 million for new flight projects to be started in fiscal 1977. Moreover, OMB recommended that the Space Telescope be funded as a new start. Although they conceded the cost was large, the Office of Management and Budget argued that it was roughly on a par with a major spaceflight mission to the planets, and agreed that the scientific potential was very large.

However, in a speech at the White House on October 6, 1975, President Ford, disturbed by a rising deficit and aiming to balance the books within three years, announced a cut of another $28 billion from the forthcoming federal budget.[31] NASA had to shoulder its portion of the burden, and so the new and decidedly unpleasant problem facing Fletcher and his staff was how to meet OMB's direction to delete $305 million from the budget NASA had submitted only the month before.

The Office of Management and Budget wanted to minimize the impact of the cuts on the development of the Space Shuttle. But, as OMB contended initially, this would require extensive "belt tightening" across the whole of NASA, the cancelling of at least one ongoing flight project (probably Pioneer Venus), and making relatively large reductions in the number of the agency's civil service employees. If this plan was followed it would still mean a six-month delay in the Space Shuttle schedule.

This was too thin a gruel for Administrator Fletcher to feed upon. He protested vigorously to the director of the Office of Management and Budget. His first point was that the cut would be bound to force a major delay in the Shuttle's schedule. This would lead in turn to "increases in total cost, large reductions in employment in 1976 as well as 1977, possible loss of foreign contributions, and a serious disruption for many months in a program that is the central focus of the entire space program on which all our plans for the future are based." For another two-and-a-half pages, Fletcher marshalled arguments on why the NASA budget should not be cut, but then he turned to what actions the agency would take if OMB did not alter its decision. He emphasized that NASA would not cut or stretch out any major ongoing flight projects. If Pioneer Venus were to be cut, for example, it would mean a loss of the $65 million already spent. He did concede, however, that "we would feel obliged to cut in about half the outlays included in our FY 1977 budget for replacement project starts in research and development."[32]

The new start of the Space Telescope was now under serious threat. Moreover, if the Office of Management and Budget approved NASA's method of reaching the $305 million cut, the Space Telescope would be in direct competition with the much cheaper Solar Maximum Mission for inclusion in the President's budget. The Solar Maximum Satellite was also time limited; that is, it would defeat its purpose to launch the satellite at a time when solar activity was not at its maximum. A delay to the Solar Maximum Mission was critical; in contrast, the Telescope had no particular launch date to meet.

Fletcher, as he claimed to one of the astronomer-lobbyists a few months later, had fought the issue for some time and had managed to lower the amount to be cut below $305 million. He had even, he remembered (although there is no documentary evidence for this), taken the Space Telescope twice to President Ford. But Ford had been concerned about an "indefensible" new start while he was cutting social programs. It had indeed been widely expected that the Democratic Congress would find the Republican Ford's reductions in social programs unacceptable and so increase the expenditures in the fiscal year 1977 budget.[33]

Fletcher had also begun to see what he said were weak spots in the Telescope program. Further possible cost savings were, he recalled, coming to light, but had not yet been evaluated. His advisors had thus told him that in view of these failings and the known opposition in the Congress—particularly in the shape of George Shipley—it would be a mistake to press for the Telescope in fiscal year 1977. A new start proposal in fiscal year 1978 would be stronger and stand a better chance of succeeding.[34] Another point against the Telescope was that the executive branch had accorded an ERDA (Energy Research and Development Agency) proposal to build a $78 million colliding beam accelerator relatively higher priority than the Telescope for scarce new start funding.[35] OMB was also concerned to ensure that the construction of the Space Telescope would be phased with the Shuttle program so that Telescope monies would be needed *after* Shuttle funding had reached its peak. The Space Telescope would then reap the harvest of what was known among OMB staffers as the "Shuttle dividend," the availability of a growing amount of funds that would be freed by completion of the development of the Space

Shuttle.[36] Yet, however the numbers were juggled, the cut in the NASA budget would compel a slip in the Shuttle schedule, undermining in OMB's opinion the case for starting the Telescope in fiscal year 1977. Another factor in play was that, for a period, the Department of Defense opposed the building of the Telescope, or at least the building of one that might incorporate items of, or processes for building, technology employed in satellites used for national security purposes, in particular photoreconnaissance satellites. The Telescope's dominant technical heritage must be from photoreconnaissance satellites, but given the distinct ends to which they are directed, there must be significant differences between the designs of astronomical space telescopes and those deployed for reconnaissance. As Presidential science advisor George Keyworth put it in 1985, there is "no question that it would have been a very much more difficult task [to build the Space Telescope] if we had not already acquired considerable expertise in both talent and industrial manufacturing. The [Space Telescope] is new, but it draws upon technologies used in military systems." And as Deputy Administrator George Low noted in his diary in 1976, if the Telescope went ahead immediately, NASA and its contractors could not "make use of some possibly existing classified systems."[37]

From Fletcher's viewpoint, the odds had become overwhelming. NASA decided there was too much political capital to be lost by continuing to push for the Telescope. The position NASA and OMB thereby reached in their negotiations was that the Solar Maximum Mission would be included in the President's budget. The Space Telescope, despite the fact that this would save only $4 million in fiscal year 1977, would not.[38]

## THE ASTRONOMERS REACT

The President's budget was officially embargoed until it reached the Congress in January 1976, but on December 22, 1975, news of the Space Telescope's omission was leaked to John Bahcall. His reactions, as well as those of many other astronomers when they heard the news, were surprise, dismay, and anger. To add insult to injury, there were not even funds in the budget for further studies.

The Space Telescope had already suffered delays on account of Congress's direction to reevaluate the program's scope and to seek international participation. There were still powerful critics in the Congress. The contractors had contributed heavily towards the costs of the technical studies they had performed and would be hesitant to risk more of their own capital and resources on a program that appeared to have such flimsy political support. It even seemed to some observers that the Space Telescope might well meet the fate of other programs that had failed to be approved for several years, that is, eventually be dropped. Some of the astronomers now turned their anger on the Space Shuttle, the program that underpinned NASA's future space activities and the program that its top managers deemed essential to the agency's survival. Indeed, during the early 1970s, the building of the Telescope itself had moved toward a more central position in the agency's set of objectives in part because NASA packaged it—literally and in a marketing sense—with the Shuttle.

Space scientists had, on the whole, never been enthusiastic about the Space Shuttle. Some had attacked it publicly, claiming that the U.S. had no compelling need for such a spacecraft, a spacecraft that would drain money away from what they believed were worthier projects.[39] Nor had scientists had any real say in its design characteristics, and they, after all, would be among its major users. As one prominent space scientist would recall, "scientists were told, there's the Shuttle. Figure out how to use it."[40]

Bahcall, along with other advocates of the Space Telescope, was outraged that NASA had used the scientific payloads it would be able to fly as one of the central justifications of the Space Shuttle, but with the Shuttle sold, science was apparently pushed aside. He made exactly this point in a letter to Administrator Fletcher, protesting that it is "shocking that out of a total NASA budget of 3.7 billion dollars, priorities would not be arranged" to fund the Telescope at some low level. "I am afraid," Bahcall wrote, "that the scientific community will conclude that NASA is intent on obtaining funds to support its own institutional needs in preference over wider goals. I fear that scientific support for the Shuttle program (over 1 billion dollars in the present NASA budget) will be decreased. Many will conclude that NASA cares most about its space vehicle (the Shuttle) and much less about what science it is doing with the Shuttle."[41]

A similar threat was made by C. R. O'Dell, NASA's project scientist for the Space Telescope. "Space Telescope has been a strongly supported scientific payload for the Shuttle era," O'Dell reported to a headquarters manager. "This is very important at a time when the discontent of scientists being forced to accept the Shuttle development has not really died away. This strong support was not always present, but is the result of a carefully orchestrated activity over the last few years to educate the ground-based astronomers about the potential of [Space Telescope] and to convince them to support this rather than the continued construction of many large ground-based telescopes. We are now on a crest of their support, but if we fail to capitalize on it, we may lose it . . . "[42]

What, however, were the astronomers to do? Bahcall now sought a means of restoring Space Telescope to the budget. He looked to Sidney Drell for guidance. Drell, a veteran of science politics, was an associate director of the Stanford Linear Accelerator, a major scientific facility. During the previous budget cycle, Stanford had expected new start funding for an addition to the accelerator with money provided by the Energy Research and Development Agency.[43] The Office of Management and Budget had deleted the funding, but the director of the Stanford Linear Accelerator and his staff, by appealing directly to Congress, had been successful in having it reinstated at a low level for fiscal year 1976. The physicists had kept their sponsoring agency informed unofficially and informally of everything done. This ensured that no one's toes were trodden on in ERDA.

During a telephone conversation with Drell, in which they discussed this lobbying activity, Bahcall fastened upon the idea of adopting the maneuvers exploited by the physicists.[44] The first step was to secure approval from NASA to start lobbying. By the end of the day, after his call to Drell, Bahcall had spoken twice with Hinners and had told him that the astronomers would consider an effort to get congressional restoration of funds only if they had his implied blessing. Hinners agreed. He had already supplied lists of people to contact, and was in touch with representatives of the contractors to get their reactions to the Telescope's omission from the budget.[45]

The contractors, too, had been dismayed that the Space Telescope had not been listed as a new start. Their message to Hinners was that a new start should be pursued in fiscal 1977. They had used large amounts of their own funds to perform studies to position themselves for the detailed and development phase contracts, and the earlier NASA study contracts had met only a fraction of their outlays. The contractors wanted firm decisions soon to make the best use of the teams they had working on the Space Telescope. They were in business to make money and if the Telescope was not to go ahead, they would reassign their teams immediately.

Bahcall polled ten leading optical astronomers on whether or not to push for reinstatement of funds at a low level for fiscal 1977. Such a course carried a decided element of risk. If it failed and the law-makers became antagonized, it might backfire and delay Space Tele-scope for a number of years.[46]

But with Hinner's concurrence with a lobbying campaign, and the backing of a number of astronomers, Bahcall and the other lead-ing astronomer-lobbyists decided to accept the risks and drive for-ward. They would appeal directly to the Congress to restore funding for fiscal year 1977. In so doing they would launch a campaign whose audacious goal, at least as they saw it, was nothing less than to outflank the Office of Management and Budget and the top NASA management.

## AN INTEREST GROUP

A massive lobbying campaign began with telephone calls, visits, arti-cles planted in influential journals,[47] and letters to congressional staff-ers, congressmen, and anybody else who might help. Such move-ments derive their power not just from the quality of the arguments presented, but also from the number of people involved and their de-termination. Hence the invocation by the campaign's leaders that the volume of mail, telephone, and personal calls was very important. Participation by astronomers and physicists with no direct interest in the Space Telescope was seen as especially helpful because it demon-strated a broad base of support. At no one point, however, did the leading astronomer-lobbyists—Bahcall, George Field of the Harvard-Smithsonian Observatory, Spitzer (some thirty years after first advo-cating a space telescope), and George Wallerstein of the University of Washington—create a formal committee to run the campaign. Rather, while they circulated memoranda to each other, most of their links were by telephone.[48]

One of their most important tasks was to contact other astrono-mers and encourage them to join in the campaign. Once this had been done, and with little coaching, the astronomers generally took the initiative themselves.[49]

Certainly this was more of a grass roots campaign than the

hastily constructed effort of 1974. The astronomers were more
united and were, in effect, acting as an interest group, although not
formally organized as one. "Of course," one writer points out,
"Americans' love affair with interest groups is hardly a new phenom-
enon. From abolitionists to abortionists there has never been a lack
of issue-conscious organizations."[50] Nevertheless, by acting as they
did, the astronomers' behavior mirrored changes within the wider
political culture of the United States in the 1960s and 1970s, for it
was during this period that there was an explosion in the number of
groups lobbying in Washington.[51] The astronomers had stumbled
blindly into the political process, but their eyes had been opened
quickly, in large part because they had been opened for them by contractors and some NASA managers.

The interests of the industrial contractors and those of the astronomers had now merged for both groups had the common short-
term goal of securing funds for the Space Telescope. The contractors conducted their own lobbying but also offered the astronomers
background information on the important people to contact and
their political preferences and the best ways to gain entry to their offices. Speaking in 1983, Bahcall recalled that "Lyman [Spitzer] and
I met on several occasions in this office [at Princeton] with contractual people . . . and they were just enormously well informed, and
they were using us in the same way we were using them. . . . The
crucial thing for us was information . . . how do we get to talk to
people, who are the people that are in the offices, what are their interests, the things that are going to sell to this Congressman or this
Senator? The best information we had on that was from professional
lobbyists for these companies. They were really good."[52] Names of
firms likely to receive Space Telescope contracts, broken down by
state and size, were provided to Bahcall, for example. These lists
could then be exploited to persuade members of Congress that their
constituents would be well served by the construction of the Space
Telescope.

The contractors' own efforts were also loosely coordinated in
NASA Headquarters by T. Bland Norris, the recently appointed head
of the Astrophysics Division in NASA Headquarters. The funding
problems had thus brought into existence an energetic and determined ad hoc coalition of astronomers pursuing professional interests, and contractors pursuing economic interests. There was never-

theless significant NASA input and some measure of oversight, and firm, indeed at times highly enthusiastic, support from a number of people in the White House and Congress as well as sympathetic journalists.

What was the nature of this coalition? Some political scientists argue that major features of the American political process are the formation and operation of so-called iron triangles.[53] Iron triangles are informal but enduring units linking executive bureaus (such as NASA, for example), congressional committees, and interest groups with a stake in a particular program. The iron triangles then exert all-powerful control over the link between politics and administration, between policy goals and their implementation.

This concept, however, does not really fit the case of the Space Telescope. For the Telescope, the organization was much more fluid than that suggested by an iron triangle. That people moved in and out of the selling process, and that a coalition had to be carefully constructed, is better illustrated by what political scientist Hugh Heclo terms an "issue network," a loose grouping that shares knowledge about some aspect of public policy.[54] These issue networks may or may not be mobilized into a shared-action group (by creating a coalition), or, a shared-belief group, thereby becoming an interest organization. In the case of the Space Telescope, those in the issue network, that is, those interested in the pursuit of space astronomy, had deliberately sought to draw in outsiders. And at the same time as this process, there had coalesced a group who shared the belief that the Space Telescope should be built, and had then started to lobby for it, thereby acting as an interest group. But perhaps Henry Lambright's term "ad hocracy" best captures the process by which approval for the Telescope was sought. Ad hoc policy-making is a process in which a decision, such as whether or not to approve the Space Telescope, is constantly being reframed, and the issues surrounding the decision reshuffled and repackaged. Certainly, an appeal to "ad hocracy" reflects better than an issue network that the Telescope designs and scientific objectives and the planned program to build the Telescope were themselves constantly being revised and repackaged, in part by the demands of coalition building and the need to extend and strengthen the coalition that favored the Telescope.[55]

However one might want to describe the policy-making process, a lobbying campaign by the coalition of astronomers and contractors and their supporters was, in fact, just what Hinners had hoped for. When the Space Telescope had been removed as a new start, Hinners, unknown to the astronomers, had gone even further and deleted all Space Telescope funding. As he recalls, " . . . the money wouldn't have done much for us. So my strategy was not to put something in, and get the outside world really antagonized. And it worked. Panic!"[56]

The use of an apparent cancellation of a project to strengthen its political position is not an uncommon maneuver of federal agencies in dealing with Congress and the Executive Branch, and by the Congress in its interactions with the Executive Branch. This maneuver is the well-known "Washington Monument Game."[57] Hinners, in playing a version of the Washington Monument Game, would remove all Space Telescope funds as a clear sign to astronomers and contractors that the program was in trouble. They would then, Hinners hoped, rise up and give vent to their wrath. In this apparently contradictory manner, Hinners sought to rally support for the Telescope, and start a lobbying campaign. Hinner's tactic had fanned what a note in the Office of Management and Budget files refers to as a "firestorm" amongst the astronomers, but the fire had been sparked by the omission of the Space Telescope as a new start.

Some of the lobbying was aimed directly at Fletcher, whose motives were now widely distrusted by the astronomers. One member of the group of astronomers most closely involved in planning for the Telescope knew Fletcher well from his work as chairman of NASA's influential Physical Sciences Committee. This was George Field, director of the prestigious Harvard-Smithsonian Observatory.

Field's senior positions as an astronomer and member of NASA's advisory apparatus meant he could be fairly direct with Fletcher. Indeed, Field posed the central question when he wrote to the NASA administrator: "Why have the astronomers reacted so strongly? Astronomers who are normally quite restrained have become passionate because they feel so frustrated." Field pointed tactfully to what he saw as failures in NASA's handling of recent events. "As things are now," he reported, "there are serious doubts among the senior astronomers as to NASA's true intentions." Field knew Fletcher had offered a strong endorsement of the Space Telescope at "An International Discussion of Space Observatories" in January, but the message, Field wrote, had not been conveyed to the astronomers.[58] Field confided, "most of all, Jim, the astronomers need to meet with you face to face so that you can allay the fears which cripple effective action and so that your own interest and excitement about ST can be communicated to all."[59]

Within a few more weeks, plans were laid for a meeting on May 19, to be attended by Fletcher, several other NASA officials, and some twenty-nine leading astronomers. There were to be formal presentations on the benefits of astronomy to society, and on the science and technology of the Space Telescope.[60]

At the meeting, Fletcher announced to the astronomers that he was determined to press ahead with a new start in fiscal year 1978. His audience was far from mollified. From their perspective, Fletcher showed remarkably little grasp of the Telescope. Bahcall, for one, thought he had been "astoundingly ignorant."[61] More alarmingly, during the question period Fletcher had, in the opinion of the astronomers, revealed himself to be possibly willing to drop the Space Telescope program in favor of two more Space Shuttles to be used by the military but paid for by NASA.[62]

The meeting with Fletcher was held in May, but by this time much had already passed on Capitol Hill. The astronomer-lobbyists had first sought a small amount of money to initiate the Space Telescope program in fiscal 1977. They had met with success in the House Authorization Subcommittee, chaired by aerospace enthusiast Don Fuqua, which had always backed the Telescope. In late February, the Subcommittee recommended a new start with funding of $3 million reprogrammed from within the NASA budget.

The Senate Authorization Subcommittee disagreed. It committed itself only to stating that the Space Telescope should receive "highest priority" for a fiscal 1978 start. Faced with a discrepancy between the Senate and House Authorization bills, the astronomers' next step was to attempt to gain full authorization when the House and Senate resolved their differences. To do this, astronomers had to find an advocate in the Senate. Bahcall and Spitzer turned again to Republican Charles Mathias of Maryland who had assisted the Telescope in 1974.

Bahcall and Spitzer visited two senators and several staffers on March 31, one of whom was Mathias. They were accompanied by astrophysicist Richard C. Henry of the Johns Hopkins University in Baltimore, Maryland, to add "local color," a typically careful touch.[63] Bahcall had ready a draft of remarks for Mathias to read in the full Senate session of April 1. Here Mathias requested the senior body follow the House in providing the $3 million authorization from re-programmed funds.[64]

A few days after the meeting with Mathias, Fletcher was writing to a highly placed official in the Office of Management and Budget:

> It appears we had underestimated the commitment to the Space Telescope that had grown over the years among scientists, industrial organizations, and members of Congress. We have been inundated with severe criticism from virtually every academic institution associated with astronomy. We have been urged forcefully by the aerospace and optical contractors to do something to alleviate the costs of their holding together effective engineering teams in order to be able to bid on the telescope project if and when it were authorized and funded.[65]

As the astronomers had realized, Fletcher's attitude towards the Telescope was crucial. Fletcher had been sworn in as the NASA administrator in April 1971, a difficult time for the space agency as it struggled to come to terms with a loss of some of its political support and a budget much diminished from the heady days of the early 1960s and the race to the moon. And here it is perhaps worth referring again to a memorandum sent to Fletcher in late 1971. As noted earlier, Homer Newell, a highly placed and experienced NASA science manager, had described to Fletcher some recent problems the agency had had with the scientific community. In Newell's opinion, these had arisen in part because the agency had pushed projects before the scientific community had a full appreciation of what they involved. Newell had even suggested when the time came to consider building a Space Telescope, the agency should wait until the pressure for it "is so great that we can hardly fail to accede to it." In his marginal comments, Fletcher had written "good point."[66] Had Fletcher now decided in mid-1976 that Newell's criterion had at last been met, that the support for the Telescope *had* indeed become overwhelming? Such a view is supported by the comments made by a senior NASA manager in February 1976. When the astronomers asked if NASA's top management was willing to fight for the Telescope, he replied that in August 1975, Fletcher had had doubts about getting the Telescope through the Congress. However, Fletcher was now "confident" of its chances of success because of the Congress's reaction to the Telescope's omission from the fiscal year 1977 budget.[67]

In any case, Fletcher now proposed, and the agency took this line on Capitol Hill, that the "Request for Proposals" for the Telescope be issued later in 1976. However, the decisions on which contractors were to build the Space Telescope would not be made until *after* the budget cycle for fiscal 1978 had been completed. This action, while it would not commit the administration in advance of the budget process, had the advantage for Fletcher that it would help to dissolve the pressure on the agency. The Space Telescope program's momentum would be preserved and " . . . will place us in a sound position to proceed with the project if it is approved during the coming [budget] cycle. Conversely, we feel that to take no steps until mid-1977 would result in serious program discontinuities and even some inequities."[68]

The House Appropriations Subcommittee was still the major stumbling block for the Space Telescope's supporters. By 1976, Edward P. Boland, the chairman, had swung firmly against the Telescope because of its cost. A Democrat from Springfield, Massachusetts, Boland was a twenty-three-year veteran of the House and had solid credentials as a supporter of federally funded research and development. He had vast experience in the politics of science and technology.

Boland's reservations about the Telescope had been highlighted during NASA hearings on February 18, 1976. These featured the most trenchant exchanges on public record between opponents and supporters of the Space Telescope. At one point Boland asked Hinners, who was known to be an unabashed advocate, "If we don't have the Space Telescope, the world is not going to come to an end anyway, is it?" Boland argued that, "I think the problem that many members of this Subcommittee have with the Space Telescope is basically one of priorities. . . . The Large Space Telescope is unquestionably a fascinating and interesting project, but it might get up to $500 million. You know we could fund many different applications satellites that would have a more immediate payout." Further on in the hearing, Boland added: "You know, someone said, what good is it going to do when you get it out there? What does it do? What does it find? And somebody says 'more of the same.' Is that correct?" When the NASA witness replied "I fail to understand why the acquisition of basic knowledge and the intellectual stimulation are not regarded as applications to the human endeavor," Boland complained, "Hadn't we spent enough?"[69]

Those sentiments were also aired by Richard N. Malow, an influential staffer to Boland's subcommittee and on whom Boland relied (and relies) heavily for technical advice. Malow was strongly opposed to the Space Telescope, and as George Low had discovered in April 1976, "he doesn't see such a telescope at all for quite a few years. He states that the Shuttle will fly in 1979 or 1980, and at that time we should be in a position to fly a large number of payloads which appeal to the Congress and to the general public, and that the telescope is not such a payload." Malow wanted more funding for applications satellites and other areas; "In fact," Low lamented, "in any area other than the space telescope."[70]

From the scientists' point of view, Boland (and Malow) was completely immovable. His subcommittee would not approve a new start appropriation. When the House and Senate came together to iron out differences in their respective NASA appropriations, he remained insistent that NASA not be allowed to release Requests for Proposals for the contractors to build the Telescope *before* a new start was authorized. The Senate Appropriations Subcommittee, too, opposed selecting contractors in this unorthodox manner. But again, the lobbyists won a partial victory when a compromise was struck allowing Requests for Proposals to be released as soon as the fiscal year 1978 budget was submitted by the President to Congress in January 1977. This did not mean that new start would be granted automatically. A tough fight still lay ahead in fiscal 1978.

## REFLECTIONS

The efforts to secure new start funding in 1976 had helped to shape a well-organized coalition with supporters among the astronomers, contractors, and parts of NASA, as well as the Congress and White House. New start funding had not been won, but the activities in 1976 had, it would turn out, laid the basis for a successful campaign in 1977. However, the coalition building had started earlier than 1976. Coalition building had very much been the goal of the Spitzer committee of the late 1960s that reported for the National Academy of Sciences on "The Scientific Uses of the Space Telescope," for example.

The campaigns undertaken by the astronomers between 1974 and 1977 played an important role in winning approval for the

Space Telescope. Here the astronomers were following in the steps of George Ellery Hale and other astronomer entrepreneurs who, earlier in the century, had financed the building of new telescopes by persuading the wealthy and the generous of the telescope's worth. In the 1970s, the patrons were not rich individuals, but NASA, the Office of Management and Budget, and the Congress. The selling campaigns for the Space Telescope were also of a very different character from those conducted by Hale and other leaders of the astronomical community of his time. In fact, the essence of the campaigns launched by the advocates of the Telescope was the large number of astronomers who participated, and who, by 1977, had been mobilized into an effective lobbying group. Before this time, space astronomers had been content to leave the selling of their programs to NASA; with the Space Telescope this was no longer the case, and so it would also be for planetary scientists in the following year when the Galileo Mission appeared for new start funding.

It would, however, be a mistake to view the astronomers as acting in isolation; rather, one has to see them as joining with sympathetic journalists, a number of government officials, as well as with professional lobbyists for the contractors with an ad hoc coalition. The contractors, in addition to their own lobbying activities and the powerful arguments they were able to make in terms of jobs to be won by the Telescope, were also able to help educate the astronomers to the ways of Capitol Hill and what selling the Telescope would actually entail. Nor should one ignore the fact that NASA also played a crucial role in selling the Telescope, even helping to form and in part to guide the coalition of contractors and astronomers.

Nor was the Telescope's expected scientific performance isolated from the political activities. To begin with, the Telescope's scientific performance had to be sufficiently impressive to a substantial number of astronomers for it to even stand a chance of getting off the drawing board. This is what had made the redesign of the Telescope between 1974 and 1977 such a difficult and delicate task. The main driver in this process for NASA was the need to reduce costs to make the Telescope politically feasible, to match the planned program to what the market would bear. Yet, if this had led to cuts in scientific performance that the astronomers had judged too drastic, the Telescope would have been just as dead as if it had died at the hands of the Congress. While a politically feasible Space Telescope did result, in the selling process the Telescope had been both oversold and underfunded. It would—as George Shipley had predicted in 1975—soon prove itself to be a buy-in.

## ACKNOWLEDGMENTS

By permission of Cambridge University Press, portions of this paper are reprinted from Robert W. Smith's (with contributions by Paul A. Hanle, Robert H. Kargon, and Joseph N. Tatarewicz) *The Space Telescope: A Study of NASA, Science, Technology, and Politics* (New York: Cambridge University Press, 1989). This paper is also based upon work partially supported by the National Aeronautics and Space Administration under Contract NASW-3691 and the National Science Foundation under grant SES-8510336. Any opinions, findings, and conclusions expressed herein are those of the author and do not necessarily reflect the views of NASA. In addition, I would like to thank the American Institute of Physics for the award of a grant to travel to Houston to conduct several interviews with C. R. O'Dell.

I am also grateful to the participants at the NASA/NASM Seminar for their comments, a number of which have been incorporated into this version of the paper. I am especially grateful to the paper's commentator, Henry Lambright, for some stimulating remarks, in particular for suggesting the notion of ad hocracy. Suggestions that several people made in reviewing the manuscript of *The Space Telescope: A Study of NASA, Science, Technology, and Politics* have also been incorporated into the present paper, and I would like to thank Sylvia Fries, the late Leo Goldberg, Paul Hanle, Robert Kargon, and most particularly Joe Tatarewicz for numerous helpful discussions.

Staff at the NASA History Office, NASA Headquarters, as well as at the Marshall Space Flight Center and the Goddard Space Flight Center helped guide me through the maze of NASA documents. Thanks are also due to the staff of the Gerald R. Ford Library for assistance, and to Memphis Norman for his help in tracing OMB files. John Bahcall and Lyman Spitzer Jr. very generously allowed my colleague Paul Hanle to work through their personal files. The oral histories cited in the references, unless specified otherwise, have been processed in the Department of Space Science and Exploration of the National Air and Space Museum, Smithsonian Institution, and I am deeply grateful to Martin Collins and his staff for the superb support they have provided over several years.

## NOTES

1. James E. Webb, *Space Age Management: The Large Scale Approach* (New York: McGraw Hill, 1969), 89.

2. Robert W. Smith and J.N. Tatarewicz, "Replacing a Technology: The Large Space Telescope and CCDs," *Proceedings of the IEEE* 73 (1985): 1221–1235.

3. H. N. Russell, "Where Astronomers Go When They Die," *Scientific American* 149 (1933): 112–113.

4. Douglas Aircraft Company, September 1, 1946, Appendix 5 to "Preliminary Design of an Experimental World-Orbiting Spaceship," Douglas Aircraft Company, Inc., Santa Monica Plant Engineering Division, Report No. SM-11827, May 2, 1946.

5. G. Kuiper to O. Struve, May 29, 1953, F. K. Edmondson Active Files. I am most grateful to Professor Edmondson for bringing this letter to my attention.

6. See, for example, F. Hoyle, *Man in the Universe* (New York: Columbia University Press, 1966), 6.

7. *Scientific Uses of the Large Space Telescope* (Washington, D.C.: National Academy of Sciences, 1969). See also L. Spitzer Jr., "Astronomical Research with Large Space Telescope," *Science* 161 (1968): 225–229.

8. Homer Newell, "Space Astronomy Program of the National Aeronautics and Space Administration," in *Astronomy in Space* 1–8 (Washington, D.C.: NASA SP-127, 1967), 7.

9. Memorandum, H. Newell to J. Fletcher, undated by December 1971, NASA Headquarters, Newell Papers, 255-79-0649, Box 25 file AA (reading file).

10. See, for example, Memorandum for the Record, J. Downey III, "Enclosure A-LST Meeting in Headquarters with Drs. Fletcher and Low, December 21, 1972." January 9, 1973, MSFC Presentation File (File Briefing to Dr. Low at Headquarters, 12/21/1972).

11. "President Ford's Budget Message" in *Issues '78: Perspectives on Fiscal Year 1978 Budget* 1–6 (Washington, D.C.: OMB, 1977), 3.

12. See Claude E. Barfield, *Science Policy From Ford to Reagan* (Washington, D.C.: American Enterprise Institute for Public Policy Research, 1982); James Everett Katz, *Presidential Politics and Science Policy* (New York: Praeger, 1978), 180–239.

13. Memorandum, Jim Cannon, "Meeting with James Fletcher and George Low," April 3, 1975, Ford Papers, White House Central Files, Box OS 8/9/74 (Exec) to OS 3 Space Flight 7/3176 (Exec), (File OS 8/9/74–12/22/75), Gerald R. Ford Presidential Library.

14. U.S. Congress, 93rd Congress, 2nd Session, August 21, 1974, H.29693. See also C. R. O'Dell, to "Dear Colleague," August 22, 1974, Project Scientist Papers (Reading File 1974), Marshall Space Flight Center.

15. A short account is P. Hanle's "Astronomers, Congress, and the Large Space Telescope," *Sky and Telescope* (April 1985): 300–305. Chapter 4 of Robert W. Smith's (with contributions by Paul Hanle, Robert Kargon, and Joseph Tatarewicz) *The Space Telescope: A Study of NASA, Science, Technology, and Politics* (New York: Cambridge University Press, 1989) examines the campaign in more detail.

16. G. Low, Memorandum for the Record, "Large Space Telescope," June 17, 1975, NASA Administrator's Papers, 255-80-0608, Box 4 (File Astronomy 3-1, 1975–1977 Space Telescope).

17. U.S. Congress, House of Representatives, Committee on Appropriations, *Department of Housing and Urban Development Independent Agencies Appro-*

*priations for 1976*. Hearings before the Subcommittee on HUD-Independent Agencies, pt. 2, NASA, 94th Congress, 1st Session, March 4, 1975.

18. It was certainly the view in OMB that the "Congress appears to want NASA to conduct more initiatives to applying NASA technology in areas such as energy, earth resources, etc." Background Material for the Director's Meeting with Dr. Fletcher, July 3, 1975, Domestic Council—Schleed Papers (File NASA, 1975: General, January–July), Gerald R. Ford Library. On the development, Pamela Mack, "The Politics of Technological Change: A History of Landsat," (unpublished Ph.D. dissertation, University of Pennsylvania, 1984).

19. U.S. Congress, House of Representatives, Committee on Appropriations, *Department of Housing and Urban Development Independent Agencies Appropriations for 1976*. Hearings before the Subcommittee on HUD-Independent Agencies, pt. 2, NASA, 94th Congress, 1st session, March 4, 1975, p. 427.

20. See, for example, John Tyndall, *Lectures on Light—Delivered in the United States in 1872–73* (New York: D. Appleton and Company, 1873), 174–183.

21. David F. Noble, *Forces of Production: A Social History of Industrial Automation* (New York: Oxford University Press, 1984), 13. These points were made and amplified by Michael D. Reagan, *Science and the Federal Patron* (New York: Oxford University Press, 1969), 40–45. Pushed to its extreme, the "scientific pool" argument becomes the claim that all technological developments depend on advances in basic science and that technology is hierarchically subordinate to science. For an excellent recent review on the relationship between science and technology, see Edward T. Layton Jr., "Through the Looking Glass, or News from Lake Mirror Image," *Technology and Culture* 28 (1987): 594–607.

22. See, for example, Barry M. Blechman, Edward M. Graunlich, and Robert W. Hartman, *Setting National Priorities, The 1975 Budget* (Washington, D.C.: The Brookings Institution, 1974), 133.

23. This point was made, for example, by George Field in congressional testimony: Congress, House of Representatives, Committee on Appropriations, *Department of Housing and Urban Development Independent Agencies Appropriations for 1978*. Hearings before the Subcommittee on HUD-Independent Agencies, pt. 7, 95th Congress, 1st session, March 31, 1977, pp. 142–151, 150.

24. U.S. Congress, House, Committee, *Testimony of W. Panofsky on the Stanford Accelerator Power Supply,* Hearing before the Joint Committee, 88th Congress, 2nd session, January 29, 1964, pp. 24–25. A fascinating account of the changing justifications of basic research in the context of funding by the Office of Naval Research is provided in Harvey M. Sapolsky, "The Office of No Return? The Office of Naval Research and the Issue of Relevance," paper presented at Workshop on the Military and Post-War Academic Science, The Johns Hopkins University, April, 1986.

25. Oral History Interview, J. Bahcall with P. Hanle, December 20, 1983, p. 64.

26. G. Low to distribution, October 28, 1975, NASA Administrator's Papers, 255-80-0608, Box 4 (File Astronomy 3-1 1975-77 Space Telescope). See also Memorandum, Assistant Administrator for Public Affairs to Deputy Administrator, November 5, 1975, NASA History Office (File Space Telescope Documentation).

27. E. M. Burbidge, to G. Low, November 13, 1975, included in enclosures to LST Operations and Management Working Group, February 6, 1976, Project Scientist Papers, Marshall Space Flight Center.

28. G. Low, to E. M. Burbidge, January 28, 1976, Aucremanne Papers (File LST 1975 [sic]). But see also S. Sobieski to C. R. O'Dell, June 18, 1975, included in enclosures to LST Science Working Group minutes, July 16–17, 1975, and Ernst Stuhlinger's suggested change of name in 1974: O'Dell Notes, August 29, 1974, O'Dell Papers, Rice University.

29. James T. Lynn to James C. Fletcher, July 25, Fletcher Papers, NASA History Office (File Correspondence 1976).

30. James Fletcher to James T. Lynn, September 1975, OMB Papers (File Directors Review Book FY 1977).

31. See, for example, "Ford Asks Slash in Tax, Matched by Spending Cut," *The New York Times* (October 7, 1975), 1. A detailed analysis of the fiscal year 1977 budget as it affected research and development is provided by Willis H. Shapley in *Research and Development in the Federal Budget FY 1977* (Washington, D.C.: American Association for the Advancement of Science, 1976).

32. James C. Fletcher to James T. Lynn, October 20, 1975, OMB Papers (File Director's Review Book FY 1977).

33. Shapley, *Research and Development in the Federal Budget FY 1977*, p. 55.

34. George B. Field to File, March 2, 1976, Field Papers, Smithsonian Institution Archives (File Space Telescope Congressional Action 1974–1978). See also John Bahcall, to "Dear Colleague," February 19, 1976, Bahcall Papers; James Fletcher to President Ford, November 26, 1975, White House Central Files, Box 13 (File FI4/FG 131-164), and James Fletcher to James T. Lynn, November 20, 1975, White House Central Files, Box 13 (File F!4/FG 131-164), Gerald R. Ford Presidential Library.

35. Issue Paper on "Earth Orbiting Space Telescope." OMB Papers (File Director's Review Book FY 1978).

36. The Shuttle's peak development years were expected to be in FY 1977 and FY 1978.

37. George Keyworth, quoted in J. Kelly Beatty, "HST and the Military Edge," *Sky and Telescope* (April 1985): 302, and George M. Low, personal notes 160, February 7, 1976, Box 65, folder 4, George M. Low papers, Rensselaer Polytechnic Institute Archives, Troy, New York.

38. See, for example, briefing paper "FY 1977 Budget [NASA]," Staff Secretary—Special Files, Box 10 (File FY-1977—Fifty Issues [1]), Gerald R. Ford Library. See also Craig Covault, "Aeronautic Stress, Shuttle Stretch Planned by NASA," *Aviation Week and Space Technology* (January 26, 1976): 30–33.

39. For the view of one robust critic, see James A. Van Allen's "Statement," in *A Compilation of Papers Prepared for the Subcommittee on NASA Oversight of the Committee on Science and Astronautics U.S. House of Representatives, Ninety-First Congress, Second Session on the National Space Program—Present*

*and Future,* pp. 90–92; See also Oral History Interview, J. Van Allen, with David DeVorkin and Allan Needell, August 6, 1981, pp. 355–359.

40. "Science on the Skids: A Conversation with Thomas Donahue," *Spaceworld* (November 1986): 16–20.

41. J. N. Bahcall to J. Fletcher, January 22, 1976, NASA Administrator's Papers, 255-80-0608, Box 4 (File Astronomy 3-1 1975-77 Space Telescope). For Fletcher's reply, see J. Fletcher to J. N. Bahcall, February 3, 1976, same file. See in addition John Bahcall, February 3, 1976, same file. See in addition John Bahcall to John Walsh, January 23, 1976, Bahcall Papers, and John Walsh, "Astronomers Go into Orbit," *Science* 191 (1976): 544–545. For letters in a similar vein to Bahcall's, see, for example, Ivan King to James Fletcher, January 30, 1976, Bahcall Papers, and Robert Danielson to James Fletcher, February 3, 1976, Bahcall Papers.

42. C. R. O'Dell to John Naugle, January 2, 1976, Project Scientist Papers (File Reading 1976), Marshall Space Flight Center.

43. This was the PEP, or Positron Electron Project.

44. Memorandum, J. Bahcall, "Regarding the Restoration of PEP Construction Funds by Congress to the ERDA Budget for FY '76," January 8, 1976, Bahcall Papers.

45. J. Bahcall to L. Spitzer, January 9, 1976, Bahcall Papers. At this time Spitzer, who generally worked very closely with Bahcall in the lobbying activities, was physically distant from the action as he was visiting the Institute d'Astrophysique in Paris.

46. J. Bahcall to L. Spitzer, January 9, 1976, Bahcall Papers.

47. See, for example, Harold L. Davis, "New Support for Basic Research," *Physics Today* (April 1976): 96.

48. Oral History Interview, J. Bahcall with P. Hanle, November 3, 1983, p. 23.

49. Ibid. See also the numerous letters to Congressmen, copies of which were often sent to NASA: Administrator's Papers, 255-80-0608, Box 4 (File Astronomy 3-1 1975-77 Space Telescope). See, for example, Phillip Morrison to Edward P. Boland, February 20, 1976.

50. Hugh Heclo, "Issue Networks and the Executive Establishment," in *The New American Political System,* ed. Anthony King (Washington, D.C.: American Enterprise Institute, 1979), 87–124.

51. See Allan J. Cigler and Burdett A. Loomis, eds., *Interest Group Politics* (Washington, D.C.: Congressional Quarterly Press, 1983), particularly Chapter 1, "Introduction: The Changing Nature of Interest Group Politics," pp. 1–30. On lobbying see, for example, Lewis Anthony Dexter, *How Organizations Are Represented in Washington* (Indianapolis: The Bobbs-Merrill Company, 1969) and *The Washington Lobby,* 4th edition (Washington, D.C.: Congressional Quarterly Press, 1982).

52. Oral History Interview, J. Bahcall with P. Hanle, November 3, 1983, p. 32.

53. See, for example, J. Leiper Freeman, *The Political Process: Executive Bureau-Legislative Committee Relations* (New York: Random House, 1964);

*Douglas Cater, Power in Washington* (New York: Vintage, 1964), and Gordon Adams, *The Politics of Defense Contracting* (New Brunswick: Transaction Books, 1982).

54. On issue networks, see Heclo, "Issue Networks and the Executive Establishment."

55. The notion of ad hocracy was suggested by W. H. Lambright in his commentary to the draft of this paper delivered at the June 1987 NASA/NASM Seminar.

56. Oral History Interview, N. Hinners with R. W. Smith and J. Tatarewicz, October 17, 1984, p. 24. In 1985, O'Dell, in recalling the omission of all Space Telescope funds, said, ". . . it makes you really wonder if they're not going to scrap the whole damn thing, when they do something like that." Oral History Interview, C. R. O'Dell with R. W. Smith, American Institute of Physics, May 21–23, 1985, Session II, p. 27. This, of course, was exactly the response Hinners had hoped for.

57. For examples of the Congress's use of the Washington Monument Game, see William Greider, *The Education of David Stockman and Other Americans* (New York: New American Library, 1986), 50.

58. *An International Discussion of Space Observatories: Report of a Conference held at Williamsburg, Virginia, January 26–29, 1976* (Washington, D.C., and Paris: National Academy of Sciences, European Science Foundation, 1976).

59. George Field to James Fletcher, February 12, 1976, Bahcall Papers. See, too, J. Bahcall, E. M. Burbidge, A. Code, G. Field, and L. Spitzer to J. Fletcher, January 21, 1976, Bahcall Papers.

60. George Field to John Naugle, March 2, 1976, Bahcall Papers, and George Field to John Naugle, May 14, 1976, Bahcall Papers. The agenda was worked out in advance by Naugle and Field.

61. J. Bahcall to George Field, May 20, 1976, Bahcall Papers.

62. On the May 19 meeting, see Oral History Interviews, E. Margaret Burbidge with R. W. Smith, November 29, 1984; John Bahcall with P. Hanle, December 20, 1983, p. 78, and C. R. O'Dell with R. W. Smith, American Institute of Physics, May 21–23, 1985, Session II, p. 28. See also John Bahcall to George Field, May 20, 1976, Bahcall Papers; George Field to James Fletcher, May 26, 1976, Field Papers; O'Dell Daily Notes, May 19, 1976, O'Dell Papers, and the material in the file "Meeting with Fletcher Headquarters, May 19, 1976," Project Scientist Papers. The latter contains the text of the four talks that were delivered: "Scientific Uses of the Space Telescope," by Lyman Spitzer, "Technological Challenges and Spin-offs of the Space Telescope," by Art Code, "The Benefits of Astronomical Research," by George Field, and "Astronomy at Century's End: A Prophecy for the Space Telescope Era," by Phillip Morrison. Fletcher's notes of the meeting are in the Fletcher Papers (File Correspondence 1976), headed "Meeting with Astronomers – 5/19/76," NASA History Office.

63. L. Spitzer note, "Chronology 1976–77 Campaign Re LST," dated February 17, 1982, Spitzer Papers, and Oral History Interview, R. C. Henry with R. W. Smith and P. Hanle, November 29, 1983, p. 45.

64. U.S. Congress, Senate, *Congressional Record,* 94th Congress, Second Session, April 1, 1976, S9063-4.

65. James A. Fletcher to James L. Mitchell, April 12, 1976, OMB Papers 51-81-1 3/33: 24-7 (File "SSET: SSPB: NASA FY1976 [sic] Space Telescope"). See also Memorandum, Memphis A. Norman to SSET: Science and Space Programs Branch, "NASA's Proposal for Early Selection of a Contractor for the Space Telescope," April 14, 1976, same record file.

66. Memorandum, H. Newell to J. Fletcher, undated, but December 1971, NASA Headquarters, Newell Papers, 255-79-0649, Box 25 (File AA Reading File).

67. Minutes of Science Working Group, February 6, 1976, Project Scientist papers, Marshall Space Flight Center.

68. See also Memorandum, George Low to James C. Fletcher, April 21, 1976, "Additional Items of Interest," Fletcher Papers, NASA History Office (File Correspondence 1976).

69. U.S. Congress, House of Representatives, Committee on Appropriations, *Department of Housing and Urban Development Independent Agencies Appropriations for 1977,* Hearings before the Subcommittee on HUD-Independent Agencies, pt. 2, NASA, 94th Congress, 2nd session, February 18, 1976, pp. 146–147.

70. George M. Low to James C. Fletcher, April 21, 1976, Fletcher Papers, NASA History Office (File Correspondence, 1976).

*W. Henry Lambright*

# Commentary

These are both fine papers; they are rich in facts and deep in analysis. They cite the right people. However, a few words need to be said about the kind of work they represent and the disciplinary premises they embody.

I might begin by saying how differences in each contributor's background and disciplinary perspective come through in the words they choose. For example, in the essay of Smith, a historian, there is greater detail, more facts. McCurdy, a political scientist, is trained to be less interested in individuals, and more concerned with organizations, and thus emphasizes NASA. The historian refers more to individuals; for the political scientist, the preferred unit of analysis is the organization, the bureaucracy, the political system — larger-scale entities.

There are, however, commonalities. They both present policy histories, not studies of science or technology. When one talks about policy, clearly people and institutions are being discussed. One can see how the historian can contribute to understanding policy, and how someone interested primarily in policy (the political scientist) can contribute to history. That comes across nicely in these papers.

Both essays are also guided by a similar model. The implicit model steering both papers is that of the innovation process. In this process, you have a sequence of formulation and implementation. There is someone who is pushing for something new, namely a particular technological innovation, such as Space Telescope and Space Station. When a model underlies the analysis, it is open to question, if not attack, about its implications. This is because models imply values. In innovation, for example, you have someone customarily pushing for change and someone resisting. The language of innovation—push, resist, proponents, opponents—has values adhering to it. Other words that come to mind, such as technology, are also value-laden. Technology implies rationality and "progress." The point that I would like to make is that politics and technological rationality are different sides of the same coin. Why? Because processes of policy-making and innovation involve multiple actors engaged in this process over time, and these multiple actors have different points of view.

It is often said that where you stand on an issue depends on where you sit. You can look at a set of facts from the standpoint of those trying to bring into the world a wonderful new technology, and in the Space Telescope case, it may be the view of the astronomers or it may be that of NASA. You see the world from their point of view. What if, however, you are writing the same set of facts from the perspective of the Office of Management and Budget (OMB)? What if you are trying to see the world, not as a process of innovation, but as a process of arresting something you do not necessarily think is good for the country? There is a body of policy literature about terminating programs that are not considered good, and one could write the same set of facts from this different point of view. Here, the 'good guys' would be those trying to stop a technology, and the 'bad guys' would be those encouraging it.

If you look at policy analysis over the course of years, you would be astounded at how values can change concerning a given innovation. Consider, for example, not space, but nuclear technology. There was a point in history, not so long ago, when the 'good guys' were the nuclear engineers. They were the ones who were technologically rational. They were promoting a hope for the world. The atom would make electricity too cheap to meter. The 'bad guys' were, then, the forces of resistance—a group of Luddites. Then another decade comes. The environmentalists move onto the scene. All of a sudden, it is the nuclear engineers who are the 'bad guys,' and the 'good guys' are those trying to stop this particular technological innovation. Policy analysis then, tends not only to reflect the biases of an author, but also the biases inherent in the mood of the time.

Policy history is hard to write without implicitly taking sides, and the two papers reflect this, whether the writers intended to do so or not. There is a pro-innovation bias favoring Space Telescope and Space Station. The papers deal with multiple actors, and these actors are engaged in a contest. The contest is often bitter; the stakes can be very high. When an innovation (Space Telescope or Space Station) is written about from the standpoint of people who are promoting programs, then technological rationality is really bureaucratic rationality. Success in innovation is attuned to selling a government program. Failure occurs when the program is not approved or funded adequately. Success and failure derive from a policy analysis driven by an innovation model, in which the key actors are the innovators, whether they are scientific entrepreneurs (Space Telescope) or administrative entrepreneurs (Space Station).

Within a context of pro-innovation studies, these are excellent papers. The principal players are identified and their strategies made clear. The issues and problems are delineated. One could go further, however, and outline the policy implications. If sections were added to the end of each paper, those sections should list and analyze implications for public policy. I recommend that those two sections be added because the reader wants to know what these cases mean in a larger sense.

In my opinion, the contributions illuminate patterns of policy with respect to large-scale technological innovation. There are three patterns or models that emerge. One is the leadership model of policy-making. This is an innovation process that is likened to the Apollo days. This is where you have coalition building, orchestrated by strong leaders with great power. The President of the United States who makes historic decisions, the dynamic administrator of an agency who knows what he is doing—these are central to the leadership model. The leadership model operates within a working consensus, short of commitment. Commitment is a misnomer because essentially it conveys something that does not exist in America—namely, certainty in implementation. There was no commitment to go to the Moon—there was a *decision* to go to the Moon, and that decision had to be reaffirmed every year, and it involved NASA winning various battles along the way. Apollo symbolizes the leadership model; there was leadership from the President and leadership from the head of NASA. They regained the commitment and maintained the working consensus. This is alluded to, particularly in McCurdy's paper, where he tries to explain the Space Station decision and relate it back to the 'good old days' of Apollo.

The second model, which is indicated by Smith's paper on Space

Telescope, is the iron triangle model. Many political scientists regard this model as illustrating the way policy is made. While it applies in some cases, it does not in many others, including that of space today. The iron triangle model conveys the notion that you have a very strong agency, you have a strong set of congressional committees that work closely with that agency, and you have powerful interest groups that work as an alliance, making policy year after year after year, providing stability in the system. Presidents come and go. The triangle remains.

This model is relevant to the world of the National Institute of Health (NIH), not that of today's NASA. NIH receives more money each year than the President wants it to get because it has strong congressional committees on its side along with a very powerful medical research interest group constituency. The iron triangle describes the Department of Defense world, to the extent that there is stability in that function of government. But that model does not apply to NASA.

The two contributors suggest that the applicable model is the issue networks model. This assumes a linkage of individuals across institutions who are concerned with a given area of policy. Actually, issue networks do not really fit the reality that the authors have described. The reality is more of an ad hocratic model. The ad hocratic model is not stable or consistent in membership. One year's success is nullified by another year's failure. One President decides and another President reverses, and you are constantly repackaging your programs, shuffling your designs, cutting back or adding on to make them more sellable.

"Decision-making by the yard" is an administrator's terminology of this view of reality. That is not a sound way to make decisions, but that is what is being described in these two papers. It is an unstable issue network guided by a policy stance of ad hocracy.

An implication to draw from this kind of policy process—the kind indicated by the papers—is that this is a difficult time to be a space-policy entrepreneur. Trying to be an innovator in the present environment is almost impossible. What is the incentive for being a policy entrepreneur? These papers suggest that no matter what I do, it's going to be undone next week by someone else. In this kind of ad hocratic context, you cannot really accomplish long-range programs. In the 1970s, we asked: If we can go to the Moon, why can't we do x, y, and z in this country? In the 1980s, we are in danger of saying that we can not do x, y, and z. Was the Moon program an aberration? Maybe the modern (i.e., post-Apollo) world of NASA is more like that of the Housing and Urban Development and the Department of the Environment than that of the Department of Defense. And if that is the case, it's not good—at least, if your biases favor programs like Space Telescope and Space Station.

NASA needs more historians and policy analysts who can look around Washington and track programs that have come and gone. It should learn from history, from past mistakes. The leadership model of policy-making (illustrated in Apollo) is not likely to be possible in the foreseeable future. Hence, it may be more useful to examine how programs grow and succeed under ad hocratic situations. Are there any policy entrepreneurs who are succeeding, in a relative sense, today? In the science and technology field, NSF's leader has linked his agency to the "competitiveness" issue, and thus made the best of these ad hocratic times.

The questions I have for the two authors are: How can you do what you want to do, build a Space Telescope or build a Space Station, in an environment of ad hocracy? What lessons can you learn from the past and the present that are applicable for this environment? How does an agency go forward with major, long-term programs for which there are no resources? In Apollo days, there was not a decade-long commitment, but there were conditions of a working consensus, within which leadership was possible.

Today, iron triangles have broken down and issue networks have become ad hocratic. As a result, the contributions illustrate programs that are taking too long, costing too much, and may not produce technologies that perform. This is obviously an undesirable situation. We have to ask the question: What is to be done about this situation in our country? These contributions have certainly shown us the problems, which are profound. Are there any answers rooted in history and contemporary reality?

# Part 2. Space Science and Scientific Communities

# Introduction

Historians of science are faced with an increasingly complex task in detailing the organization of postwar science and technology. The proliferation of technologies and the diversification of traditional disciplines, as well as new kinds of institutional affiliations, has changed many professions and blurred previously accepted distinctions among others.[1] For several of the sciences, most notably branches of physics, the Second World War was a period of transformation and redefinition. When enrolled in the war effort, these sciences produced rapid technological advancement as well as new professional opportunities. And for the first time, large numbers of scientists in these fields found themselves in close relationships with the federal government.

Of course, some elements of the organization of prewar science remained in force—informing, coexisting with, and influencing new technologies, new areas of research, and their communities of practitioners.[2] The two papers that follow each look at the complicated structures of scientific communities in these transforming years, and at subsequent results for both old and new professions. In particular, they look at the establishment of professional communities in, respectively, solar science and planetary science. Of special interest is the fact that most postwar developments in these fields were shaped by new and enormously expensive technologies—rockets, sophisticated electronics, and, later, satellites—which could be supported only by the government. Both solar science and planetary science reflect the complex sets of relationships that arose when new technologies offered opportunities for carving out new disciplines—in these cases, drawing practitioners from astronomy, as well as physics and geology — *and* when these new specialties found themselves dependent on government for support and, sometimes, direction.

While the impact of government patronage on science in the postwar period has been widely acknowledged and discussed by historians and other scholars, no consensus has been reached on a suitable historiography for explicating the complex postwar links among government, science, and technology.[3] The papers by Hufbauer and Tatarewicz exhibit some of this historiographical tension. Both authors start from a well-established approach for studying scientific disciplines: the primary unit of analysis is the discipline, with emphasis on its formation and membership (a professional society), on means of communication among the discipline's members and with relevant external constituencies (society meetings and specialized journals), and on a distinct domain of scientific inquiry.[4] The rationale often advanced for the formation and development of a discipline is an internal dynamic of science based on problem-solving and the advance of theory, governed by a set of norms for communicating and reviewing research. Implicit in this earlier historiography of scientific communities is that the interesting questions are how scientists organize *themselves* to advance knowledge. Much less attention was given to the ways in which scientists and their professional institutions have interacted with the larger society, especially federal government.[5]

The two papers here rely on the older historiography as a touchstone, but broaden their analyses to include the impact of federal involvement in science in the postwar period. The picture that emerges is of disciplines that are less autonomous — in terms of necessary technologies, funding, and even problem choices — and are more intricately tied to the political processes of government. And if the session's two papers are indicative, each discipline is affected differently in its relationship with its government sponsors. The relationship may vary depending on the strength and leadership of a discipline's professional and advisory bodies, both national and international; the influence of key individual research centers; and, of course, on the government's needs, both technical and political, in any particular area of endeavor. Modified by these factors, government involvement in science, in some sense, shapes a discipline's professional and scientific activity. Hufbauer's and Tatarewicz's papers can be viewed as attempts to provide a more concrete understanding of how these influences operate in the cases of, respectively, solar science and planetary science.

Hufbauer in his presentation on the evolution of the solar physics community, is particularly concerned with the effects of technologies and funding on the establishment of a new discipline.[6] During World War II, solar scientists were active contributors to the war effort, studying the effects of solar emissions on radio communications. While this marked the beginning of active government support for solar science, there was no well-defined specialty field; physicists worked on solar science as a part of the astronomy community. After the war, new technologies made above-the-atmosphere solar research possible for the first time. And it was these technologies, and the promise they held for both the military and the space program, which helped the practitioners of solar physics to define and promote themselves as a distinct scientific community.

Hufbauer presents an interesting composite of the group drawn to the small new field, evenly divided among established prewar scientists, researchers who had entered the field during the war, and postwar recruits. Thus, from the beginning, tradition and innovation worked side-by-side in the evolving community. The new above-the-atmosphere scientists may have eclipsed the traditional ground-based observation specialists in the amount of public attention received, but both had strong voices in the formation of the new discipline.

For their parts, the military and NASA were interested in the new discipline for pragmatic reasons: to yield potentially useful military technologies, to explore the space environment with an eye toward future manned flights and, when possible, to garner by association some of the scientific prestige associated with the new space science. Hufbauer details the ways in which solar scientists, during the days of seemingly limitless government spending on space, both established themselves as a well-defined community and managed to infuse substantial funding into the more traditional ground-based research as supports for above-the-atmosphere work. Part of a larger study on the development (and, later hard times) of the solar science community, Hufbauer's presentation accentuates both the "bargaining" power of those practitioners associated with the revolutionary new space-related technologies of the postwar period, as well as the complexities facing historians seeking to preserve their story.

In his presentation on the evolution of the community of planetary scientists out of the broader astronomy community, Joseph

Tatarewicz details a somewhat different story with equally complex equations of patronage and scientific organization. Although planetary science did not have a direct role to play in World War II, the emerging field benefited in the postwar years from increased general funding to astronomy, from new instrumentation and technologies, and from wartime geophysical studies raising new questions about space research. In these years, a small group of planetary scientists, practicing as astronomers, were based at a few key institutions (such as Lowell Observatory) and received support primarily from the military.

But with the launching of Sputnik in 1957, both military and civilian interest in the Moon gave sudden impetus to the formation and expansion of a field of planetary science, joining astronomers with chemists, physicists, and geophysicists to serve as guides to what was perceived as newly opened territory. By 1965, NASA had launched a vigorous program to promote planetary science. Looking forward to the post-Apollo years of space exploration, NASA realized that the number of well-trained scientists in the field would be inadequate. Tatarewicz outlines the ways in which NASA deliberately created a scientific infrastructure dedicated to the exploration of the solar system. Through its own Lunar and Planetary Program Office, NASA built (and determined the use of) major optical observatories, provided research grants, established a predoctoral training program, and advanced its own planetary probe program.

The result was a community heavily dependent on NASA for support and direction. Although Tatarewicz details the efforts of the emerging community in establishing professional associations, journals, and so forth, the end picture is of what might be called a "hollow" community. As a composite of various scientific disciplines, there was no traditional structure in the field—NASA itself served as the focal point. And in the mid-1970s, when support for the space program declined, planetary science and its practitioners found themselves without a focus or a forum.

This study provides an extreme example of how government involvement altered the usual role and functioning of a discipline's professional apparatus. More than Hufbauer's paper, it demonstrates the degree to which scientific activity is *not* autonomous but part of a complex interplay between a discipline and its institutional environment. Both papers make clear that a discipline may not be neatly defined strictly by its scientific activities and norms of research. In addition, they also suggest the distinctive character of the government -science interplay for individual disciplines. These studies highlight the need for a historiography of scientific disciplines and subdisciplines that fully recognizes the complex interconnections and loosely defined boundaries among the institutions of science and government.

In his commentary, Thomas Gieryn addresses this historiographic issue by providing a sociological context for these two historical assessments. Of special concern to Gieryn is how these papers relate to current trends in the sociology of scientific communities. In recent years there has been a rejection of traditional studies on specialists as community-members — the difficulty and arbitrariness of identifying professional boundaries is compounded by the lack of a general social theory of specialty formation. Given the absence of general methodological tools for studying specialty formation and development, the trend in sociological scholarship, Gieryn argues, is toward a series of micro and macroscopic studies of disciplines. This trend is based on recent studies which indicate that the discipline as primary unit of analysis is both too large and too small.[7] More and more, sociologists look not at who is in or who is out of a given scientific specialty, but at how scientists work, what they do, and what they say about their work. On a larger scale, these sociologists look at the relationships between scientific specialties and their social, political, and cultural worlds.

The results emerging from these studies echo the conclusions of the session's papers: science is a diffuse enterprise, closely connected with its social context, and its disciplines exhibit distinctive practices in local research and professional settings. While historians and sociologists approach the problems of defining and analyzing communities in postwar science from different perspectives, they both are contributing to a more detailed understanding of science and its context. The papers and commentary in this session point the way to a number of interesting lines of research.

## NOTES

1. Two points should be raised regarding terminology. First is the inconsistent usage of and relation among terms such as "discipline," "subdiscipline," "specialty," "profession," and "community" in the historical and sociological litera-

ture. In this session's papers, for example, Tatarewicz calls planetary science a "discipline," while Hufbauer designates solar science as a "subdiscipline." Second, as the commentary by Thomas Gieryn suggests, these terms, while useful in colloquial discourse, lack precision when these 'communities' are themselves the object of study. Meaningful operational definitions with unambiguous criteria for deciding, say, whether a community exists, who is a member of a community, or what areas of inquiry are encompassed by its activities are hard to achieve. This difficulty in developing analytical definitions is in part a reflection of the organizational complexity of postwar science and the 'muddiness' of the boundaries among practitioners, federal sponsors, managers, and the institutional framework within which they interact. It is also in part a function of greatly enhanced roles for scientists in mediating these interactions as government advisors and managers. See note 5 for additional discussion of this point.

2. For another analysis in which prewar developments predominate and combine with war research in the formation of a new research area see Spencer R. Weart, "The Solid State Physics Community," *Physics Today* 41, no. 7 (1988): 38–45.

3. While postwar patronage of science has unique and important differences from its antecedents, earlier examples can be noted. On prewar government patronage see Hunter S. Dupree, *Science in the Federal Government: A History of Policies and Activities,* 2nd edition (Baltimore: Johns Hopkins University, 1986). On foundation and industry patronage for university research in the interwar period see Stanley Coben, "American Foundations as Patrons of Science: The Commitment to Individual Research," in *The Sciences in the American Context: New Perspectives,* ed. Nathan Reingold (Washington, D.C.: Smithsonian Institution Press, 1979) and Roger Geiger, *To Advance Knowledge: The Growth of American Research Universities, 1900–1940* (Oxford, London, New York: Oxford University Press, 1986).

4. The classic expression of this methodology and normative view of science is found in the collected writings of Robert K. Merton, *The Sociology of Science* (Chicago: The University of Chicago Press, 1973).

5. While these papers focus on solar and planetary scientists as scientists and community members, it should also be noted that the postwar period saw the evolution of new roles: most notably as government advisor and as manager and administrator of large projects. The implications of this heightened involvement in public life have been amply examined in the political science and public policy literature. For an overview see *Daedalus* (103), Special Issue on "Science and Its Public: The Changing Relationship."

6. Hufbauer's essay published here is a revised version of "The Solar Physics Community Since Sputnik," a chapter from his book *Exploring the Sun: Solar Science Since Galileo* (in press, Johns Hopkins University Press).

7. See notes 14 through 19 in Gieryn's commentary on the session.

*Karl Hufbauer*

# Solar Observational Capabilities and the Solar Physics Community Since Sputnik, 1957 to 1988

## INTRODUCTION

Launched on October 4, 1957, Sputnik was billed by the Soviet Union as a contribution to the International Geophysical Year. It was that, and much more.[1] The satellite was a tribute to modern dreams of space exploration. It was a hitchhiker on the Soviet Union's new intercontinental ballistic missile. It was an avowal of that nation's determination to be second to none. Together with subsequent Soviet space firsts, Sputnik provoked a rapid buildup of American missile forces, motivated the creation of the National Aeronautics and Space Administration, and stimulated a major expansion in funding for science and technology.[2] Nothing less, most Americans believed, would maintain the nation's security and prestige.

By catalyzing so many developments, Sputnik accelerated the growth of solar observational capability. The scientists who took advantage of the fresh opportunities for solar research pursued three main strategies. Some placed instruments for studying the Sun on stratospheric balloons, high-altitude aircraft, rockets, and spacecraft. Others obtained new telescopes or substantially upgraded existing ones at ground-based observatories. And a very few established solar-neutrino detectors in subterranean facilities. As solar observing evolved into a sizable enterprise between 1957 and 1975, the solar physics community grew apace. Before long, solar physicists wanted special organizations and forums to represent their interests in the larger world and to expedite their communications with one another.

Once in place, these subdisciplinary institutions fostered a certain parochialism within solar physics.

As national priorities shifted away from science in the 1970s, solar physics moved from an era of exuberant growth into one of frustrating limits. The solar physics community's adjustment to this new context was not without pain. Indeed, lean budgets forced some solar physicists out of the field. Nonetheless, the community seems to have emerged from this difficult transition stronger than ever. Solar physicists have become more alert to their field's symbiotic relationship with the rest of astronomy. And, making the most of the funds available to them, they have managed to continue improving their observational capabilities.

This paper focuses on the relationship between patronage for solar observing and the solar physics community's development since Sputnik. It first considers the rise of what might be called the international space science movement between 1957 and 1975. Then it zeroes in on solar physics, characterizing the rapid growth of the field's observational capabilities and the consequent emergence of subdisciplinary institutions. Next it explores the solar physics community's successful adaptation to the lean times that began in the 1970s.

## THE RISE OF SPACE SCIENCE, 1957–1975

Political and military leaders made, and still make, the basic agenda for competition in space. This is not to say, however, that national leaders ignored scientific counsel. Had they done so, science in space would have been pretty much limited to activities with obvious propagandistic or strategic utility. The fact that national space programs have had a scientific component from their inception suggests instead that scientists have played an important advisory role in setting priorities.

In the mid-1950s, both the United States and the Soviet Union volunteered to launch satellites during the International Geophysical Year. Their motives for doing so were mixed. Both governments anticipated that successful launchings would enhance national prestige. President Dwight D. Eisenhower's administration also regarded the International Geophysical Year as an excellent opportunity to establish the freedom of space for future American reconnaissance satel-

lites.[3] Besides these considerations, the scientists of both countries
had their own reasons for wanting satellites to be launched during
the International Geophysical Year. In particular, they were eager to
begin studying phenomena that were beyond the observational capabilities of sounding rockets. Their seriousness, and persuasiveness,
were manifest in the many scientific instruments that were placed in
orbit during 1957 and 1958 by the Soviet Union on *Sputnik 1, 2,* and
*3,*[4] and by the United States on *Explorer 1, 3,* and *4, Vanguard 1,*
and *Pioneer 1.*[5]

While scientists played important parts in the early American
and Soviet space programs, their influence on the American program
was substantially greater. It might have been otherwise. Eisenhower
and many of his closest advisors thought space should remain the
province of the Department of Defense. Significant opposition to this
viewpoint emerged, however, from the President's own Science Advisory Committee, which was formed in November 1957 after the Soviet launch of *Sputnik 2.*[6] The committee, which was chaired by
James R. Killian Jr., wanted a space agency that, like the Atomic Energy Commission, would have considerable autonomy from the military. Eisenhower resisted this idea on military and fiscal grounds. For
instance, the Minutes of a meeting in early 1958 with Killian and
others reported that he

> said that space objectives relating to Defense are those to which the
> highest priority attaches because they bear on our immediate safety. . . .
> He did not think that large operating activities should be put in another
> organization, because of duplication, and did not feel that we should put
> talent, etc., into crash programs outside the Defense establishment.[7]

But a month later, perhaps wanting to buttress the case for the freedom of space, Eisenhower endorsed a civilian agency. The upshot of
intense congressional scrutiny and revision was a bill reconstituting
the National Advisory Committee for Aeronautics as the National
Aeronautics and Space Administration, or simply NASA. On October
1, 1958, just before the first anniversary of *Sputnik 1,* the new
agency began operations.

As Congress was shaping NASA, the National Academy of Sciences took action to assure continued scientific participation in the
setting of priorities for space after the International Geophysical
Year.[8] Throughout the winter and spring of 1958, not only the

Academy's committees for the International Geophysical Year, but also the directors of the National Advisory Committee for Aeronautics and the National Science Foundation had been expressing concerns about this issue. In June the Academy's president, Detlev W. Bronk, responded by establishing the Space Science Board. He appointed Lloyd V. Berkner, the first proponent of the International Geophysical Year, as chair and asked the board

> to survey in concert the problems, the opportunities, and the implications of man's advance into space, and to find ways to further a wise and vigorous national scientific program in the field.[9]

Over the summer, the board canvassed scientists across the nation for research proposals. And during NASA's start-up in the fall and winter of 1958–1959, the board actively represented the scientific community's interests in discussions of the agency's priorities.

In the meantime, Berkner and others had been campaigning for the creation of an international equivalent to the Space Science Board.[10] The International Council of Scientific Unions responded by establishing a provisional Committee on Space Research in order

> to provide the world scientific community with the means whereby it may exploit the possibilities of satellites and space probes of all kinds for scientific purposes and exchange the resulting data on a cooperative basis.

The Council's Executive Committee immediately asked Homer E. Newell Jr., who was in the midst of transferring from the Naval Research Laboratory to NASA, to convene the new committee's organizing meeting in London. All went smoothly at the London meeting in November 1958. Those present agreed to seek permanent status, drafted a charter, and elected Hendrik C. van de Hulst, a Dutch theoretical astrophysicist representing the International Astronomical Union, as president. The Committee on Space Research's second meeting—at The Hague in March 1959—was more exciting. The Soviet delegate started off by complaining that all the other delegates were from the advanced capitalist nations. Heated debate led to a decision to redraft the charter in order to assure Soviet participation. Later that year, the revised charter opened membership to all interested nations and reserved certain positions on the executive committee for representatives from Eastern bloc countries.

Besides forcing a revision in the charter, the Soviet complaint provoked an early announcement of American plans for cooperation in the exploration of space.[11] Prior to the meeting at The Hague, these plans had been the subject of detailed but inconclusive discussions between the National Academy's Space Science Board and NASA. The American delegate, Richard W. Porter, was so piqued by Soviet insinuations that the United States wanted to exclude the smaller nations from space that he phoned Hugh L. Dryden of NASA to insist on the urgency of announcing American intentions. The following day, Porter was able to report that NASA stood ready to help the scientists of other nations put instruments or even complete scientific satellites into orbit. His announcement was welcome news indeed. No longer would scientists outside the United States and the Soviet Union need to wait until their own countries had developed launch capabilities to participate in space research.

During the next few years, motivated both by a desire to take advantage of NASA's cooperative program and anxiety about being left behind, scientists around the globe won support for space science programs in their own nations. The spread of space research is nicely exemplified by developments in Holland. The first advocate of a Dutch program was probably van de Hulst, the president of the International Committee on Space Research. His colleague Jan Oort, a respected leader in studies of galactic structure and dynamics since the mid-1920s, soon rallied to the cause. In April 1959, as it happened, Oort was the featured speaker at the annual meeting for the Royal Netherlands Academy of Sciences. He used the opportunity to discuss the potential value of space travel for science, recounting recent Soviet and American achievements.[12] Over the next year, the Academy's committee for the International Geophysical Year was won over to the idea of a Dutch space program.[13] Upon its recommendation, the Academy reconstituted the committee in March 1960 as the Committee for Geophysics and Space Research and named van de Hulst as chair.[14]

Van de Hulst and his colleagues established a small but quite respectable Dutch program of space research.[15] They secured funding for three projects: (1) a work group in Utrecht under the leadership of the solar physicist Cornelis de Jager for space research on the Sun and stars; (2) a work group in Leiden for space research on cosmic rays; and (3) a work group for studying the ionosphere above Surinam during the impending solar minimum. They arranged lecture series for Dutch physicists and engineers who wanted to go into space science. And in the international arena, they effectively represented Dutch interests at the Committee on Space Research and in the negotiations and planning that gave rise to the European Space Research Organization.

Initiatives like those taken by the Dutch scientists rapidly spread space research.[16] By 1965, the number of Western bloc nations with space science programs—programs to use spacecraft as platforms for scientific investigations—had climbed to eleven.[17] Thereafter, thanks in good measure to the Soviet Union's decision to establish a cooperative program similar to that of NASA, space research spread into several Eastern bloc countries and one developing nation—India.[18] By 1975, consequently, scientists in more than twenty nations had joined those in the United States and Soviet Union in studying natural phenomena with the aid of spacecraft.

As space research was spreading around the globe, scientists in the United States and Soviet Union were using the ample resources made available to them to increase the sophistication of their own space science programs. With the aid of rocket manufacturers and engineers, they were sending larger spacecraft on longer journeys. With the aid of radio and computer specialists, they were transmitting commands to and retrieving information from their spacecraft with greater speed and reliability. With the aid of specialized shops and firms, they were including more capable and diverse instruments in their scientific payloads. This was not all. As their programs matured, American and Soviet space scientists came to see that their success depended not only on the progress of space technology but also on the progress of ground-based observing programs and theoretical research.[19] In order to make the most of the resources at their disposal, they both promoted greater support for and cultivated closer ties with scientists using traditional approaches. By the 1970s, consequently, the space science programs of the United States and, to a lesser degree, the Soviet Union had evolved into highly sophisticated enterprises that were tackling ever more varied, difficult, and interesting problems.

## BOUNTIFUL TIMES, 1957–1975

For some fifteen years after Sputnik, solar physicists and other scientists seeking to expand solar observational capabilities fared extremely well in their pursuit of funds and resources. They got ever more capable instruments for observing the radiations and particles emitted by the Sun into space. Less dramatic but every bit as important, they constructed a new generation of ground-based solar telescopes and steadily enhanced the efficacy of their auxiliary instrumentation. A few scientists even went underground in an attempt to find observational evidence of the energy-generating processes in the Sun's interior.

### Spacecraft As Solar Observing Platforms

The case for using spacecraft as platforms for observing solar radiations and particles was strong from the outset. The glimpses of the Sun provided by rocket-borne instruments prior to the International Geophysical Year had hinted at a wealth of discoveries to be made with prolonged observations from above the atmosphere. In addition, new solar results could be obtained with comparative ease because of the Sun's brightness and large angular diameter. Last, knowledge of solar emissions would be essential both for designing adequate shielding for astronauts and for distinguishing surreptitious nuclear tests from violent solar events. In short, solar observations from space were seen as having scientific merit, technical feasibility, and practical utility.

Initially, Soviet scientists led the way in using spacecraft as solar observing platforms. As early as November 1957, indeed, S. L. Mandel'shtam and his colleagues at the Lebedev Physical Institute in Moscow were able to orbit a set of electronic counters for measuring the intensities of solar X-ray and Lyman-alpha radiation aboard *Sputnik* 2.[20] They succeeded in getting a set of readings from their instrument. Subsequently, however, it became clear that they had failed to obtain clean solar measurements. Their data was seriously compromised by radiations from what soon came to be known as the Van Allen radiation belts.[21] All, or almost all, of the spacecraft launched by the Soviet Union during the next three years evidently included at least one instrument for observing solar radiations or particles in their payloads.[22] The first solar measurements from a spacecraft that have stood the test of time were obtained by a team from the Soviet Academy's Radio Engineering Institute in Moscow. Their ion traps aboard *Luna 2*, which was launched on September 2, 1959, measured the flow rate of what some theorists were beginning to call the solar wind.

Later that month, Herbert Friedman and his associates at the Naval Research Laboratory got the first American solar instrument into orbit on *Vanguard 3*.[23] However, their X-ray and Lyman-alpha photometers were, like those of Mandel'shtam's group, swamped by electrons from the Van Allen radiation belts.[24] Success did not long elude Friedman. His team's photometers on *Solrad 1* monitored fluctuations in solar X-ray and Lyman-alpha intensities from July into November 1960.[25] Soon, despite their later start, American scientists were setting the pace in the use of spacecraft for observing solar phenomena. They consistently put more solar instruments into space than did Soviet scientists. Moreover, to judge from their reports, their instruments generally had greater capabilities than did the Soviet instruments.

American leadership in studying the Sun from space was the result both of the influence of American scientists in the making of space policy and of the success of American engineers — especially in electronics and computing — in implementing that policy. In particular, the United States put more plentiful resources and sophisticated manpower than did the Soviet Union into the selection, development, production, and deployment of space-based solar instruments. For instance, American scientists were evidently able to do much more by way of testing prototypes than were their Soviet peers. They made frequent use of high altitude aircraft, stratospheric balloons,[26] and especially sounding rockets[27] for trying out early versions of solar instruments that were subsequently placed in orbit.

The scientists who used spacecraft as solar observing platforms naturally focused on emissions that were either entirely blocked or severely attenuated by the earth's atmosphere and hence more or less inaccessible to ground-based facilities. One important class of such emissions comprised particles emanating from the Sun's atmosphere. In the interest of brevity, it suffices here to indicate two features of this work. First, the observational study of the particles emitted by the Sun was essentially a new branch of solar physics. Those who created the particle spectrometers, magnetometers, and plasma-wave detectors used in this area could not have acquired the requisite expertise in the traditional areas of solar research. Second, these newcomers to solar physics obtained a sizable fraction of the spacecraft berths allocated to solar instruments. One reason was that observations of solar particles had much new light to shed on the Sun and its influence in the solar system. In addition, the instruments used for observing solar particles made ideal hitchhikers on long-range space-craft not only because they were relatively inexpensive and light but also because they could double as tools for investigating conditions in space near the Moon and planets.

The other important class of solar emissions observed from space comprised the Sun's radiations that could not be satisfactorily observed through the terrestrial atmosphere. A fair number of the scientists behind the solar-radiation instruments placed on spacecraft were, like those behind the solar-particle instruments, newcomers to solar research. But the dominant figures here were either physicists who had been using rockets as solar observing platforms or ground-based solar astronomers who were excited by the prospects of getting an unobstructed view of the Sun. The influence of these groups was manifest in NASA's increasingly sophisticated *Orbiting Solar Observatories 1* through *8* and *Skylab*.

Although Newell and other early planners of NASA's science program started off with grand ideas for using spacecraft as solar observing platforms, an enthusiastic pragmatist—John C. Lindsay—played the lead role in initiating the agency's solar observatory series.[28] An experimental physicist by background, Lindsay did not get involved in solar research until 1955 when he joined Friedman's team at the Naval Research Laboratory. He participated there in Friedman's campaign to observe flares with rocket-borne instruments. He also served as the project manager for the solar photometers that Friedman's group developed for the Vanguard program. Then in the fall of 1958, like Newell and many others associated with the Naval Research Laboratory's rocket program, Lindsay transferred to NASA. He went to the agency's Goddard Space Flight Center in Greenbelt, Maryland. His first major job there was serving as project manager for *Explorer 6,* which was successfully launched in August 1959.

Meanwhile, impatient to exploit the advantages that satellites would have over rockets for the study of flares, Lindsay was urging that NASA begin its program of solar research with a modestly endowed spacecraft instead of a highly sophisticated, and costly one.[29] Before June 1959, he won Ball Brothers Research Corporation of Boulder, Colorado, a young firm that specialized in the production of pointing controls for American sounding rockets, over to the idea of a low-budget solar observatory. He also won some solar physicists — notably Michigan's Leo Goldberg, whose postwar enthusiasm for space research had been rekindled by Sputnik — over to this pragmatic approach. In August, Lindsay succeeded in getting his spacecraft included in NASA's official ten-year program. By the end of October, he had a contract for Ball Brothers to produce the satellite. And on March 7, 1962, about three years after he began agitating for a satellite dedicated to solar observing, *Orbiting Solar Observatory (OSO) 1* — the first spin-stabilized spacecraft with pointing control and several solar instruments — was in orbit.[30]

Shortly before launch, NASA informed the press that the *Orbiting Solar Observatory 1* was the lead satellite in a series of spacecraft that would study the Sun over an entire eleven-year sunspot cycle.[31] By this time, Lindsay had clearly gone some distance toward transforming his single mission into an ongoing program.[32] His progress had been made possible by the acquisition of two allies in 1960. One was Laurence T. Hogarth, a suave yet tough manager who was Lindsay's administrative counterpart. The other was the Astronomy Subcommittee of NASA's Space Sciences Steering Committee.[33] Working with these allies, Lindsay had received authorization for a second solar observatory that would include instruments from such respected scientists as Richard Tousey of the Naval Research Laboratory and Leo Goldberg, who had recently moved from Michigan to Harvard University. He had also obtained approval for preliminary planning of additional series spacecraft and an Advanced Orbiting Solar Observatory. Thus, in the spring of 1962, Lindsay had every reason to be optimistic about his program.

Things went well for Lindsay and his program during the next year and a half.[34] NASA recognized the success of *Orbiting Solar Observatory 1* by giving Lindsay its highest individual award. Meanwhile, with Hogarth riding herd, Ball Brothers and the principal investigators readied the second orbiting solar observatory and its instruments for launch. In addition, the Space Sciences Steering Committee's new Solar Physics Subcommittee, which included solar physicists from outside as well as inside the agency,[35] approved payload proposals for the third, fourth, and fifth satellites in the series. And, after competitive design studies, NASA awarded a contract to Republic Aviation Corporation for the first stage of work on the Advanced Orbiting Solar Observatory.

In 1964, however, Lindsay's luck changed.[36] At the beginning of the year, the U.S. General Accounting Office criticized NASA for wasting $799,000 by forcing the pace of the solar observatory program. Much worse, in April when the second observatory was being mated to the third-stage rocket at Kennedy Space Flight Center, static electricity ignited the engine. The satellite was badly damaged and three engineers were killed. Then in February 1965, when the re-built satellite was successfully sent into orbit, its most sophisticated instrument—Goldberg's ultraviolet spectrometer-spectroheliograph—was immediately put out of commission by electrical arcing. A few months later, rumors began circulating that NASA was about to divert the budget for Lindsay's advanced spacecraft to other projects.[37] Then in August, the third solar observatory failed to make orbit because the third-stage rocket fired prematurely. The pressure was too much for Lindsay. He died of a heart attack while mowing his lawn in late September 1965. Not long afterwards, NASA cancelled the Advanced Orbiting Solar Observatory program on budgetary grounds.

Had the case for using spacecraft as solar observing platforms not been so compelling, all these setbacks might have meant the end of Lindsay's program. In fact, however, it soon recovered. Over the next decade, NASA got another six Orbiting Solar Observatories into space. In doing so, the agency gave scientific teams from some fourteen institutions in the United States, Britain, France, and Italy opportunities to observe the Sun with ever greater photometric, spectral, spatial, and temporal resolution. The program did not stop with collecting data. As the quality of the results improved, NASA devoted greater attention to fostering their use by solar physicists who were not direct participants in the missions.[38] Hence, rebounding from the setbacks of 1964–1965, NASA's solar observatory series ultimately compiled a record that matched or surpassed all of Lindsay's expectations.

In the meantime, NASA had embarked on the most ambitious solar mission that has ever been sent aloft—what came to be known as the Skylab Apollo Telescope Mount. Before his death, Lindsay and others had discussed the possibility of putting a manned solar observatory into orbit.[39] They were attracted to the idea partly because astronauts would have the versatility needed both to take advantage of unexpected observational opportunities and to handle unanticipated difficulties. They were also stimulated, however, by the very challenge of giving astronauts an integral role in solar research. But the most that Lindsay had been able to accomplish was to arrange a contract with Ball Brothers to explore how a manned spacecraft could, despite crew movement, achieve the requisite pointing stability.

The prospects of a manned solar observatory improved substantially in December 1965 when NASA's Office of Space Sciences and Applications took up the cause.[40] Homer Newell, the Office's chief, had been spurred into action by the decision to kill the Advanced Orbiting Solar Observatory program. He immediately set about recruiting the disappointed principal investigators for an Apollo observatory mission that, if approval could be won, would complement the Apollo lunar program. In March 1966, having gotten a favorable response, he made a strong bid for the creation of such a program under his direction. Newell's initiative aroused the competitive instincts of George E. Mueller who, as chief of NASA's Office for Manned Space Flight, was ultimately responsible for the new Apollo Applications Program. Mueller emerged triumphant from the ensuing turf war. In July 1966, NASA announced that the Apollo Telescope Mount would be managed by the Marshall Space Flight Center in Huntsville, Alabama. Rein Ise, a seasoned Marshall engineer, was charged at once with organizing a project office there. And four scientists who had been negotiating with Newell's deputies were notified soon afterwards of their selection as principal investigators.

The original responsibility of the principal investigators for the Apollo Telescope Mount—Leo Goldberg of Harvard College Observatory, Richard Tousey of the Naval Research Laboratory, Gordon Newkirk of the High Altitude Observatory, and Ricardo Giacconi of American Science and Engineering in Cambridge, Massachusetts— was to have improved versions of their instruments ready for launch by late 1968. The instrument teams and other solar physicists were, to judge from a meeting of NASA's Solar Physics Subcommittee in September 1966, not at all happy with the initial constraints on the mission, especially those resulting from the presence of astronauts:

> The three experimenters present, Harvard, HAO, and NRL, expressed concern over tight delivery schedule compromising experiment design. Also general agreement was reached that OSO measurements were advantageous over the limited [i.e., brief] ATM measurements. ATM is not a substitute for OSO. Also great dissatisfaction was expressed with proposed hard-mount for ATM experiments which requires no movement by the 2 or 3 astronauts for 20 minutes at a time. Urine disposal ap-

pears to form a cloud around ATM at 200 miles altitude which is of
great concern.[41]

Over the next three years, such concerns were partially met by re-
finements in spacecraft design, by extension of the mission from a
single crew with a two-week observing period to three successive
crews with longer observing periods, and by postponements of the
schedule launch date to mid-1972.[42] All the while, the principal investigators' teams were busily developing a set of telescopes that were
more sensitive than any solar instruments orbited thus far.

As they solved their most difficult design problems, the principal
investigators paid increasing attention to operational issues. They
wanted sufficient flexibility to assure a quick response to flares and
other sudden solar phenomena. Accordingly, they arranged for the
astronauts to get enough training in solar physics to be confident
about taking observational initiatives. They also persuaded NASA to
give representatives of their teams fairly direct access to the astronauts during the mission. Besides flexibility, the scientists wanted a
mutually satisfactory means of avoiding disputes over observing priorities. They achieved this objective in 1971 by agreeing, in emula-
tion of the instrument teams for *Orbiting Solar Observatory 6,* upon
a set of coordinated observing routines. The passage of time was,
meanwhile, accompanied by a significant turnover in scientific personnel. Goldberg received an offer to serve as the Director of the Kitt
Peak National Observatory in Arizona. Unwilling to forego this opportunity, he passed the job of principal investigator for Harvard's
instrument on to Edmund M. Reeves. Likewise, Newkirk, who was
appointed Director of the High Altitude Observatory, passed his hat
as principal investigator on to his colleague, Robert M. MacQueen.

Finally, on May 14, 1973, NASA launched the unmanned Skylab with the Apollo Telescope Mount. The four main solar instruments alone represented a major investment—$40.9 million for the
Naval Research Laboratory's ultraviolet spectrograph and spectrohe-
liograph, $34.6 million for Harvard's ultraviolet spectroheliometer,
$14.7 million for the High Altitude Observatory's white light coro-
nagraph, and $8.3 million for American Science and Engineering's
x-ray telescope.[43] Hearts must have sunk when it became clear soon
after launch that all was not well with the spacecraft. The micrometeoroid shield, which was also intended to serve as a sun screen,

and two of the spacecraft's six solar-power panels were not functioning properly. During ascent, the shield had broken loose, taking one
of the solar panels with it and jamming the other. The launch of the
first crew was postponed while NASA engineers worked around the
clock to diagnose the problems, devise a remedial strategy, and re-
hearse the astronauts in its implementation. Then on May 25,
Charles Conrad Jr., Joseph P. Kerwin, and Paul J. Weitz were sent
up to restore the ailing spacecraft to working order. They managed
to replace the micrometeoroid shield with a special parasol that soon
reduced temperatures to a livable level. They also freed up the
jammed solar panel, thereby increasing the power supply to the
range needed for sustained operations.

Once repaired, Skylab was an extraordinary solar observatory.[44]
Over the next eight months, the original and two follow-up crews
worked in close coordination with the ground-based instrument
teams which, in turn, were backed up by a global observing network. Altogether the astronauts devoted 953.3 hours to obtaining
127,047 photographs of the Sun as well as myriads of related electronic data. Thus, contrary to the dire expectations of the Solar
Physics Committee back in 1966, the Apollo Telescope Mount was
a great success — partly because the solar physicists obtained a major
say in instrument design and operation and partly because the astronauts performed so capably as repairman and observers.

### Ground-Based Solar Observing Facilities

Besides funding solar research from spacecraft, the generous scientific
budgets after Sputnik accelerated the development of ground-based
observational capabilities. Solar physicists argued that the advance of
technology, especially electronics, put major enhancements in resolv-
ing power within easy reach. Moreover, as the solar data acquired in
space became increasingly precise, they were wont to maintain that
concurrent ground-based observing was essential for its interpretation. Finally, as manned missions increased in frequency, they could
point out that a reliable flare patrol would facilitate the protection of
astronauts from intense solar emissions.

Armed with such arguments, solar physicists obtained substantial funding for new telescopes between 1957 and 1975. Robert R.
McMath, one of the pioneers in solar cinematography, was the chief

figure behind the largest of these new instruments.[45] During the mid-1950s, he chaired a National Science Foundation panel that articulated the need for a national optical observatory and supervised the search that settled on Kitt Peak, Arizona, as the best site. He persuaded the panel, which included Goldberg, that a solar telescope should be included among the new observatory's instruments. Approved by Congress after Sputnik, this telescope was dedicated in November 1962. President John F. Kennedy sent his congratulations:

> The great new solar telescope at the Kitt Peak National Observatory in Arizona is a source of pride to the nation. The largest instrument for solar research in the world, it presents American astronomers with a unique tool for investigating the nearest of the stars, our Sun. This project is of exceptional interest to all our citizens, for the observatory is financed by the Federal Government through the National Science Foundation. . . . Bold in concept and magnificent in execution, the instrument is the crowning achievement of the career of the late Robert R. McMath, builder of solar telescopes, for whom it is named.[46]

The $4 million McMath Solar Telescope was indeed gargantuan. Its three mirrors, including the 150-cm objective, directed the Sun's rays along a 244-m path before forming a 90-cm solar image in an underground observation room.

Although other teams building solar telescopes between 1957 and 1975 worked on a smaller scale than did McMath and his colleagues, several ended up with instruments that produced images of comparable or greater clarity than those from the Kitt Peak giant. Those who did so, all managed, in one way or another, to avoid the local heating and air movements along the optical path that often blurred the McMath Solar Telescope's image. Some had the additional advantage of sites with less atmospheric turbulence and hence better "seeing" than Kitt Peak.[47]

In addition to building new telescopes, solar physicists were constantly improving the auxiliary instrumentation of existing telescopes. Step by step, they replaced the weakest components in their apparatus with ones that would improve their ability to analyze the Sun's richly complex signals. They were particularly successful in narrowing the passbands of monochromatic filters, in substituting electronic subsystems for electromechanical components, and in computerizing control and data systems. The labors of Robert F. Howard between

1959 and 1974 on Mt. Wilson's magnetograph exemplify this process of refinement.[48] In 1959, working with the instrument's inventor, Horace Babcock, he installed a new cathode-ray tube for displaying the solar magnetic fields. Three years later, he replaced the spectrograph's grating to improve the spectral resolution of the input signal. In the mid-1960s, he thoroughly overhauled the magnetograph. He increased the spatial resolution to 11,000 sectors on the solar disk, installed a guider with a digital logic system for controlling the stepwise scan of these sectors, developed an electronic subsystem that could determine both the magnetic field and rotational velocity of each sector and digitize the results for storage on computer tape, and devised a servo-plotter with two colored pens for producing magnetograms. Around 1970, he tackled the optics, replacing the telescope's 30-cm objective and the spectrograph's feed lens with cemented triplet achromatic and apochromatic lenses respectively. Finally in 1974, no longer satisfied with his guidance and data-handling systems, he computerized his operations. Such upgrading was, of course, expensive. It was thanks to the Office of Naval Research, the Air Force Cambridge Research Laboratories, the National Science Foundation, and NASA that Howard attained the capability of analyzing subtle changes in solar magnetic and velocity fields over extended periods of time.

While solar physicists actively pursued opportunities to acquire new telescopes and auxiliary apparatus, they evinced no interest whatsoever in establishing subterranean facilities for solar research. Yet according to a growing number of nuclear scientists and theoretical astrophysicists, just such facilities would enable observation of the neutrinos from the nuclear reactions powering the Sun.[49] The two key advocates of this idea were Raymond Davis Jr., a nuclear chemist at Brookhaven National Laboratory, and John N. Bahcall, a theoretical astrophysicist at the California Institute of Technology. If the Sun produced enough neutrinos, Davis began arguing in 1955, he could detect these massless and chargeless particles that travel with the speed of light by their ability to transmute the nuclei of chlorine 37 into argon 37. Some seven years later, he persuaded Bahcall, an expert on stellar interiors, to undertake the difficult task of predicting the flux of solar neutrinos. Bahcall's prediction was high enough to justify a serious attempt at detection.

Davis and Bahcall mounted a campaign for funding that led in mid-1964 to a grant of $600,000 from the Atomic Energy Commission for the installation of a neutrino detector in South Dakota's deep Homestake Mine. Three years later, Davis began measuring the rate at which solar neutrinos were transmuting the chlorine in some 400,000 liters of commercial cleaning fluid, tetrachloro-ethylene, into argon. The rate turned out to be so much lower than Bahcall's predicted flux that it was near or below the threshold of detection. Davis was delighted. Nothing is quite so satisfying to an experimentalist as coming up with a solid result that is at odds with theory. But Bahcall was initially disappointed and depressed at the failure of his prediction. He soon recognized, however, that Davis's null result could well indicate the need for a major revision in stellar or neutrino theory.[50] The discrepancy between observation and theory was, in any case, sufficiently intriguing to warrant round after round of further refinements in Davis's subterranean solar telescope.

Between Sputnik and the mid-1970s, therefore, the American government spearheaded the expansion of patronage for solar research. A major share of the new money went into the development and exploitation of solar observing from spacecraft. However, substantial amounts were also expended on ground-based observatories and subterranean neutrino detectors. Meanwhile, to foster the interpretation of the data acquired, increasing funds were also going toward the support of theorists and their computational needs. One consequence of the expanded patronage was that the solar physics community roughly doubled in size, reaching about 150 established investigators in the United States and some 300 worldwide.[51] Another to which we now turn, was the emergence of subdisciplinary institutions.

## SUBDISCIPLINARY TRENDS IN SOLAR PHYSICS, 1965–1975

As their numbers grew, solar physicists came to think that they needed more opportunities for communicating with one another about practical concerns and scientific problems. They found it increasingly difficult to get as much time and space as they wanted for discussing solar issues in the main astronomical societies and journals. This difficulty made them ever more aware of the limitations of their long-standing institutions. The triennial meetings of solar committees of the International Astronomical Union were too infrequent and the focus on solar statistics of the *Quarterly Bulletin on Solar Activity* was too narrow to fulfill their needs for mutual access. From the mid-1960s, therefore, solar physicists formed new institutions — the Solar Physics Division of the American Astronomical Society, the Joint Organization for Solar Observations in Europe, and, most notably, the journal *Solar Physics* — that gave their field standing as a subdiscipline by 1975. In doing so, they were participating in a much broader process of subdisciplinary formation that occurred throughout the republic of science during the bountiful times following Sputnik.

### *Organizing*

In April 1965, the chief solar physicist at NASA headquarters, Henry J. Smith, initiated the train of events that gave rise to the American Astronomical Society's Solar Physics Division. He proposed at a meeting of NASA's Solar Physics Subcommittee that NASA-funded solar physicists meet regularly to discuss common problems.[52] In the ensuing discussion, Leo Goldberg offered an alternative — that the American Astronomical Society sponsor an annual solar meeting, "perhaps as a first step in establishing a section for Solar Physics." After the meeting, Goldberg, who was president of the American Astronomical Society at the time, considered how he might follow through on his suggestion. He decided that it would be imprudent to raise the issue directly with the society's council. Many councilors were likely to oppose any move that would undermine astronomy's unity. Accordingly, Goldberg[53] asked John W. Firor Jr., the director of the High Altitude Observatory in Boulder, to take the initiative.

That July, Firor[54] presented the council with a proposal that an annual solar meeting be held under the auspices of the American Astronomical Society. He opened by drawing the council's attention to the rapid growth of solar research:

> One of the fastest growing fields of astronomical research is the study of the Sun. The advent of new techniques of observing the Sun — on the ground, from balloons and rockets, from space; in optical and radio

wavelengths; and with fast particles and magnetic fields — has brought new people and new enthusiasm to solar research.

This growth, he suggested, had created a need for special solar meetings. While this need could be met by the American Geophysical Union or some other organization, he believed that:

> if the AAS takes the lead at this time in bringing together the varied aspects of solar research, the traditional and valuable connection of solar studies to the rest of astronomy will be symbolized and encouraged. A meeting devoted to solar astronomy may appear as step away from the desired unity of astronomy as a subject, but specialization of meetings is an inevitable consequence of the growth of science, and no amount of nostalgia will bring back the situation in which a large fraction of the attendees at a general AAS meeting is competent to discuss most of the contributions. In any case, the gain from bringing into our Society those now studying the Sun with new techniques should outweigh the advance in specialization represented by a solar meeting.

He went on to propose that the annual solar meetings be held in the western United States because of the "considerable concentration" of solar research there and that a start be made with a three-day meeting in Boulder in October 1966.

The American Astronomical Society's Council would not be rushed. It approved the meeting in Boulder, but declined to make any long-range commitments.[55] The solar meeting in Boulder was "a great success, and it was the unanimous opinion of those present that another such meeting should be held within a year or so."[56] However, when asked once again to approve annual scheduling,[57] the council evidently refused to do more than endorse a second solar meeting in Tucson in February 1968. The solar meeting in Tucson drew over two-hundred scientists as had its predecessor.[58] Later that year, consequently, the council yielded to the advocates of specialized meetings whose ranks had grown to include the planetary astronomers and high-energy astrophysicists. It approved the formation of subdisciplinary divisions within the American Astronomical Society, giving them the right to organize separate meetings under the society's auspices.[59]

Planning for the society's Solar Physics Division commenced at a third special solar meeting in Pasadena in February 1969 and culminated with a founding meeting at NASA's Marshall Space Flight Center in November 1970.[60] The solar physicists attending the meeting in Huntsville adopted a constitution and elected the first set of officers. During the next few years, as membership climbed above 180, the Solar Physics Division's main activity was organizing solar meetings.[61] But it did take on a few additional responsibilities. In December 1973, for instance, it sponsored a symposium on Skylab's coronal observations at a regular meeting of the American Astronomical Society. And the following year it started raising funds for a Hale Prize Lectureship to be awarded to an outstanding contributor to solar physics.

Across the Atlantic, meanwhile, the Europeans were also forming solar associations. Organization seemed essential for acquiring instruments that would keep them competitive with the Americans. K. O. Kiepenheuer took the lead at the Prague meeting of the International Astronomical Union in 1967, polling several West European colleagues about their interest in a solar observatory that would surpass the best American facilities.[62] They were receptive to the idea, so he called a planning meeting at the Fraunhofer Institute in July 1968. The eleven solar physicists from six countries who came to Freiburg agreed to undertake a cooperative survey along the Mediterranean seaboard for a site with exceptional 'seeing' ability. At a second meeting in March 1969, twenty-one representatives from eight countries worked out the details for site testing that summer in Sicily and Portugal. Nine months later, the group reassembled in Catania, Sicily, to discuss initial results and plan the survey's next stage. In two years, therefore, Kiepenheuer had organized a thriving cooperative enterprise by providing his European solar colleagues with a strategy for outdoing the Americans.

All was going so well, in fact, that Kiepenheuer and nine of his colleagues—two each from France, Germany, and Italy, and one each from The Netherlands, Norway, Sweden, and Switzerland—took steps to formalize the venture.[63] At the Catania meeting in December 1969, they constituted themselves as a Provisional Board for the Joint Organization for Solar Observations and selected Kiepenheuer as president and Cornelis de Jager of Utrecht as secretary. They envisioned the completion of site testing in 1973 at a cost of $450,000 and the construction of the joint observatory by 1976 at a cost of about $900,000. Subsequent progress was slower than anticipated, partly because the board was unable to arrange major funding and partly because it broadened the site search to include the Canary Islands.[64] Still, by 1975, when the search narrowed down to Tenerife and La Palma in the Canaries, the Joint Organization for Solar Observations had secured the ongoing participation of solar physicists representing Spain, Austria, Greece, and Israel.

Besides conducting its site survey, the Joint Organization of Solar Observations took the initiative in forming a general association of European solar physicists. Kiepenheuer, and especially de Jager,[65] became convinced that success in obtaining cooperative funding for the Large European Solar Telescope would require support from the broader solar community. As a step in this direction, they arranged for the provisional board's next meeting to coincide with that in March 1974 of the three-year-old Committee of European Solar Radio Astronomers.[66] The two groups appointed a twelve-member committee to plan the first European Solar Meeting.[67] Held in Florence a year later, this meeting attracted 223 participants.[68] A session on the issue of how best to promote solar research instructed the planning committee to lay the groundwork for a Solar Physics Section in the Astronomy and Astrophysics Division of the European Physical Society. Thus, in Western Europe as in the United States, solar physicists stood ready to join into new subdisciplinary ventures.

### Publishing

This same spirit was evident in the publication of solar research. The journals that had traditionally carried the best solar papers—the *Astrophysical Journal* in the United States, *Nature* and the Royal Astronomical Society's *Monthly Notices* in Britain—continued to be important outlets for new work. But competition to get into these journals was increasingly severe. Anxious to publish quickly, solar physicists were eager to find additional outlets. They ended up placing much of their better work in two journals. Many solar physicists—especially those who were primarily interested in solar emissions with pronounced terrestrial effects—came to regard the rapidly expanding *Journal of Geophysical Research* as their journal of choice. Others—especially those interested in optical studies of the Sun—leaned toward *Solar Physics: A Journal for Solar Research and the Study of Solar Terrestrial Physics,* which first appeared in 1967.

From its inception through 1975, *Solar Physics* swiftly evolved into the central forum of the international solar physics community.[69] Its press run climbed to 1,500 copies and the annual output to six thick volumes. But the journal's large circulation and enthusiastic reception were not the only indications of its primary place in the new community's life. The most telling indication was an argument within the solar physics community during 1972 and 1973 over the fledgling journal's standards. By 1974, *Solar Physics* reorganized its editorial board and raised its review standards. *Solar Physics* stood as an emblem of the emergent community. The impressive circulation numbers demonstrated the vitality of the field, and the concern for quality revealed that leading solar physicists had come to regard the journal's performance as a collective responsibility.

## LEAN TIMES, 1975–1988

During the early 1970s, after treating science generously for a decade and a half, American politicians and bureaucrats brought the growth of scientific budgets to a halt. They turned parsimonious for two main reasons. The costs of the Vietnam War, the Arab oil embargo, and social and environmental programs raised doubts about the desirability of continuing the expansion of federal patronage for science and technology. And the growth of opposition among scientists to America's foreign and military policies engendered questions about the idea that scientific spending automatically promoted national security. In particular, conservatives and moderates were increasingly skeptical that support for pure science was essential for maintaining American military superiority. Exploiting this skepticism, Senator Mike Mansfield and other liberals who wanted to reduce the military's presence in American society waged an effective campaign to limit armed forces' patronage to research and development projects having a demonstrable value to their missions.[70]

As American leaders curbed scientific spending between 1970 and 1975, most of their counterparts around the globe followed suit. To be sure, the governments of Japan and a few other countries appreciated that continuing adherence to an expansive science policy would enhance national scientific standing. But most were relieved that fewer sacrifices would be required to maintain a respectable presence in science. Consequently, the leveling off of scientific budgets in the United States inaugurated an era of limits in world science that is likely to persist for a long time to come.

### The Solar Physics Community's Struggle Against Its Insularity

Like other scientists, solar physicists saw by the mid-1970s that lean times were upon them. One harbinger of future stringencies was the High Altitude Observatory's closing of its Climax Station.[71] Another was NASA's termination in September 1973 of the ninth and tenth Orbiting Solar Observatories.[72] Yet another was the U.S. Air Force's decision to abandon the Sacramento Peak Observatory.[73] Although two major missions—Skylab and *Orbiting Solar Observatory 8*—softened the transition for solar physicists, they could see that maintaining current levels of support would be difficult.

American solar physicists, who had done especially well in the halcyon years following Sputnik, were especially worried. Their concern gave the Solar Physics Division's chairman in 1975—Robert W. Noyes of the Harvard-Smithsonian Center for Astrophysics—the opportunity that he had wanted for a decade to fight solar separatism.[74] Noyes made a persuasive case that the division should hold most of its meetings in the future with the American Astronomical Society.[75] He also arranged for the creation of a committee to suggest strategies for reducing solar physics' insularity and consequent vulnerability.[76] It was surely not chance that the committee's chair—Noyes's Harvard colleague Andrea K. Dupree—and six members shared his opposition to solar separatism.

Dupree's committee made a hard-hitting report.[77] It portrayed "the current situation" as grave:

> solar physics, which once was an integral part of astrophysics and the astronomical community, appears now to be a distinctly separate and isolated field of astrophysical research. Communication and cross-fertilization among the subdisciplines of astrophysics has declined. The astronomical community is largely unaware of and maybe indifferent to current research in solar astronomy. Adverse effects . . . could result from the loss of interest and hence support from the astronomical com-

munity. Lack of support for solar physics on a national and local level can endanger funding as well as encourage a further decrease in faculty positions in solar physics. Few students are then produced or even exposed to the problems and potential in the study of the Sun.

The result was that solar physicists were almost alone in realizing that their subject was "a significant, active, and vital field [with] numerous substantial, exciting, and unsolved problems [that had] broad interdisciplinary extension."

Dupree and her committee suggested several actions that might remedy the situation. They urged the Solar Physics Division to continue meeting jointly with the American Astronomical Society, to nurture relations with other societies that might be interested in solar phenomena, and, at every opportunity, to encourage interdisciplinary lectures, symposia, and research projects. In addition, they urged the division's members "to act individually" on solar physics' behalf. Here, they stressed the importance of promoting faculty appointments in the field so that astronomers and students in universities would be exposed "to active programs of solar research." Furthermore, they emphasized the desirability of placing "solar papers of general interest" in *The Astrophysical Journal,* proposing that only narrow papers "of strictly solar interest" should be given to *Solar Physics.* They also exhorted their peers to be constantly on the alert for opportunities to apply their techniques to nonsolar problems, write semipopular papers, give lectures, issue press releases, and serve on advisory committees.

Many American solar physicists apparently saw merit in the case for strengthening their field's ties with the rest of astronomy. In 1977, for instance, the division started appointing members to act as liaisons to neighboring subdisciplines.[78] A year later yet, the division's Hale Committee arranged for the prize's first recipient—the prominent theorist Eugene N. Parker of the University of Chicago—to give his lecture to the society as a whole.[79]

Besides seeking a greater presence within the discipline of astronomy, solar physicists updated George Ellery Hale's arguments for their field's significance. Their campaign, which opened at about the same time in Europe[80] as in the United States,[81] has continued to this day.[82] It has underscored four contributions of solar physics to astrophysics—new instruments, new diagnostic techniques, new interpretive insights, and new observational tests for existing theory.

Among the campaigners, Parker has been especially active and eloquent. The "range and intensity of solar radiation," according to his summary of a 1975 report to the National Academy's Space Science Board,[83] "have favored the development of sophisticated . . . spectroscopic and imaging instruments . . . that have subsequently found application in other areas of astrophysics." In addition, the "sun is the principal laboratory for developing and testing theoretical diagnostic tools with which to determine such physical properties as temperature, density, ionization equilibrium, systematic and random velocity fields, mass loss, heating and radiative losses, and chemical abundances." Of still greater importance, "the sun, our daytime star, is sufficiently near [to reveal] a variety of phenomena that at first sight defy rational explanation . . . but ultimately stimulate the theoretical understanding of new effects . . . elsewhere in physics and astrophysics." Finally, "the sun has been, and continues to be, the 'testing ground' of [stellar] astrophysics, where theories of nuclear energy, convection, radiation transport, and other phenomena may be confirmed or refuted." In short, as Parker[84] insisted at a semipopular symposium on the "new solar physics," the field was the "mother of astrophysics" because it was "the one area in which hard science — the critical interplay of theory and measurement — can function."

### Solar Observational Capabilities — A Mixed Record

Solar physicists have had a mixed record in their struggle since the mid-1970s to sustain the advance of their observational capabilities. On the one hand, they have suffered many disappointments. They have failed to prevent reductions in the numbers of spacecraft and ground-based facilities engaged in solar observing. They have also witnessed one postponement after another of several projects that would significantly enhance their ability to investigate solar phenomena. On the other hand, they have chalked up many successes. They have sent some remarkable instruments into space and constructed some excellent telescopes at ground-based observatories. Moreover, they have gotten access to extremely sensitive radio telescopes originally designed for galactic work and found various ways — including setting up instruments at the South Pole — to refine observational knowledge of the Sun's vibrational modes. In short, despite many setbacks, solar physicists can now observe the Sun at higher photometric, spectral, spatial, and temporal resolutions than ever before.

The reduction in the number of spacecraft used as solar observing platforms since the mid-1970s has certainly been noticeable. Two developments have evidently combined to cause this decline. First was NASA's decision to develop the reusable Shuttle Orbiter as its main Space Transportation System.[85] Bringing the Shuttle fleet into service turned out to be a much more difficult, costly, and time-consuming process than its advocates within the agency anticipated. The consequence was not only that funds for space science were tight but also that those missions that won approval were subject to repeated delays.[86] The second development behind the declining number of spacecraft with solar instruments was the emergence of strong competition from stellar and extragalactic astrophysicists for access to space. Thanks in large measure to the achievements of space-based solar observing, these rivals no longer had trouble arguing that instrumental sensitivity and spacecraft pointing were sufficient for research on celestial objects much fainter than the Sun. As a consequence, funds that might well have gone to solar missions in the 1960s and early 1970s were allocated to nonsolar astrophysical missions such as the *International Ultraviolet Explorer* [launched January 1978], the *Einstein High Energy Astronomical Observatory* (launched November 1978), the *Infrared Astronomical Satellite* (launched January 1983), and the Hubble Space Telescope [launched in April 1990].

At the present writing (November 1988), the prospects that the number of spacecraft with solar instruments will return to the levels of the late 1960s and early 1970s are nil. In fact, since the *Challenger* accident, it has been hard to imagine that the number of such missions will soon return to the reduced levels of the late 1970s and early 1980s. In general, the tragedy tempered the optimism of space-science planners not only in the United States but also in the other spacefaring nations.[87] In particular, the loss of the *Challenger* led to several changes in NASA's plans for solar observing from space. For instance, the agency postponed the launch of *Ulysses*—a European spacecraft for observing the solar wind from above the Sun's poles—for at least four years. More serious, NASA abandoned development of a solar telescope with a 130-cm primary mirror that would have provided a sustained view of features half the size of those visible from the best ground-based telescope because, contrary to original plans, the Shuttle would only rarely be available for flying the instrument.[88]

The reduction since 1975 in the number of spacecraft with solar instruments observing from space has been accompanied by a reduction in the number of ground-based solar observing programs. Several routine monitoring programs have, to judge from the staff of World Data Center in Boulder,[89] either ended completely or lapsed into irregular activity. Three losses have been particularly noteworthy. At the end of 1976, after 102 years of measuring sunspot positions and areas, Greenwich discontinued its program of daily sunspot photography.[90] Four years later, Zurich abandoned its traditional responsibility as the center for sunspot statistics. Then, in 1984, the Carnegie Institution of Washington decided to close Mt. Wilson Observatory including the solar telescopes that Hale, his colleagues, and his successors had used so successfully for eight decades.[91] All the while, the Sacramento Peak Observatory—arguably the world's premier solar observatory—has been at risk. In 1976, as the result of a concerted campaign by European as well as American solar physicists, the National Science Foundation assumed responsibility for Sac Peak from the Air Force.[92] Since then, it has been operated for the foundation by the same academic consortium that operates Kitt Peak National Observatory.[93] But Sac Peak's future is far from secure for important voices within this consortium want to consolidate solar observing at Kitt Peak as a means of freeing funds for other endeavors.[94]

Although the solar physics community has had many reversals in these lean times, it has also managed to strengthen its observational capabilities in several directions. Solar physicists have sent dozens of instruments into space that, by and large, were more precise and durable than earlier instruments. In fact, thanks to projects begun in the United States, Europe, and the Soviet Union during the late 1960s and early 1970s, spacecraft with four or more solar instruments continued to go up at a good pace until the fall of 1978. Since then, although the pace has slowed considerably, several major missions have been totally or mainly dedicated to observations of solar radiations and particles.

The best equipped solar mission since 1975 has been a NASA spacecraft for the study of flares.[95] The Solar Maximum Mission, which was the agency's last major solar mission launched by expendable rocket, was put into orbit on February 14, 1980—just five years after work began on its payload at eight American and five European scientific centers. At first, all seven of the satellite's instruments deliv-

ered excellent results. Soon, however, component failures in three instruments hampered their performance. Worse yet, nine months after
launch, the spacecraft's pointing system went out of commission.[96]
Since the backup system could only point within a few degrees of the
Sun, this failure transformed the satellite from a first-rate flare observatory into a modest solar monitor.

Such a turn of events had not gone entirely unanticipated.
Thinking that Shuttle-borne astronauts should be able to retrieve and
repair ailing satellites, NASA had designed the spacecraft with a
graspable trunnion and modular electronic system.[97] In 1982, once
the Shuttle was fully operational, therefore, NASA requested $50
million for a Solar Maximum Repair Mission.[98] Congress yielded to
an intense lobbying effort not only from the scientists but also from
the Department of Defense that, like NASA, was eager to demonstrate the capacity of astronauts to undertake serious extravehicular
work in space. On April 6, 1984, after two years of preparation,
NASA sent Robert Crippen and his crew of four up in the *Challenger* to make the repair.[99] The astronauts were hard pressed to get
the satellite into the orbiter's bay. But once successful, they succeeded
in repairing the spacecraft's pointing system and coronagraph in less
than two-thirds of the twelve hours scheduled for the job. The outcome was that, at a cost considerably below that of a comparable
spacecraft, but considerably above the most expensive ground-based
solar telescope, the Solar Maximum Mission was ready for another
five or so years of operation.[100]

Meanwhile, at the many ground-based solar observatories that
have remained open, solar physicists around the globe have continued drawing upon new electronic and computing technology to up-
grade their auxiliary instrumentation.[101] This is not all. Japanese,
German, Swedish, Soviet, and French solar physicists have managed
to obtain support for several good-sized vacuum solar telescopes. By
doing so, they have approached or matched the standard set by Richard Dunn and his colleagues at the Sacramento Peak Observatory. Indeed, with the completion of the 90-cm telescope at Tenerife, the
French may well surpass this standard.

Ground-based solar physicists have also secured support since
the mid-1970s for observing the Sun from two surprising sites—
Socorro, New Mexico, and the South Pole. They were attracted to
Socorro by the Very Large Array, an immense radio telescope that
was built primarily for galactic and extragalactic astronomy.[102] Its use

for studying the Sun was inaugurated by the University of Maryland's Mukul R. Kundu, an Indian-born radio astronomer who has focused on solar research since his graduate studies in France. He evidently secured observing time on the Very Large Array by arguing that this radio telescope's ability to pinpoint the origin of radio emissions from flares would be crucial for interpreting high-resolution optical observations from ground-based facilities and NASA's forthcoming Solar Maximum Mission. He and his colleagues made their first observations at Socorro on July 25, 1977 and May 12, 1978.[103] The success of these trials provided adequate justification for Kundu's group and a few others to use the Very Large Array as a radioheliograph during the Solar Maximum Mission's first year and thereafter.[104]

Two converging motivations gave rise to solar observing programs at the South Pole.[105] In the mid-1970s, the geophysicist Martin A. Pomerantz, director of the Bartol Research Foundation in Swarthmore, Pennsylvania had the idea of using the American polar station as a base for establishing an astronomical observatory. Stellar astronomers did not think that the advantages of observing through the long night of the polar winter warranted going to this trouble. But a few solar physicists were enthusiastic about the prospects of observing from the South Pole. Their reason was that they could make continuous observations of the Sun during the Antarctic summer for as many days as the skies remained cloudless. This would enable them to determine the frequencies of the photospheric oscillations that, according to quite recent work, would reveal the Sun's internal structure. The first solar physicist to collaborate with Pomerantz was a former colleague—Arne A. Wyller, professor of Astrophysics at the Royal Swedish Academy. In January 1979, the Swedish and Bartol groups demonstrated the feasibility of continuous solar observing from the South Pole.[106] A year later, a French team led by Eric Fossat of Nice and his graduate student Gerard Grec joined with the Bartol group in securing an uninterrupted record of solar oscillations for more than five days.[107] Since these early successes, solar observing has been a regular activity at the American station during the Antarctic summers.

Thus, although solar physicists have had to struggle for support since the mid-1970s, they can investigate many solar phenomena that were earlier beyond their reach. Their instruments in space, while fewer than in the years leading up to Skylab and *Orbiting Solar Observatory 8*, are generally more precise, more versatile, and more reliable. They are acquiring a new generation of high-resolution solar telescopes at ground-based facilities. They are upgrading their auxiliary instrumentation as new technologies become available. And, to judge from the new solar observing programs at the Very Large Array and the South Pole, they still have opportunities for undertaking fresh ventures.

## CONCLUSION

Patronage for solar physics grew by leaps and bounds from the late 1950s through the early 1970s. Impressed by the military and political implications of Sputnik, national leaders in advanced nations around the world substantially increased support for science and technology. Meanwhile, their scientific and technical advisors, who were mindful of solar physics' immediate prospects and utility, devoted a small yet generous share of the new monies to the improvement of solar observational capabilities. In the 1970s, changed priorities brought an end to the era of plenty in research and development. Having fared relatively well during the bountiful times following Sputnik, solar physicists have been hard pressed to come up with the resources needed for new space missions and ongoing programs of research at ground-based facilities. Still, the current level of worldwide support for solar work remains well above that of the 1950s.

Thanks to increased support, solar physics has become a substantial enterprise. The number of established solar physicists around the globe has reached some three hundred. They have created subdisciplinary associations and a journal. Most important, with the technical assistance of outsiders ranging from rocket engineers to nuclear scientists, they have acquired an increasingly versatile and sensitive array of instruments for observing the Sun. They have gained access to particles from the Sun's atmosphere and neutrinos from its interior as well as the entire electromagnetic spectrum. And while doing so, they have attained ever higher photometric, spectral, spatial, and temporal resolutions. But to what effect? Elsewhere I begin to explore how improvements in solar observational capabilities since Sputnik have contributed to the progress of solar physics in the last three decades.[108]

## NOTES

1. W. A. McDougall, . . . *The Heavens and the Earth: A Political History of the Space Age* (New York: Basic Books, 1985).

2. J. R. Killian Jr., *Sputnik, Scientists, and Eisenhower: A Memoir of the First Special Assistant to the President for Science and Technology* (Cambridge: MIT Press, 1977); B. B. Clowse, *Brainpower for the Cold War: The Sputnik Crisis and National Defense Education Act of 1958* (Westport: Greenwood Press, 1981).

3. W. A. McDougall, . . . *The Heavens and the Earth: A Political History of the Space Age.*

4. G. E. Wukelic, ed., *Handbook of Soviet Space-Science Research* (London: Gordon and Breach, 1968).

5. W. R. Corliss, *Scientific Satellites* (Washington, D.C.: NASA, 1967), NASA SP-133.

6. J. R. Killian Jr., *Sputnik, Scientists, and Eisenhower: A Memoir of the First Special Assistant to the President for Science and Technology.*

7. P. B. Stares, *The Militarization of Space: U.S. Policy, 1945 to 1984* (Ithaca: Cornell University Press, 1985), 42.

8. L. V. Berkner and H. Odishaw, "A Note on the Space Science Board," in *Science in Space,* ed. Berkner and Odishaw (New York: McGraw-Hill, 1961), 429–436; N. S. Hetherington, "Winning the Initiative: NASA and the U.S. Space Science Program," *NASA Prologue* (Summer 1975): 99–108.

9. Berkner and Odishaw, *Science in Space,* 430.

10. R. W. Porter, "International Scientific Community: International Council of Scientific Unions and COSPAR," *International Cooperation in Outer Space: A Symposium,* ed. E. Galloway (Washington, D.C.: U.S. Government Printing Office, 1971); H. S. W. Massey and M. O. Robins, *History of British Space Science* (Cambridge, England: Cambridge University Press, 1986).

11. A. W. Frutkin, *International Cooperation in Space* (Englewood Cliffs: Prentice-Hall, 1965); H. E. Newell Jr., *Beyond the Atmosphere: Early Years of Space Science* (Washington, D.C.: NASA, 1980), NASA SP-4211.

12. J. H. Oort, "Ruimtevaart en Haar Betekenis voor de Naturwetenschap," *Koninklijke Nederlandse Akademie van Wetenschappen: Jaarboek (1958–1959),* 147–171.

13. Letter from DeJager to Karl Hufbauer regarding the background and early history of the Dutch Committee for Geophysics and Space Research, 1986, NASA History Office, Washington, D.C.

14. J. Veldkamp, "Verslag van de Nederlandse Commissie voor Geofysica en Ruimte-Onderzoek over 1960." *Koninklijke Nederlandse Akademie van Wetenschappen: Jaarboek (1960–1961),* 201–202.

15. Veldkamp, ibid. *(1961–1962),* 222–224; *(1962–1963),* 283–286; *(1963–1964),* 280–301; *(1964–1965),* 256–265.

16. Massey and Robins, *History,* 1986.

17. A. W. Frutkin, *International,* 1965.

18. U.S. Congress: Congressional Research Service, *World Wide Space Activities: National Programs Other than the United States and Soviet Union* (Washington, D.C: U.S. Government Printing Office, 1977); *Soviet Space Programs: 1976–80,* pt. I (Washington, D.C.: U.S. Government Printing Office, 1982).

19. J. N. Tatarewicz, "'Where Are the People Who Know What They Are Doing?' Space Technology and Planetary Astronomy, 1958–1975" (Ph.D. dissertation, Indiana University, 1984).

20. H. H. Guendel, "Solar and Cosmic Electromagnetic and Charged-Particle Radiations," in *Handbook,* ed. G. E. Wukelic (1968), 215–302.

21. S. L. Mandel'shtam, "Studies of Shortwave Solar Radiation in the USSR," *Applied Optics* 6 (1967): 1834–1844; J. A. Van Allen, *Origins of Magnetospheric Physics* (Washington, D.C.: Smithsonian Institution Press, 1983).

22. Guendel, 1968.

23. W. R. Corliss, *Scientific Satellites.*

24. H. Friedman, "Recent Experiments from Rockets and Satellites," *Astronomical Journal* 65 (1960): 264–271.

25. R. W. Kreplin, T. A. Chubb, and H. Friedman, "X-Ray and Lyman-Alpha Emission from the Sun As Measured from the NRL SR-1 Satellites," *Journal of Geophysical Research* 67 (1962): 2231–2253.

26. R. W. Newkirk and J. D. Bohlin, "Coronascope II: Observation of the White Light Corona from a Stratospheric Balloon," *Annales d'Astrophysique* 78 (1065): 234–238.

27. W. R. Corliss, *NASA Sounding Rockets, 1958–1968* (Washington, D.C.: NASA, 1971), NASA SP-4401; L. N. Ezell, *NASA Historical Data Book, vol. 3: Programs and Projects, 1969–1978* (Washington, D.C.: NASA, 1988), NASA SP-4012.

28. Biography of John C. Lindsay, NASA History Office, Washington, D.C.; A. Bester, *The Life and Death of a Satellite* (Boston: Little, Brown & Co., 1966).

29. Bester, *Life and Death,* 1966; U.S. General Accounting Office, *Certain Weaknesses in the Management of Solar Observatory Projects, NASA, for the Period January 1959 through December 1962* (Washington, D.C.: Government Printing Office, 1964); L. Goldberg, "Solar Physics," in *Space Science Comes of Age: Perspectives in the History of the Space Sciences,* A. Hanle and V. D. Chamberlain (Washington, D.C.: Smithsonian Institution, 1981), 15–30; L. N. Ezell, *NASA Historical Data Book, vol. 2: Programs and Projects 1958–1968* (Washington, D.C.: NASA, 1988), NASA SP-4012.

30. NASA, *Orbiting Solar Observatory Satellite OSO I: A Project Summary* (Washington, D.C.: NASA, 1965), NASA SP-57.

31. NASA, OSO Fact Sheet, News Release Number 62-32 (NASA History Office, Washington, D.C., February 22, 1962).

32. Bester, *Life and Death,* 1966.

33. H. E. Newell Jr., *Beyond the Atmosphere: Early Years of Space Science* (Washington, D.C.: NASA, 1980), NASA SP-4211.

34. Bester, *Life and Death,* 1966; Ezell, *Data Book,* vol. 2, 1988.

35. NASA, Summary Minutes: Solar Physics Subcommittee of the Space Sciences Steering Committee (NASA Headquarters, Washington, D.C., September 13–14, 1962).

36. Bester, *Life and Death,* 1966.

37. J. E. Karth, "NASA Authorization for Fiscal Year 1966," *Congressional Record,* Appendix (June 17, 1965), A3178.

38. H. Glaser, "Orbiting Solar Observatories (OSO) Workshop" (NASA History Office, Washington, D.C., OSO File, August 28, 1969).

39. Bester, *Life and Death,* 1966.

40. R. W. Newkirk, I. D. Ertel, and C. G. Brooks, *Skylab: A Chronology* (Washington, D.C.: NASA, 1977), NASA SP-4011; W. D. Compton and C. D. Benson, *Living and Working in Space: A History of Skylab* (Washington, D.C.: NASA, 1983), NASA SP-4208.

41. R. E. Davis and W. A. Ostaff, Memorandum for Laurence T. Hogarth regarding Solar Physics Subcommittee meeting (NASA History Office, Washington, D.C., September 21, 1966).

42. Newkirk et al., *Skylab,* 1977; Compton et al., *Living and Working,* 1983.

43. Compton et al., *Living and Working,* 1983.

44. J. A. Eddy, *A New Sun: The Solar Results from Skylab* (Washington, D.C.: NASA, 1979), NASA SP-402; Compton et al., *Living and Working,* 1983.

45. R. R. McMath and A. K. Pierce, "The Large Solar Telescope at Kitt Peak," *Sky and Telescope* 20 (1960): 64–67, 132–135; R. M. Petrie, "Builder of Solar Observatories," *Sky and Telescope* 23 (1962): 187–190; J. E. Kloeppel, *Realm of the Long Eyes: A Brief History of Kitt Peak National Observatory* (San Diego: Univelt, 1983).

46. Kloeppel, *Realm* (1983), 69.

47. R. B. Dunn, "High Resolution Solar Telescopes," *Solar Physics* 100 (1985): 1–20.

48. R. F. Howard, "Studies of Solar Magnetic Fields," *Solar Physics* 38 (1974): 283–299; id., "The Mount Wilson Solar Magnetograph: Scanning and Data System," *Solar Physics* 48 (1976): 411–416.

49. T. J. Pinch, "Theoreticians and the Production of Experimental Anomaly: The Case of Solar Neutrinos," in *The Social Process of Scientific Investigation,* ed. K. D. Knorr, R. Krohn, and R. Whitley (Dordrecht: Reidel, 1980), 77–1906; id., "Theory Testing in Science—The Case of Solar Neutrinos: Do Crucial Experiments Test Theories or Theorists?," *Philosophy of the Social Sciences* 15 (1985): 167–187; id., *Confronting Nature: The Sociology of Solar Neutrino Detection* (Dordrecht: Reidel, 1985).

50. J. N. Bahcall, "Neutrinos from the Sun," *Scientific American* 221 (June 1969): 28–37.

51. H. J. Smith et al., *Report of the Solar Astronomy Task Force.*

52. NASA, Summary Minutes: Solar Physics Subcommittee of the Space Science Steering Committee, NASA Headquarters, Washington, D.C. (April 29–30, 1965).

53. L. Goldberg, letter to J. W. Firor Jr., requesting a proposal for American Astronomical Society sponsorship of regular solar meetings (May 11, 1965). Leo Goldberg Papers, Kitt Peak National Observatory, Tucson, Arizona.

54. J. W. Firor Jr., letter to L. Goldberg with "An Annual Solar Astronomy Meeting: A Proposal to the American Astronomical Society" (July 16, 1965). Leo Goldberg Papers, Kitt Peak National Observatory, Tucson, Arizona.

55. L. Goldberg, letter to J. W. Firor Jr., regarding the AAS Council's response to his proposal (September 30, 1965). Leo Goldberg Papers, Kitt Peak National Observatory, Tucson, Arizona.

56. L. Goldberg, letter to N. U. Mayall asking whether Kitt Peak National Observatory would host the next solar meeting (November 22, 1966). Leo Goldberg Papers, Kitt Peak National Observatory, Tucson, Arizona.

57. L. Goldberg, letter to A. K. Pierce reporting that the issue of annual solar meetings would be brought to the AAS Council in June (April 17, 1967). Leo Goldberg Papers, Kitt Peak National Observatory, Tucson, Arizona.

58. J. W. Firor Jr., letter to G. C. McVittie describing the first two solar meetings and requesting AAS sponsorship of annual solar meetings (March 4, 1968). Leo Goldberg Papers, Kitt Peak National Observatory, Tucson, Arizona.

59. L. Goldberg, letter to H. W. Babcock reporting the AAS Council's approval of annual solar meetings (July 22, 1968). Leo Goldberg Papers, Kitt Peak National Observatory, Tucson, Arizona; M. Schwarzschild, "Introduction," *Bulletin of the American Astronomical Society* 1 (1969):1; J. N. Tatarewicz, *Space Technology and Planetary Astronomy* (Bloomington, Indiana: Indiana University Press, 1990).

60. "Abstracts of Papers Presented at the Meeting of the Division on Solar Physics, Held 17–19 November 1970 at Huntsville, Alabama," *Bulletin of the American Astronomical Society* 3 (1971): 259–266; Anonymous, "AAS Division on Solar Physics," *Bulletin of the American Astronomical Society* 4 (1972): 376.

61. Anonymous, "Solar Physics Division: 1973," *Bulletin of the American Astronomical Society* 5 (1973): 484; P. A. Sturrock, "Division on Solar Physics: 1974," *Bulletin of the American Astronomical Society* 6 (1974): 494–495.

62. K. O. Kiepenheuer, "The Aims and Prospect of the Joint Organization for Solar Observations," *Joint Organization for Solar Observations: Annual Report* (1970), 8–20; C. De Jager, "Introduction," *Joint Organization for Solar Observations: Annual Report* 3 (1970); C. De Jager and P. Maltby, "Report of Activities of JOSO in 1970 and Preceding Years," *Joint Organization for Solar Observations: Annual Report* (1970): 32–36.

63. Anonymous, "Statement of Intentions (June 1970)," *Joint Organization for Solar Observations: Annual Report* (1970), 4–7.

64. K. O. Kiepenheuer, "European Site Survey for a Solar Observatory," *Sky and Telescope* 48 (1974): 84–87; K. O. Kiepenheuer, "The JOSO Observatory Coming into Sight," *Joint Organization for Solar Observations: Annual Report* (1974), 4–9.

65. C. De Jager, "The Formal Organization of JOSO in Relation to General Solar Research in Europe," *Joint Organization for Solar Observations: Annual Report* (1973), 13–18.

66. A. D. Fokker, "CESRA," in *Proceedings of the First European Astronomical Meeting*, Athens, September 4–9, 1972, vol. 1: *Solar Activity and Related Interplanetary Phenomena*, ed. J. Xanthakis (Berlin: Springer, 1973), 178–179.

67. G. M. C. Reijnen, "Concise Report of the Combined JOSO-CESRA Meeting, 7 March 1974, Berne, Switzerland," *Joint Organization for Solar Observations: Annual Report 1973* (1974), 38–40.

68. A. D. Fokker, "Cooperation in Solar Physics," *Joint Organization for Solar Observations: Annual Report* (1976), 88–90.

69. K. Hufbauer, "Solar Physics' Evolution into a Subdiscipline (1945–1975)," paper for Utrecht University's 350th Anniversary Symposium on New Trends in the History of Science, August 29, 1986.

70. R. W. Nichols, "Mission-Oriented R & D: Senator Mansfield's Questions Sharpen Congressional Uncertainties about Federal R & D Patterns," *Science* 172 (1971): 29–37.

71. O. R. White and J. T. Jefferies, "Reports on Solar Instruments," *Transactions of the International Astronomical Union* 15A (1973): 67, 75–76.

72. Ezell, *Data Book*, vol. 3, 1988.

73. A. von Alvensleben, "Report of the Eighth Meeting of the Provisional Board of JOSO in Florence," *Joint Organization for Solar Observations: Annual Report* (1974), 27–33.

74. Back when Leo Goldberg and John Firor opened the campaign for regular solar meetings under the auspices of the American Astronomical Society, Noyes had anticipated that this innovation might weaken solar physics. "I would be somewhat concerned," he wrote Goldberg,

> over any change which would tend to divide the solar astronomers from the rest of the astronomical community. I think there is already too much tendency for solar physics to be insular, due I suppose to the isolation of some of the observatories (Sac Peak is a prime example) and the complexity of the detailed analysis required by the detailed nature of solar observations. I do not think it is good, for instance, for an astronomer to spend his life studying oscillations in the solar atmosphere to the exclusion of all other astronomy!
> I fear that either creating a separate solar astronomy subsection or devoting one meeting of the AAS each year to solar astronomy would work in just that direction.
> The solar people would come only to 'their' meeting, would see only their solar colleagues and would be seen by no others.[1965]

75. L. L. House, "Division of Solar Physics: 1975," *Bulletin of the American Astronomical Society* 8 (1976): 401.

76. J. D. Bohlin, "Division of Solar Physics: 1975," *Bulletin of the American Astronomical Society* 8 (1976): 589.

77. A. K. Dupree, J. M. Beckers, L. W. Fredrick, J. W. Harvey, J. L. Linsky, L. E. Peterson, and A. B. C. Walker, "Report of the Ad Hoc Committee on Interaction Between Solar Physics and Astrophysics" (NASA History Office, Washington, D.C., June 18, 1976).

78. J. D. Bohlin, "Division of Solar Physics," *Bulletin of the American Astronomical Society* 9 (1977): 698.

79. J. D. Bohlin, "Division of Solar Physics," *Bulletin of the American Astronomical Society* 10 (1978): 723–724.

80. E. H. Schroter, "Trends and Problems in Optical Solar Research," *Joint Organization for Solar Observations: Annual Reports 1973* (1974), 19–33; C. Zwaan, "Why Optical Solar Research?," *Joint Organization for Solar Observations: Annual Reports 1973* (1974), 34–37; J. C. Pecker and R. N. Thomas,

"Solar Astrophysics: Ghettosis from, or Symbiosis with, Stellar and Galactic Astrophysics?," *Space Science Reviews* 29 (1976): 217–243.

81. H. J. Smith et al., "Report of the Solar Astronomy Task Force to Ad Hoc Interagency Coordinating Committee on Astronomy" (Washington, D.C.: Federal Council for Science and Technology, 1975); E. N. Parker et al., "Report on Solar Physics to the National Academy of Sciences' Space Science Board," August 1975; P. A. Sturrock, "Division on Solar Physics: 1974," *Bulletin of the American Astronomical Society* 6 (1974): 494–495.

82. Eddy, *A New Sun,* 1979; R. W. Noyes, letter to L. Goldberg about the dangers of solar separatism, July 26, 1965; E. N. Parker, "The Future of Solar Physics," *Solar Physics* 100 (1985): 599–619.

83. E. N. Parker, "A Broad Look at Solar Physics: Adapted from the Solar Physics Study of August 1975," in *Solar System Plasma Physics,* vol. 1, ed. E. N. Parker, C. F. Kennel, and L. J. Lanzerotti (Amsterdam: North-Holland Publishing Co., 1979), 5, 7, 10, 12.

84. E. N. Parker, "Solar Physics in Broad Perspective," in *The New Solar Physics,* ed. J. A. Eddy (Boulder: Praeger, 1978), 1–8.

85. J. M. Logsdon, "The Space Shuttle Program: A Policy Failure?," *Science* 232 (1986): 1099–1105; Ezell, *Data Book,* vol. 3, 1988.

86. R. J. Smith, "Shuttle Problems Compromise Space Program," *Science* 206 (1979): 910–914; M. M. Waldrop, "Space Science in the Year of the Shuttle," *Science* 231 (1981): 316–318.

87. M. M. Waldrop, "The *Challenger* Disaster: Assessing the Implications," *Science* 231 (1986): 661–663; id., "A Crisis in Space Research," *Science* 235 (1987): 426–429; D. Dickson, "Europe Assesses Its Options," *Science* 231 (1986): 665; id., "Space: It Is Expensive in the Major Leagues," *Science* 237 (1987): 1110–1111; R. A. Brown and R. Giacconi, "New Directions for Space Astronomy," *Science* 238 (1987): 617–619.

88. H. Zirin, letter to K. Hufbauer regarding the cancellation of the Solar Optical Telescope (April 7, 1986), NASA History Office, Washington, D.C.; "Solar Telescope Cancelled," *Sky and Telescope* 73 (1986): 126–127.

89. H. E. Coffey, "Problems in Gathering and Archiving Ground-Based Solar Synoptic Data: Talk to the National Academic Panel on Long Term Observations" (February 1986), NASA History Office, Washington, D.C.

90. G. A. Newkirk Jr., ed., "Commission 10: Solar Activity," *Transactions of the Astronomical Union* 176A (1979): 11–48.

91. "A Second Life for Mount Wilson Observatory?" *Sky and Telescope* 68 (1984): 203–204; L. J. Robinson, "Why Mount Wilson Shouldn't Be Scrapped," *Sky and Telescope* 69 (1985): 197; R. F. Howard, "Eight Decades of Research at Mt. Wilson," *Solar Physics* 100 (1985): 171–187.

92. J. W. Evans, "Sacramento Peak Observatory," *Bulletin of the American Astronomical Society* 9 (1977): 243–244.

93. L. E. Cram, "Sacramento Peak Observatory," *Solar Physics* 69 (1981): 411–418.

94. M. M. Waldrop, "Sacramento Peak Observatory to Close?" *Science* 235 (1985): 36; "Sac Peak Scare," *Sky and Telescope* 70 (1985): 105.

95. C. Covault, "Solar Max Mission Will Increase Sun Data Twofold," *Aviation Week and Space Technology* 111 (December 17, 1979): 52–56; D. M. Rust, "The Solar Maximum Observatory," *Johns Hopkins University: Applied Physics Laboratory Technical Digest* 5 (1984): 188–196.

96. C. Covault, "Fuse Failure Curbs Solar Max Vehicle," *Aviation Week and Space Technology* 114 (1981): 14–15.

97. Covault, "Solar Max," 1979.

98. A. Chaikin, "Rescuing Solar Max," *Sky and Telescope* 63 (1982): 236; Rust, "Solar Maximum," 1984.

99. C. Covault, "Orbiter Crew Restores Solar Max," *Aviation Week and Space Technology* 120 (April 16, 1984): 18–20.

100. S. P. and B. E. Woodgate, "A Second Chance for Solar Max," *Sky and Telescope* 67 (1984): 498–500.

101. Dunn, "High Resolution," 1985.

102. W. Tucker and K. Tucker, *The Cosmic Inquirers: Modern Telescopes and Their Makers* (Cambridge: Harvard University Press, 1986).

103. M. R. Kundu, E. J. Schmahl, and A. P. Rao, "VLA Observation of Solar Regions at 6-cm Wavelength," *Astronomy and Astrophysics* 94 (1981): 72–79.

104. M. S. Roberts and R. J. Havlen, "National Radio Astronomy Observatory," *Bulletin of the American Astronomical Society* 12 (1980): 288–311; id., "National Radio Astronomy Observatory," *Bulletin of the American Astronomical Society* 13 (1981): 308–344; id., "National Radio Astronomy Observatory," *Bulletin of the American Astronomical Society* 14 (1982): 370–410; M. R. Kundu, "Probing the Radio Sun," *Sky and Telescope* 64 (1982): 6–10.

105. J. W. Harvey, M. A. Pomerantz, and T. L. Duvall Jr., "Astronomy on Ice," *Sky and Telescope* 64 (1982): 520–523.

106. H. L. Shipman, "Bartol Research Foundation and University of Delaware," *Bulletin of the American Astronomical Society* 12 (1980): 21–25.

107. G. Grec, E. Fossat, and M. A. Pomerantz, "Full-Disk Observations of Solar Oscillations from the Geographic South Pole," *Solar Physics* 82 (1983): 55–66.

108. K. Hufbauer, *Exploring the Sun: Solar Science Since Galileo* (in press, The Johns Hopkins University Press).

*Joseph N. Tatarewicz*

# Space Technology and Planetary Science, 1950–1985

## INTRODUCTION

Planetary science and solar science offer many points of similarity and difference. Both have at various times in history been in the mainstream of astronomy, perhaps even dominating astronomical research for brief periods. Both have had very strong ties to several other disciplines of the physical sciences, drawing large numbers of scientific workers to study the Sun and planets in search of data on physical conditions that could not be duplicated in the laboratory on Earth. Both shifted out of the mainstream of astronomy at mid-century, and emerged from the Second World War well poised for a period of intense growth and articulation. Both planetary science and solar science, each in its unique way, offered the promise of practical results applicable to agendas far from basic science. And both were arenas where the budding U.S. space science program could achieve immediate and impressive results with extensions of the technology at hand.

The planetary exploration program, which grew out of the reaction to Sputnik, transformed the study of solar system bodies. Direct access to the planets by space probes allowed observations impossible from earth, setting the study of the solar system on a new observational and theoretical footing. In addition, the exploration of the solar system was prosecuted on the basis of ground-based study, and provided the means by which astronomers and others "rediscovered" the merits—and limits—of an expanded program of more conventional ground-based planetary astronomy.[1]

In 1959, when the decision was made to engage in a program of exploration of the solar system from space probes, NASA planners were unaware of the rudimentary state of solar system studies. When NASA officials were finally convinced in the early 1960s of the value of ground-based planetary astronomy, and of the improbability of the needed research being done without direct NASA support, the agency responded with a multifaceted program that transformed the field. Observatories were constructed, instruments acquired, astronomers trained, research programs funded, and other activities supported, all of which aimed at increasing the fund of ground-based knowledge of the planets. These developments had profound consequences for the established discipline of astronomy and for the emerging multidisciplinary area of planetary studies.[2]

The immediate stimulus for encouraging the development of a planetary science community and providing it with substantial resources came from NASA's lunar and planetary flight programs. But just as the expanded space program put into place in the aftermath of Sputnik capitalized on scientific, technical, political, and social forces that had been gathering since World War II, so, too, the renewed activity in planetary astronomy had roots stretching back at least as far. NASA drew on the expertise of individuals, such as Harold Urey, Gerard Kuiper, and Clyde Tombaugh, who had long been active in planetary research. NASA also drew upon, and enlarged, the resources of institutions such as Lowell Observatory, which had similar interests. Before NASA, and concurrent with NASA support, many of these same individuals and institutions had been supported in their planetary work by the military and other federal agencies.

## SECOND WORLD WAR

Except for a few very interesting exceptions, planetary science could not promise the same kind of direct operational benefit to the war effort offered by solar science. However, insofar as planetary science could be seen as "earth science writ large," whatever benefits geophysics and other earth sciences accrued during and after the war ultimately made their way into planetary science. The study of Earth as a planet was (and this is not Whig history) for some individuals with grand visions a way of developing and exercising in situ techniques and instruments to be applied later when the technology would be available to send similar instruments to other planets.[3]

Planetary astronomy benefited from the war in a number of ways. The increased availability of money helped alleviate the financial pressures that had constrained all of astronomy. The liberal funding environment especially aided the planetary specialty, which had not been in the immediate prewar years a major concern of mainstream astronomy.

New instrumentation, developed during the war, helped open the infrared wavelengths beyond the photographic range, a spectral region important for discerning molecular constituents of planetary atmospheres. Radar techniques opened the microwave and shorter wavelength regions, allowing radiometry to be applied with far more precision and flexibility than that of the prewar studies.

Wartime experience had drawn increasing attention to various scientific problems that were on the boundaries of astronomy and geophysics: structure, composition, and optical properties of the atmosphere; nature and dynamics of the aurora and skyglow and their connection with solar activity; dynamics of Earth's weather and global circulation patterns; and many others. Deeper understanding of Earth as a planet helped frame questions to guide research on the characteristics of other planets, while the vastly different conditions on those planets invited investigations to deepen the understanding of Earth.

Finally, rocket and missile technology, and the political nexus in which it was embedded, in time made travel to the planets a feasible and attractive goal for a variety of reasons.[4]

## POSTWAR PERIOD AND NASA

Unlike solar science, the study of other planets made only very tentative use of sounding rockets and balloons during the 1950s. In large part this was due to the rather crude spatial resolution of the instruments available to fly, combined with the equally crude pointing and guiding controls available on the vehicles. However, there was a general transfer of vehicle and instrument expertise as well as buoying of spirits in the small community.[5]

In the wake of Sputnik, the planets took on much more than

scientific interest to various parties. Segments of NASA looked to the planets as an opportunity to recover lost prestige. Segments of the military saw the Moon and even the planets as the next arena of battle. Aerospace companies, making the transition from building aircraft to building missiles and near-space vehicles saw opportunities for lucrative contracts. Engineers working in various aspects of rocketry (propulsion, guidance, and communications) saw interplanetary travel as an attractive challenge to their skills. Once the remote objects of scientific curiosity, the planets took on new significance.[6]

These extra-scientific and quasi-scientific motivations were not the sole reasons for an increase in interest in the planets. Some astronomers, already interested in planetary studies, saw a major opportunity to advance their specialty, and were prepared and able to seize it. Some geophysicists, chemists, physicists, and others also saw in the planetary program an opportunity to advance their respective specialties. A few, with grander visions, saw the possibility of uniting several disciplines to create, through space techniques, a new field of research, sometimes called comparative planetology or planetary science(s).[7]

## THE NASA PLANETARY EXPLORATION PROGRAMS

Ambitious plans for planetary exploration were made in the late 1950s but were partially diverted by the overriding emphasis placed on Project Apollo. Around 1965, as planners anticipated the peak and decline of Apollo funding, internal and external planning bodies converged on an ambitious program of solar system exploration as a post-Apollo goal. NASA expanded its support of ground-based planetary astronomy during this period, elevating it to the status of an ongoing program. NASA planners, with advice from external and internal advisory bodies, had identified two major needs: optical telescope time and instrumentation, and qualified astronomers to undertake planetary studies. To meet the first need, major optical observatories were constructed with NASA funds and with contractual guarantees of their use for lunar and planetary astronomy (Table 1). To meet the second, research grants for ground-based studies in support of probe missions swelled, NASA's predoctoral training program began to produce new Ph.D.s, and the active planetary probe pro-

gram began to produce its scientific harvest, attracting more researchers. The initial exploration of Venus (1962, 1967) and Mars
(1965, 1969) took place during this period, since only those planets
were within technological and funding reach, given the available
technology and funds. Correspondingly, the NASA-supported ground-
based program focused on the inner planets during this period (Table
2).[8]

As the Apollo lunar landings approached, NASA planners began
to look increasingly toward post-Apollo programs. Many candidates
were considered, including space stations, orbital astronomical observatories, and others. Favorite among the scientific advisory boards

**Table 1. Major NASA-Funded Telescopes for Planetary Astronomy**

| Location | Aperture (in) | Owner/Operator | Completion Date |
|---|---|---|---|
| Mt. Palomar, CA | 200 | Caltech | (1948) |
| Mt. Locke, TX | 107* | U. Texas | 1963-1969 |
| Mt. Wilson, CA | 100 | Carnegie | (1917) |
| Mauna Koa, HI | 88* | Hawaii | 1965-1970 |
| Mt. Locke, TX | 82 | U. Texas | (1939) |
| Catalina Mt., AZ | 61* | Arizona LPL | 1962-1965 |
| Mt. Wilson, CA | 60 | Carnegie | (1908) 1965-1970 |
| Mt. Palomar, CA | 60 | Carnegie | 1971 |
| Bethany Sta., MA | 40* | Yale | 1966 |
| Palestine, TX | 36* | Princeton | 1963-1970 |
| Greenbelt, MD | 36* | NASA | 1967 |
| Flagstaff, AZ | 30* | USGS | 1964 |
| Palestine, TX | 28* | Arizona LPL | 1966 |
| Table Mountain, CA | 24* | JPL | 1966 |
| Ojai, CA | 24* | UCLA | 1965 |
| White Mtn., CA | 24* | Caltech | 1965 |
| Las Cruces, NM | 24* | Northwestern | 1965 |
| Las Cruces, NM | 24* | New Mexico State | 1967 |
| Mauna Koa, HI | 24* | NASA-Lowell | 1969 |
| Cerro Tololo, Chile | 24* | NASA-Lowell | 1969 |
| Australia | 24 | NASA-Lowell | 1969 |
| India | 24 | NASA-Lowell | 1969 |
| So. Africa | 24 | NASA-Lowell | 1969 |
| Las Cruces, NM | 16* | New Mexico State | 1962 |
| Table Mtn., CA | 16* | JPL | 1963 |

*Sources:* NASA Planetary Astronomy Office Files
Table adapted from *Astronomy and Astrophysics for the 1970s* (Washington, D.C.: NASA, 1972),
vol. 2, pp. 388-393.
* NASA-funded construction of entire instrument, with owner/operator supplying dome and building.
Dates in parentheses refer to completion of original instrument.

Table 2. Planetary Exploration by Spacecraft

| Planet | Spacecraft Name | Launch Date | Encounter Date |
|--------|-----------------|-------------|----------------|
| Venus | Mariner | 28/27/62 | 12/14/62 |
| Mars | Mariner 4 | 11/28/64 | 4/14/65 |
| Venus | Mariner 5 | 6/14/67 | 10/19/67 |
| Mars | Mariner 6 | 2/25/69 | 7/31/69 |
| Mars | Mariner 7 | 3/27/69 | 8/5/69 |
| Mars | Mariner 9 | 5/30/71 | 11/13/71–<br>10/27/72 (Orbiter) |
| Jupiter | Pioneer 10 | 3/3/72 | 12/4/73 |
| Jupiter | Pioneer 11 | 4/6/73 | 12/5/74 |
| Saturn | Pioneer 11 | 4/6/73 | 9/1/79 |
| Venus | Mariner 10 | 11/3/73 | 2/5/74 |
| Mercury | Mariner 10 | 11/3/73 | 3/29/74<br>9/21/74<br>3/16/75 |
| Mars | Viking 1 | 8/20/75 | 7/20/76 (Lander) |
| Mars | Viking 2 | 9/9/75 | 9/3/76 (Lander) |

was the ambitious "Grand Tour" of the outer solar system, then technically within reach by a combination of advancing spaceflight technology and a fortuitous alignment of the outer planets. NASA's ground-based program looked increasingly toward the outer planets in preparation. Mars, Mercury, and Venus also were visited by spacecraft, and ground-based research was conducted in support of these inter-planet missions as well. During this period major NASA planetary telescopes, under construction since 1965, became operational, and were quickly set to work in support of the planetary flight program. The optical and laboratory facilities that NASA supported in the 1960s helped alleviate the shortage of telescope time that planetary astronomers had faced before the program.

The agency's emphasis shifted in the 1970s toward construction and renovation of radio and radar facilities for planetary astronomy, and the construction of a major infrared telescope. The research emphasis of the program also shifted. Whereas Venus and Mars had been emphasized in the earlier period, the new targets for the planetary exploration program—Mercury and the outer planets—required increasing ground-based reconnaissance.

In summary, NASA began the United States' exploration of the planetary system on the basis of knowledge gained from a small astronomical specialty, by then on the very fringe of astronomy and some marginal areas of geophysical sciences. Through a vast influx of a variety of resources, the agency put into place an entire scientific infrastructure dedicated to exploration of the solar system. Table 3 lists the principal varieties of support provided by NASA. Other institutions, such as the Air Force, the National Science Foundation, and the universities provided some support for this activity, but their aggregate contribution is minuscule in comparison to that provided by NASA.

**Table 3. NASA Support Provided to Planetary Science**

* Conventional research grants to fund ground- and space-based planetary research.

* Telescopes dedicated, in whole or in part, to lunar and planetary research. Such telescopes ranged in size from 107 inches, among the world's largest, to 12 inches, and included both optical and radio telescopes.

* Telescopic instrumentation, laboratories, and other research facilities.

* Predoctoral and postdoctoral training.

* Interplanetary spacecraft and the planetary flight program (perhaps the most important, due to its scientific return as well as providing the motivation and the justification for the ground-based support).

* General interest in space flight and astronomy, and the prospect of an extended, vigorous planetary exploration program, including the prospect of ultimate manned missions.

## EFFECTS OF THE NASA PROGRAMS ON PLANETARY SCIENCE

One indication of the vitality of a particular scientific specialty may be found in the relative numbers of scientists publishing in the scholarly literature. A few years ago Tom Gieryn and I did some quantitative analyses of the publishing habits of astronomers and possible impacts of NASA funding. The data and results have been published elsewhere.[9] Here I just wish to summarize some of the primary findings.

We found that planetary research among astronomers constituted a very small portion of their overall work, confirming a variety of anecdotal evidence. While work on planetary topics increased dramatically after the beginning of NASA, planetary work seems to have begun to accelerate at a rate only nearly equal to that of astronomy as a whole in the early 1960s, faltering after 1965, and recovering somewhat in 1972–1974. Planetary astronomy thus showed enough gain relative to other astronomical specialties to indicate some increasing interest, but important developments were occurring elsewhere in astronomy, particularly in stellar and high- energy astronomy, which attracted new as well as established astronomers.

For individual planets, however, there was a clear and dramatic increase in numbers of astronomers publishing on individual planetary problem areas around the times of planetary missions, but the activity dropped off in most cases rather rapidly. The drop in activity among astronomers in planetary topics was, however, generally less dramatic than some of the anecdotal testimony would lead one to expect.[10]

The amount of time spent by astronomers on planetary topics around 1970, a survey of astronomers' research interests from the same period, and the overall use of major telescopes for lunar and planetary research all agree generally with the level of support provided by NSF for lunar and planetary research from its astronomy program, and suggest a basis for what some planetary astronomers have called the "10 percent rule," referring to the observing time and funding made available for planetary research by the overall astronomical community. The survey results discussed above suggest continuing lack of interest among the majority of astronomers at least to about 1970. A similar survey conducted around 1980 found little change. These surveys also suggest that relatively few new astronomy Ph.D.s were taking up planetary research.

These and other data suggest the following sketch of one segment of the planetary science community — those affiliated with the American Astronomical Society (AAS), and thus with strong astronomical interests and ties. It was first of all a small community, growing from around 100 members in 1960 to a peak of about 400 members around 1974, but at a rate substantially less than that of the astronomical community as a whole. Around half worked exclusively on planetary topics, the rest maintaining interest in other astronomical specialties. Thus, there was a core of around 200–250 planetary workers allied with the AAS. But around 1965, those publishing exclusively in planetary topics represented a decreasing percentage. The production of new Ph.D.s in planetary science appears to have remained relatively flat during the 1970s, at around 20 per year. The data suggest that planetary specialists in the AAS were somewhat older than other specialists. Finally, the community was very heavily dependent—almost exclusively so—on NASA support.[11]

## THE PLANETARY SCIENCE COMMUNITY

This growing community of planetary researchers with multidisciplinary allegiances, and using a peculiar combination of space and ground-based research techniques on the planets, called for novel institutional arrangements. The attempts to find a "home" for planetary science within existing scientific societies and associations focused on the American Geophysical Union's Planetary Sciences Section, and the Division for Planetary Sciences of the American Astronomical Society.

The American Geophysical Union (AGU) attempted to establish such a division in 1961, very early in the space program. The Executive Committee of the AGU had been discussing the problem of where space research should be located within the union. After some preliminary planning, Homer Newell, Robert Jastrow, and Gordon J. F. MacDonald argued for a separate section exclusively devoted to planetary sciences. First, they argued, the time was coming when the planets could be studied using geophysical techniques, and pointed out the many ways in which the other planets were similar to Earth. "Thus, the techniques to be employed are those of the earth sciences, and not those of astronomy. The new areas of planetary exploration . . . will utilize many of the techniques already available in the earth sciences."[12] While the planets had been "not too highly valued a property" of the astronomers, those astronomers who were so inclined would continue to study the planets. But in addition, geophysicists "ought to join in." They saw a need for educational institutions to begin to educate workers in a broader view, encompassing all of the planets as a unified science. As to the proper home for planetary sciences, the astronomers no longer had exclusive claim—the interest of the American Astronomical Society was "on the basis of tradition and the fact that the planets are indeed astronomical bodies." The AGU, however, "has the strongest interest in this matter. For . . . the planets are indeed sisters to the earth in their relation to the solar system."[13] It took two and a half years of maneuvering, but in November 1962, the Planetary Sciences Section was created with Newell as President, Jastrow as Vice President, and Cameron as Secretary.[14]

The Planetary Sciences Section continued to grow into the late 1960s, in part representing the intense work being done on the magnetic fields and particles of Earth, Mars, Venus, and interplanetary space, and the geophysical work being done on the Moon. In the late 1960s the Planetary Sciences Section of the AGU had grown to such an extent that, as part of a general reorganization of the structure of the AGU, it was split into Planetology, which considered surfaces and interiors of planetary bodies, and Solar-Planetary Relationships, which considered particles and fields and their interaction with the solar wind.

At about the time that the AGU Planetary Sciences Section was fragmenting, another attempt to organize the diverse community of planetary workers occurred within the American Astronomical Society. Very shortly after the recommendations of a National Academy of Sciences panel on planetary astronomy in August 1968, the AAS approved the formation of a Division of Planetary Astronomy, with Joseph W. Chamberlain as chairman of the organizing committee. A pre-inaugural meeting was held at the University of Texas in December, and by the spring of 1969 the first by-laws of the group, now named the AAS Division for Planetary Sciences (DPS), were adopted. The DPS was to exist

> for the purpose of advancing the investigation of the solar system, with special encouragement of interdisciplinary cooperation. . . . Studies of the Earth and Sun fall within the scope of the Division's interests, insofar as they are oriented toward an understanding of the planetary system in general.[15]

Although originally the membership of the DPS was limited to AAS members (primarily astronomers), in March 1973 the by-laws were changed to allow a new category, affiliate membership, " . . . open to planetary scientists who wish to be associated with the Division . . . but who are members of other professional organizations actively concerned with planetary science." At the same time, a publications committee, appointed two years earlier under Clark Chapman recommended that the DPS endorse *Icarus* as the primary publication for planetary research, and that members attempt to publish in the most frequently read journals.[16]

The publications subcommittee had investigated a severe problem in planetary science, the lack of journals devoted to the field. Using various survey analyses of publication habits and a poll of the membership, the committee found that at least 60 journals published planetary science articles, and that "In order to have access to as much as 90% of important articles, the library for a planetary science group must subscribe to 15 or 20 journals; however, over 90% of the pages of such journals contain articles irrelevant to planetary science."[17] They found six journals that were the most widely used and highly regarded by planetary scientists, and published 80 percent of the most frequently cited articles in the 1960s, but found various problems of editorial restrictions, refereeing policies, publication delays, and quality with all of them. They considered various courses of action, but finally decided at the March 1973 meeting to endorse *Icarus*.[18]

*Icarus* had been founded in 1962, under the editorship of Zdenek Kopal and A. G. Wilson. Carl Sagan joined the editorial staff in 1968, and became editor in 1969. Sagan began to recruit more articles in planetary astrophysics, in contrast to the previous concentration of celestial mechanics in the journal. Table 4 lists other

**Table 4. Scientific Journals for Lunar and Planetary Research**

| Year | Title  (Comments) |
|------|-------------------|
| 1947 | *The Strolling Astronomer* (Amateur publication of the Association of Lunar and Planetary Observers [ALPO]) |
| 1959 | *Planetary and Space Science* |
| 1962 | *Communications of the Lunar and Planetary Laboratory* (G. P. Kuiper, private publication) |
| 1962 | *Icarus. Journal of Solar System Research* (Z. Kopal and A. G. Wilson, eds.) |
| 1966 | *Earth and Planetary Science Letters* |
| 1967 | *Solar System Research*  (USSR) |
| 1968 | *Icarus* (Carl Sagan, editor, various editorial changes) |
| 1969 | *The Moon* (Z. Kopal, editor; year of Apollo 11 first lunar landing and sample return) |
| 1973 | *Icarus* (changes to monthly publication and endorsed by AAS/DPS) |
| 1978 | *The Moon and Planets* (formerly *The Moon*) |

more-or-less specialized lunar and planetary journals that were established in response to the increasing activity in planetary study. Planetary science was diffused not just through several scientific fields and societies, but through a variety of journals.[19]

## CONCLUSIONS

In the thirty-five years covered by this paper, astronomy and planetary sciences experienced wide fluctuations in funding, employment patterns, and general interest. Since planetary research required tools far beyond the means of any but government groups, such trends have implications not just for the level of activity, but perhaps for the very survival of the science itself. In recent years, a number of articles and studies have appeared suggesting that in the absence of continuity of funding, some planetary science research teams were disbanding as their members struck out into new and more secure directions of research.[20] This recalls the comments in the 1968 Hall Report on Planetary Astronomy that "The absence of a greater number of active, specialized planetary science departments may reflect some skepticism about the permanence of the space effort." The authors predicted that if the federal government were to commit the nation "to a long-term planetary-exploration program, the rate of Ph.D. production in planetary science will probably increase as university confidence in the stability and continuity of the national program develops."[21]

Planetary research was a scientific enterprise whose pace and direction of development ultimately depended on considerations far beyond the scientific desiderata developed by the research community itself. The goals and priorities of the research community and those of their sponsors (NASA, Congress, the public) did not always coincide. They clashed, for example, over the early emphasis on Mars and the use of large, complex spacecraft. Most of the scientific community came to favor a more balanced approach, using simpler spacecraft to visit several planets. But the engineering community favored the more challenging Voyager-class missions. In addition, discussion within NASA centered on whether the less-glamorous agenda could capture the attention and enthusiasm of Congress and the public, and hence ultimately the funding and project approval. While a detailed comparison of the atmospheres of Mars,

Venus, and the Earth held great interest for the planetary science community, the search for life on Mars with an advanced robot explorer and the prospect of human footsteps on the Red Planet held far more allure for those who ultimately controlled the purse strings.[22]

As the degree of interest and funding in the planetary flight program went, so went ground-based planetary astronomy and planetary science. Thus the fortunes of planetary science were linked to the fortunes of the flight program, since in the absence of NASA research grants and operational support for the NASA-constructed telescopes, ground-based planetary astronomy could not be carried out. NSF did not move to increase its funding of planetary astronomy when the magnitude of NASA support faltered in the early 1970s, and the planetary programs on NASA-supported telescopes were continually in danger of being swamped by stellar and galactic programs. And in the absence of NASA-sponsored and operated transportation to the planets, planetary science was stalled.[23]

This means that planetary science is in a sense an artificial product, created and maintained at least in part by forces operating outside the science in question. The relative lack of attention given to planetary astronomy before NASA (and even during the NASA years by such organizations as NSF) can be seen as an assessment by the astronomical community of what constituted scientifically important and technically feasible research problems worthy of being attacked with the limited resources available. NASA's attempts to stimulate this field, while partially motivated by scientific sincerity and a somewhat broader vision concerning the scientific potential of space techniques, represented in some sense interference, an attempt at political control.[24]

Direct but limited access to the planets required an active and scientifically vigorous community of planetary researchers able to integrate ground- and space-based results and bring them to bear on important theoretical problems. In order to do this, as well as support the probe program, access to ground-based instruments was required and the cooperation and support of the wider scientific community was no less important. NASA was led to establish the ground-based program most immediately because it was deemed essential to the engineering success of the planetary exploration program. But of equal force as a motivation was the desire to produce a scientifically sound and productive program. But the scientific community, and astronomers in particular, did not leap at this new opportunity. Other factors were at work.

The debate during the early 1960s within NASA over just how to go about getting the planetary research it needed centered on to what degree the agency was willing to reproduce portions of the existing scientific system, but with planetary work emphasized. The method chosen by NASA can be seen as a compromise: an attempt at gentle control, through financial support of planetary work, sponsoring conferences and symposia to drum up interest in planetary research, construction of facilities dedicated in part to planetary astronomy and other planetary research, and "gifts" to the astronomical community such as the facilities, interdisciplinary grants, and predoctoral training grants through the NASA University Program. Behind this lay the hope that with such "seed" programs, and with the demonstration through the results of the ground- and space-based programs, the overall community would respond with increased enthusiasm for planetary research. To assure access to the NASA-provided facilities while waiting for the longer-term stimuli to take effect, the contracts for such telescopes had "teeth" in them, language explicitly stating to what extent planetary research and planetary astronomers on other NASA support were to have access.

NASA's use of these "levers of control" seems to have been only partially successful. It was motivated in part by a desire to disrupt the usual practice of science as little as possible by avoiding the establishment of competing institutions that would then be abandoned after their mission relevance had vanished. After planetary exploration became more commonplace, NASA planners and scientists hoped, planetary science would naturally develop into a respectable scientific specialty or discipline of its own, and with or without planetary astronomy — depending on whether further uses for planetary astronomy would emerge — the new discipline would take its place within the economy of science. But NASA became identified as the sponsor of planetary astronomy, and the community looked to this agency to take care of the specialty.[25]

Planetary astronomy was transformed by space technology and the scientific, technical, social, and political milieu in which that technology was used to explore the planets. In place of an exclusively astronomical specialty there appeared a new heterogeneous community of researchers attempting to establish a professional identity. The overall planetary science that resulted could probably claim a closer contemporary theoretical kinship to the earth sciences than to astronomy. But in the course of this overall construction of planetary science through the 1960s and 1970s, an important niche was found for planetary astronomy.

The small community of planetary astronomers that evolved to populate that niche had strong ties to the astronomical community by virtue of tradition, their education, research tools, and the overall place of the solar system within the astronomical universe. But they were equally tied to the diverse planetary science community by virtue of the overall goal of understanding the various bodies of the solar system as planets. This diffusion of identity in the disciplinary structure of the sciences made it difficult for planetary workers and especially planetary astronomers to find a true "home" within the economy of science.

To a certain extent NASA helped provide a surrogate institutional focus for planetary research. As almost the sole sponsor, such work could hardly have been carried out without the agency. But NASA's role went beyond the vast material support it provided. The agency also provided mechanisms for communication among the diverse workers, through informal means as well as through sponsorship of symposia and conferences. The agency also contributed to the cognitive direction of the specialty, by selecting which planets were to be targets of the flight program and hence in which particular areas research would be supported.

This is not to say that planetary astronomy and planetary science were total captives of a government agency. Through the American Geophysical Union's planetary sections, the American Astronomical Society Division for Planetary Sciences, and other groups, the community organized itself apart from NASA in ways more familiar to the conduct of science. Through the many committees of the National Academy of Sciences Space Science Board, planetary scientists could wield considerable influence on the scientific objectives of the NASA program. The agency could hardly appear before Congress for budget hearings and approval of programs without the backing of the Space Science Board.

A very simple and compelling argument can be constructed to show that NASA (and its Soviet counterparts) are almost solely responsible for the current, rather sophisticated, state of knowledge of the solar system.[26] Interplanetary spacecraft and the associated infrastructure, including its ground-based astronomical components, are necessary conditions for sophisticated scientific knowledge of the solar system. The more interesting and more difficult questions occur when one looks at the finer structure of this patronage. All of the developments associated with space technology and postwar government funding of science introduced new ways of conducting scientific work and choosing problems for research. Matters planetary and matters astronomical became the concerns of a much wider community, with other than purely scientific motivations.

## ACKNOWLEDGMENTS

Portions of this work were carried out with support from the National Science Foundation Division of Policy Research and Analysis, the Smithsonian Institution and National Air and Space Museum, the NASA History Office, and Indiana University, which the author gratefully acknowledges. Any opinions, findings, conclusions, or recommendations expressed in this publication are those of the author and do not necessarily reflect the views of the National Science Foundation or any of the other supporting institutions.

## NOTES

1. The themes in this presentation are developed in greater detail in Joseph N. Tatarewicz, *"Where Are the People Who Know What They Are Doing?" Space Technology and Planetary Astronomy, 1958–1975* (Ph.D. dissertation, Indiana University, 1984), published in a revised form, *Space Technology and Planetary Science* (Bloomington: Indiana University Press, 1990); *'A Strange Plea'—The Campaign for Planetary Astronomy in Support of Solar System Exploration, 1959–1962. National Air and Space Museum Research Report 1985,* 91–109; "Federal Funding and Planetary Astronomy," *Social Studies of Science* 16 (February 1, 1986): 80–103.

2. Planetary *astronomy* is the use of ground or space-based astronomical telescopes and instrumentation to study solar system bodies from afar. Planetary *exploration* is the use of space probes sent to the near vicinity of a planet to conduct observations either in situ or from very close to the planet. Planetary *science* is the multidisciplinary study of solar system bodies using geology, geophysics, chemistry, etc.

3. Homer E. Newell, *Beyond the Atmosphere: Early Years of Space Science* (Washington, D.C.: NASA SP-4211, 1980).

4. Bernard Lovell, "The Effect of Defence Science on the Advance of Astronomy," *Journal for the History of Astronomy* 8 (1977): 151, 167; Neville J. Woolf,

"The Impact of Space Studies on Astronomy," in *Impact of Space Exploration on Society*, ed. William E. Frye (Tarzania: American Astronautical Society, 1966), 180–181; Walter Fricke, "New Impetus to the Exploration of the Solar System," Inaugural Address in *Sun and Planetary System*, ed. W. Fricke and G. Teleki (Dordrecht: Reidel, 1982), 9.

5. Aoudoin Dollfus, "Pioneering Balloon Astronomy in France," *Sky and Telescope* 66 (November 1983): 381–387; Robert S. Richardson, "A Postwar Plan for Mars," *Astounding Science Fiction* (January 1944), quoted in Robert S. Richardson (Mount Wilson and Palomar Observatories) *Exploring Mars* (New York: McGraw-Hill, 1954), 19–20; Robert S. Richardson, *Some Observations Made of Mars at Mount Wilson in 1956*, Astronomical Society of the Pacific Leaflet 333 (February 1957).

6. Tatarewicz, *Where Are the People*, Chapter 1.

7. Carl Sagan, "Harold Clayton Urey—In Memoriam," *Icarus* 48 (1981): 348–352; Cyril Ponnamperuma, "Harold Clayton Urey: Chemist of the Cosmos," *Sky and Telescope* 61 (May 1981): 397; Stephen G. Brush, "Harold Urey and the Moon," op cit.; Dale P. Cruikshank, "20th-Century Astronomer," *Sky and Telescope* 47 (March 1974): 159–164, and "Gerard Peter Kuiper," *Biographical Memoirs of the National Academy of Sciences* (in press).

8. Tatarewicz, op cit., Chapter 4.

9. Tatarewicz, "Federal Funding and Planetary Astronomy;" Tatarewicz and Thomas F. Gieryn, "Federal Funding and Planetary Astronomy, 1950–1975," in the National Science Foundation Division of Policy Research and Analysis, Proceedings of the Workshop on *Federal Funding and Knowledge Growth in Subfields and Specialties of Science*, May 1983.

10. Very strong assertions about NASA "resurrecting" planetary research occur in Eli Ginzberg et al., *Economic Impact of Large Public Programs: The NASA Experience* (Salt Lake City: Olympus, 1976), "Transformation of a Science: NASA's Impact on Astronomy," 82–83, and Homer E. Newell, *Beyond the Atmosphere*, 328–329, 408.

11. Tatarewicz, *Where Are the People*, Chapter 5.

12. H. E. Newell, R. Jastrow, G. MacDonald. "A Home for Planetary Sciences." Prepared for the President's Page in *Transactions of the American Geophysical Union*, draft manuscript (June 1960) in above location. Published in *Transactions of the American Geophysical Union* 41 (September 1960): 407–409.

13. Ibid.

14. Thomas F. Malone to Newell, 11/30/62; Newell to Jastrow, 11/27/62, with attached "Conference Report, Conference on organization and planning for the new Section on Planetary Sciences . . . [Newell and Jastrow], 13 November 1962."

15. "By-Laws of the Division for Planetary Sciences, American Astronomical Society, 15 May 1969," Article 3; Chamberlain to distribution, 12/10/68; "Abstracts of Papers Presented at the Pre-Inaugural Meeting of the Planetary Division of the AAS," *Bulletin of the American Astronomical Society* 1/2 (1969): 213–219.

16. Frank Drake, Chairman, "Proposal for Change in By-Laws of the Division of Planetary Sciences;" Peter M. Millman, "Meeting Review. The Fourth An-

nual Meeting of the AAS Division for Planetary Sciences, Tucson, Arizona, March 20–23, 1973," *Icarus* 20 (1973): 346–355.

17. Report of the Publications Subcommittee, ca. March 1973. Members were Clark R. Chapman, David Morrison, R. Reynolds.

18. Report of the Publications Subcommittee; Peter M. Millman, "Meeting Review," op cit.; the six journals were *Icarus, Astrophysical Journal, Science, Journal of Geophysical Research, Astronomical Journal,* and *Journal of Atmospheric Sciences.*

19. Table 4 lists the principal journals devoted to planetary science and their founding dates.

20. U.S. Congress, Office of Technology Assessment, *Space Science Research in the United States: A Technical Memorandum* (Washington, D.C.: Government Printing Office, September 1982), 5–8; Mitchell Waldrop, "Planetary Science on the Brink Again," *Science* 206 (4424, 14 December 1979): 1288–1289; R. Jeffrey Smith, "Uncertainties Mark Space Program of the 1980s," ibid., 1284–1286; "The NASA Budget: Planetary Panic," *Science News* 120 (26 October 1981): 260.

21. Hall Report, 67–68.

22. Edward C. Ezell and Linda Neumann Ezell, *On Mars: Exploration of the Red Planet* (Washington, D.C.: NASA SP-4212, 1984); Joseph N. Tatarewicz, "The Persistence of Lowell's Legacy: Life, Mars, and the U.S. Space Program 1958–1967" (abstract), *Bulletin of the American Astronomical Society* 17/4 (1985): 828.

23. See Brunk to M. J. S. Belton, 11/18/75, AR, concerning problems at one of the NASA-sponsored telescopes: "The combination of a small planetary staff and pressures for more observing time from the larger number of non-planetary staff members are the basic causes of the problem. . . . The present university-supported staff has predominantly stellar interests."

24. The use of various "levers of control" to direct scientific activity in certain directions is explored in Wolfgang van den Daele's and Peter Weingart's, "Resistance and Receptivity of Science to External Direction: The Emergence of New Disciplines under the Impact of Science Policy," in *Perspectives on the Emergence of Scientific Disciplines,* ed. Gerard Lemaine et al. (The Hague: Mouton, 1976), 247.

25. Michael J. S. Belton, "Planetary Astronomy with the S[pace] T[elescope]," in *Scientific Research with the Space Telescope* (Washington, D.C.: NASA CP-2111, 1979); Working Group on Planetary Science, Astronomy Survey Committee, National Academy of Sciences. *Challenges to Astronomy and Astrophysics.* Working Documents of the Astronomy Survey Committee (Washington, D.C.: NASA, 1983), 108.

26. The European and Asian nations have recently entered the field of planetary exploration, especially during the recent apparition of Halley's comet. It will soon be possible to do serious international comparative studies on government influence on the direction of planetary science.

*Thomas F. Gieryn*

# Space Sociology?
# Commentary on
# Hufbauer and Tatarewicz

My comments have all the prejudices of a sociologist of science. I have never described myself as a historian of science, nor has anyone from that field ever asked me to join. My observations on these two fine reports thus come from afar, though I hope that they are not completely out of bounds.

Despite the disciplinary divide that separates the authors from me, I feel as if I am among old friends. I am comfortable with their findings: at no time was I jarred by something unexpected. The histories of solar physics and of planetary sciences unfolded in a way that was, for me, recognizable and easily anticipated. My comfort has little to do with our intertwined biographies: Hufbauer and I first met a decade or so ago over some oral histories stored at the American Institute of Physics; Tatarewicz and I first met a half-decade ago while he was finishing his dissertation at Indiana's Department of History and Philosophy of Science. No, my comfort is the result of an intellectual déjà vu. Reading the chapters is (as the rock music DJs say) "a blast from the past."

About the time I met Karl Hufbauer in the mid-1970s, I was beginning my studies in the sociology of science at Columbia University. I participated in an annual two-semester graduate seminar on the subject directed by Robert Merton and Harriet Zuckerman, and at the start of each year, students would receive a long bibliography of the "essential" readings. I believe it was 1977 when Merton and Zuckerman passed out an appendix to the syllabus that listed three pages of new studies that, in retrospect, inaugurated new wave sociology of science: the study of *scientific specialties*. Many of the refer-

ences are still familiar — they have become the classics that I assign
to my graduate students: Nicholas Mullins's work on the phage
group in molecular biology;[1] Joseph Ben-David and Randall Collins's
study of the origins of psychology;[2] David Edge and Michael Mulkay's just-published *Astronomy Transformed;*[3] reports from the Cornell group on high-energy physics by Sullivan, White, and Barboni;[4]
Small and Griffith's bibliometric co-citation mapping of specialties
and disciplines;[5] John Law's innovative study of x-ray protein crystallography;[6] Daryl Chubin's first attempt to review all this in 1976.[7]
And there were many others. Now these two studies of planetary sciences and solar physics fit neatly into that sociological category of
"specialty studies" — in terms of their analytic goals, methodological
strategies, data collection, and theoretical assumptions. In 1977, they
would have been cutting edge; in 1987 — for a sociologist — they are
a bit like a comfortable period-piece.

Please do not mistake me for a neophile! There is much about
the newer sociology of science of the last decade that I find troubling
and maybe even worthless, and much of the good old days is worth
salvaging and renewing. Still, in the sociology of science, the study
of scientific specialties — along the lines pursued in these two case
histories — is passe, and for reasons that are worth discussing. I want
to suggest that the evaporating sociological interest in "specialty
studies" is the result of both push factors and pull factors. Sociologists were pushed from the study of specialties by several roadblocks —
call them intractable problems — that simply made it impossible to
carry forth the research that began so promisingly in the mid-1970s.
But they were also pulled out of specialty studies by the appeal of
other topics and questions that had no place on the research agenda
of that era. I shall talk first about the push factors (the intractable
problems) and then the pull factors (the omitted questions). My ex-
plicit references to the papers will be few and fleeting, but I hope the
pertinence of my remarks for each of them will be obvious.

As I look back, there were two push factors, two intractable
problems that blocked progress in the sociology of scientific specialties. Call the first of these the "boundary problem." Forgive me for
once again resorting to autobiography, but so much of my own intellectual journey is inseparably linked to the life and death of specialty
studies. When I commenced my dissertation in 1977 or so, desper-
ately wanting to be part of the new wave, I began a kind of specialty
study — more precisely, an analysis of how astronomers choose prob-

lems for investigation.[8] That study required me to map the discipline of astronomy into its constituent specialties and problem areas, so that I could watch astronomers travel around the territories as they moved through their careers. I approached this task as a technical problem of measurement, solved (I thought) by using the *Astronomischer Jahresbericht*, a 93-category subject-indexed bibliography of the world's literature in astronomy and astrophysics. The 93 subject categories became problem areas, and these were grouped into eleven more encompassing regions that I labeled specialties, and I successfully defended my thesis.

Then the troubles began: Small and Griffith's co-citation maps of astronomy had little correspondence to my own; the more I talked with practicing astronomers I came to realize that each of them mapped out astronomy (and their careers) in unique ways. My crisis of confidence got worse when I read a paper by Steve Woolgar, demonstrating that the astronomical specialty of "pulsar research" could have anywhere from 509 to 760 publications (in 1968–1972) depending upon which of six equally rational and methodologically justifiable criteria for inclusion that one might choose.[9] This is the boundary problem: how can we know when solar physics leaves off and another specialty begins? What are the boundaries of planetary astronomy in terms of included topics, methods, instruments, and practitioners? Typically, the boundary problem is solved by expediency (as in my use of the *Jahresbericht*), but Woolgar's paper and my own experience confirmed that expediency could become just another word for arbitrariness. The empirical conclusions about how specialties formed and grew became a function of how one chose to bound the territory, and there were no rational or methodological rules other than expediency for deciding those demarcations.

This arbitrariness still haunts specialty studies that approach the boundary problem as a technical difficulty to be solved with "better measures." About five years ago, I gave up on the possibility of better measures of the boundaries of specialties, and began instead to study how and why participants in science—researchers, college deans, officials at NSF or at NASA, Congressmen—themselves drew different maps by locating boundaries between territories here or there.[10] The result, I think, has been a better understanding of the function of such maps—how they are used to allocate resources and rewards, for example—even though I have given up much by abandoning the hope that we can ever arrive at a definitive map of science and its disciplines and specialties. To convert the boundary problem from a technical issue of measurement into an analytical problem of its own implies that "specialties" cannot be defined or bounded in any transcendent way because they are constantly being redrawn depending upon the cartographer and his or her interests. There is no fixed reality behind the maps—the many and typically discordant maps are the reality of science.

The second push factor is a different kind of roadblock: tag it "data in search of a theory." Sociologists are inveterate extrapolators and generalizers: a case study is only useful if it can be lumped with other cases to yield a picture of typical and unusual patterns. The finished products of historians become grist for our mill: but, for sociologists trying to compare and contrast case studies of scientific specialties, we had no mill (and I am not certain that we have a mill today). A mill would be a theory of scientific specialties that would allow us to explain and predict typical patterns in their emergence, social structure, and functioning. Perhaps sociologists of science got out of the "specialties" business because we simply could not come up with a theory or set of theories that would order the diversity of case studies we were then mass producing.

There were attempts, of course. I still recall pouring over page 382 of *Astronomy Transformed,* a six-by-fifteen verbal table labeled by Edge and Mulkay "Factors in Scientific Innovation and Specialty Development." The six columns listed the major sociological studies of specialties that I ticked off before. The fifteen rows were features hypothesized to be generic characteristics in the life of scientific specialties, things like: "marginal innovators," "initial discovery in 'applied' context," "growth associated with access to graduate students," "creation of new journal," "conflict with established or parent discipline," and so on. This surely is the beginning of a theory of scientific specialties, except that the cells of the table—filled in with a "+" if the feature was present in one of the six cases, a "-" if it was not, and a "?" if information was not available— showed a mishmash: some specialties had all of the hypothesized features, others had only a few. And, so far as I know, sociologists then failed to make the next step—to account theoretically for why these features of specialties turned up in some cases but not others. We stopped instead with the lame truism that specialties are different.

There were other more ambitious attempts to come up with a theory of scientific specialties, notably the efforts of Mullins, who melded Thomas Kuhn's writings on the formation of paradigms in science[11] and Derek Price's writings on the formation of networks of science,[12] to arrive at a sequence of stages through which most specialties passed (the stages were labeled normal, network, cluster, and specialty).[13] Only a few picked up on Mullins's stage theory, perhaps because it seemed to propose a unilinear theory of evolution in the face of too many cases that simply did not fit that proposed sequence. Again, the theorizing ceased just when it would have been interesting to develop a model for why specialties conform to or depart from Mullins's stages. The step was not taken, and it has not been taken since, but the problem remains that until we arrive at some theoretical understanding of the typical patterns of specialty formation and development, the iteration of more historical case studies will add up to nothing nomothetic.

For historians of science content to tell a story about "what happened" in solar physics or planetary astronomy, that may be a gap easily lived with. Or is it? "Theory" enters historical studies when the investigator chooses the questions to be asked, the data to be assembled, and analytic methods to be used. Tatarewicz and Hufbauer each restricted their attention to some interesting aspects of their specialty, leaving others unexplored—perhaps because they worked with implicit theories that identified some features as essential and others irrelevant for the understanding of their cases. That use of theory on a case-by-case basis invites what Merton used to call "theoretical ad-hoc-ery": inventing explanations to fit the particular facts of a single case. Until sociologists of science can develop general theories of scientific specialties—accepting, rejecting, and refining hypotheses as they collide with the data—our understanding of science will remain merely historical.

Let me turn to the two pull factors: elements of science that have attracted theoretical and empirical attention, but ones that had no place in specialty studies as formulated in the 1970s. These two pull factors are related: the first came from a realization that the scientific specialty was too large a unit of analysis, while the second came from a realization that it was too small or narrow a unit of analysis. If the study of scientific specialties is like looking at science with normal vision, sociologists in the 1980s have begun to use microscopes to look for details too tiny to be seen in the context of specialty studies, while others have picked up telescopes to see better a wider universe in which specialties are embedded. I need to elaborate both the microscopic and telescopic turns in recent sociology of science.

A signal change in the language of today's microscopic sociologists of science is the growing frequency in use of the word "local." In the hands of Karin Knorr-Cetina, for example, "local" implies that scientists' behavior and interpretations are specific to the narrowly circumscribed geographical home in which they do science. In her book *The Manufacture of Knowledge*, Knorr-Cetina writes:

> research laboratories develop local interpretations of methodological rules, a local know-how in regard to what is meant and how to make things work the best in actual research practice. . . . The argument here is not that science is private or non-public, but that information obtained in natural and technological research is idiosyncratic. The selection of the research process reflects interpretations which are crystallizations of order in local contingency space. Contrary to what we may think, criteria for 'what matters' and 'what does not matter' are neither fully defined nor standardized throughout the scientific community. Nor are the rules of official science exempted from local interpretation.[14]

In the trendy language of the day, meaning and behavior is "contextually contingent." As sociologists of science turned increasingly to studies of how scientific knowledge is constructed (as opposed, say, to counting how many scientists do research on solar physics), the word "local" became a methodological dictum. Where once a sociologist of science might be content using the Science Citation Index along with a few personal interviews, my microscopic colleagues literally go and see how science gets done through ethnographic studies of laboratory life (which happens to be the title of the best anthropology of science so far, by Bruno Latour and Steve Woolgar[15]).

The result? The "scientific community" and even the "scientific specialty" becomes a figment: a fiction created by analysts to group together people and practices that are — upon microscopic inspection — not enough alike to constitute a unit of analysis. By zooming in on the daily life at a telescope or in a laboratory, sociologists have found a world completely unappreciated ten years ago. Let me give an example from a local world more familiar to this group: a microscopic study by Harold Garfinkel, Michael Lynch, and Eric Livingston of the astronomical discovery of the pulsar. Their article begins: "On the evening of the discovery of the optical pulsar at Steward Observatory, January 16, 1969, by John Cocke, Michael Disney, Don Taylor, and Robert McCallister, a tape recording in which they reported their series of observations was left running, and before it ran out recorded the evening's 'conversations' from Observations 18 through 23."[16]

Because someone forgot to turn off the tape recorder, these sociologists were blessed with a gold mine of data that would let them glimpse the social construction of a scientific discovery. I must excerpt from the transcript, for the excitement of the astronomers is matched by the excitement of sociologists trying to discover what goes on in science:

"This is run number nineteen, on S. P. Star, on South S. P. Star."
"We're on our way."
[later] "Hmmm. It's growing! Heh heh heh."
"Yeah, that's it."
"Hihh, Hihh."
"By God, we got it."
"Naow, naow."
"Hmmmm."
"I think the best way to look at these things is just to forget the dots, just look underneath, here . . . "
"Hmmmm."
"The dots at the bottom."
"Alright."
"Yeah, it looks clearer there."
"It disturbs me that it's right in the middle of the screen."
[later] "If you get the right frequency . . . "
"Uh huh."
"Then it'll be more or less in the same place, wouldn't it?"
"Yeah."
"It should be more or less, you wouldn't be exactly the same place."
"It could be . . . "
"If we have exactly the same frequency . . . If you've got the pulse dead right."
"Yeah, hmmmmmm, well that—that's, uh—that's the bloody pulse."
"Isn't it?"
"Yeah, hmmmm."
"Should we go and ring Don up?"

"Uh, let's move off that position and do somewhere else and see if we get the same thing."

"Alright?"

"My God!"

"I hope to God this isn't some sort of artifact of the, uh, instrumentation."

"My God."

"My God."

"Never saw it before."

"We didn't, no, but maybe tonight a mouse got in and chewed out some of the wires."

"Well, we didn't have the period right before, that's why."

"God damn."

"God . . . fantastic!"

"That's a bloody pulsar."[17]

Now I am not suggesting that this sort of detail is essential for understanding the emergence and development of a scientific specialty, but only this: by choosing the specialty as a unit of analysis, this microscopic picture is invisible. And this blow-up of science-as-it-happens has proved irresistibly fascinating for many.

Others among my peers have traded the naked eye for a telescope, and found still another world of science that was largely invisible in the heyday of specialty studies. I am pleased to report, that on this score, both Tatarewicz and Hufbauer are using the same telescope, for they, like some sociologists today, see scientific specialties against the backdrop of a wider political and economic world. Back in the 1970s, however, it was possible to see specialties emerging from only three conditions: a few new ideas, a few new instruments, and a few people to take up both. But where was the money to build machines, to support new research programs, to train students? And where were the political battles necessary to secure those funds? If these concerns were absent from old-style specialty studies, they are prevalent today in a sociology of science that does not often use the word "specialty."

Bruno Latour's latest book, *Science In Action,*[18] expands the population of people doing "science" by including those who are drawn into the financial support of research, or those who consume its products. Expensive instruments and laboratories do not grow on trees, and nowhere is this more apparent than in astrophysics. Scientists must enlist allies willing to spend money on their pursuits; but how? Latour says that scientists must make others want the facts that they make, by fitting their facts to others' needs or by redirecting others' needs to fit their facts. These enrolled allies become as much a part of "science" as the guy at the telescope, though they were "missing" from the old-style study of specialties. On one level, Latour's work breaks down the analytical distinction between "science" and "the social or political contexts of science" (though that split still animates the logic of these essays). The funding programs of NASA and the dots on a computer printout are now seen as caught up in a seamless web called science. In this telescopic vision, the specialty (as an autonomous and disinterested group of researchers pursuing nature through ivory telescopes) is simply too small a window for looking in on the wider reality of science.

I have concentrated too much on sociology, but let me close with one last prickly question. My colleagues at York (Michael Mulkay, Trevor Pinch, and Malcolm Ashmore) have initiated the study of accounting practices in science.[19] Simply put, the idea is to study the mechanisms of how science is written about or talked about, rather than to use such accounts to draw inferences about the reality behind the accounts. These sociologists, for example, compare the written-up professional journal account of a discovery to the often quite different off-the-record account of the same discovery by the same author. The goal is not to find out what really happened, but to figure out how and why the two accounts of science are different.

Tatarewicz and Hufbauer have offered two accounts of two scientific specialties, and we might sit around and talk about how well or poorly those accounts correspond to others' memories. But suppose, following Mulkay's lead, we take the accounts themselves as an object of sociological study, and ask how these historian's accounts might differ from accounts created by participating astronomers or by high officials in NASA. I would bet that the accounts differ in substantial ways. Why? Because all accounts are prepared in a context of identifiable goals and interests that constrain their authors, and these goals (following Latour) are intellectual but also political, social, and economic. So what are the goals of these two accounts of astronomical specialties, what are the interests of their authors, and to what ends are they written?

## NOTES

1. Nicholas C. Mullins, "The Development of a Scientific Specialty: The Phage Group and the Origins of Molecular Biology," *Minerva* 10 (1972): 51–82.

2. Joseph Ben-David and Randall Collins, "Social Factors in the Origins of a New Science: The Case of Psychology," *American Sociological Review* 31 (1966): 451–465.

3. David Edge and Michael Mulkay, *Astronomy Transformed* (New York: Wiley, 1976).

4. Daniel Sullivan, D. Hywel White, and Edward Barboni, "Co-Citation Analyses of Science: An Evaluation," *Social Studies of Science* 7 (1977): 223–240.

5. Henry Small and Belver Griffith, "The Structure of Scientific Literatures I: Identifying and Graphing Specialties," *Science Studies* 4 (1974): 17–40.

6. John Law, "The Development of Specialties in Science: The Case of X-Ray Protein Crystallography," *Science Studies* 3 (1973): 275–303.

7. Daryl Chubin, "The Conceptualization of Scientific Specialties," *The Sociological Quarterly* 17 (1976): 448–476.

8. Thomas F. Gieryn, *Patterns in the Selection of Problems for Scientific Research: American Astronomers, 1950–1975* (Ph.D. dissertation, Columbia University, 1980). For a published excerpt, see Gieryn, "Problem Retention and Problem Change in Science," *Sociological Inquiry* 48 (1978): 96–115. For a recent extension of this line of inquiry, see John Ziman, "The Problem of 'Problem Choice'," *Minerva* 24 (1986): 92–106.

9. S. W. Woolgar, "The Identification and Definition of Scientific Collectivities," in *Perspectives on the Emergence of Scientific Disciplines*, ed. Gerard LeMaine et al. (Chicago: Aldine, 1976), 233–245.

10. See, for example, Thomas F. Gieryn, "Boundary-Work and the Demarcation of Science from Non-Science and Interests in Professional Ideologies of Scientists," *American Sociological Review* 48 (1983): 781–795.

11. Thomas S. Kuhn, *The Structure of Scientific Revolutions* (Chicago: University of Chicago Press, 1967).

12. Derek J. deSolla Price, "Networks of Scientific Papers," *Science* 149 (1965): 510–515.

13. The "stage theory" is developed most fully in Mullins, *Theory and Theory-Groups in Contemporary American Sociology* (New York: Harper and Row, 1973).

14. Karin D. Knorr-Cetina, *The Manufacture of Knowledge* (Oxford: Pergamon Press, 1981), 37, 39.

15. Bruno Latour and Steve Woolgar, *Laboratory Life* (Princeton: Princeton University Press, 1986). Original 1979.

16. Harold Garfinkel, Michael Lynch, and Eric Livingston, "The Work of a Discovering Science Construed with Materials from the Optically Discovered Pulsar," *Philosophy of the Social Sciences* 11 (1981): 131–158. Quotation from p. 131.

17. Ibid., 150–153.

18. Bruno Latour, *Science in Action* (Cambridge: Harvard University Press, 1987).

19. For a sample of this work, see G. Nigel Gilbert and Michael Mulkay, *Opening Pandora's Box: A Sociological Analysis of Scientists' Discourse* (Cambridge: Cambridge University Press, 1984).

# Part 3

# Postwar Aeronautical Research in the Federal Laboratory

*Martin J. Collins*

# Introduction

Historians of science and technology have long debated the proper focus for their professional analyses. Since the 1950s, this debate has centered around the arguments of the "internalists" and "externalists," and later "contextualists" and other methodological advocates.[1] This discussion spanned those who would see science and technology as evolving principally through the logical refinement of experiment and theory, and those who see this evolution as inextricably linked to the broad social structure in which the scientist and his laboratory are embedded. As a consequence of these exchanges, by the late 1960s, the discipline was broadened to include routinely the interconnections between science and technology and cultural, political, and economic influences.[2] Most recently, and in the papers in this volume, many historians in the field have come to accept the close interdependence of these methodological divisions and look for more synthetic approaches to writing and researching developments in science and technology.[3]

Decades of interchange on the proper "focus" of historical analysis in the field have hinged on the problem of identifying essential elements in the scientific enterprise and its change over time. Was it proper to look only at theoretical or technical development? Or, were the "nuts and bolts" of science in some sense derived from the larger interplay among scientists, technologists, institutions, and society? In sorting out this question of focus, historians gained a heightened appreciation of a related historiographic problem: the role of the author's ideology, "world view," or basic assumptions in shaping a historical account through his or her selection and organization of data.

**147**

For example, should the historian of science approach his or her work *as* a scientist—by identifying the historically interesting questions on the basis of what scientists believed to be relevant? This historiographic issue has special force when studying recent history, especially that of the complex technical and institutional development of postwar aeronautical and space activities.

As earlier presentations have suggested, postwar developments in the space program have been marked by close interaction between scientists and engineers *and* their institutions and federal patrons. The very size of the space endeavor—with enormous federal input toward research and development efforts and the demand for complex and expensive technology—has made self-evident the connection between science and technology and their social context. Indeed, much of recent air and space history has concentrated on the monumental social, political, and organizational efforts that took America from faltering Vanguard rockets to the Moon in less than a decade.

But the most recognizable product of this concerted national effort has been an array of increasingly sophisticated and complex aeronautical and space *devices*. The actual work of scientists and engineers—in materials, electronics, guidance, and so forth—has dramatically advanced both space- and earth-based technology. The air and space historian, then, must take into account an ever-more complex range of "artifacts"—the actual devices and their technologies underpinning present and future advances in the field. The difficulty for the historian comes both in acquiring the expertise to access these myriad new technologies, *and* in finding the appropriate narrative voice to explain material that is relatively inaccessible to large segments of the professional and public readership.

It is precisely this kind of technical "literacy" that James Hansen advocates in his paper on the current status of aeronautical history. Hansen suggests that the need for more thorough historical writing on technical topics is twofold. First, the level of analysis needs to be deepened. The public and many historians have invested aircraft with magical, but narrowly defined, qualities. Held spellbound by the "life-stories" of aircraft—their size, their color, who flew them, where they traveled—these writers have generated, for the most part, descriptive studies. Confronted by this pervasive "coffee-table" tradition, the historian, then, owes the public a more complete picture of aeronautics—one that includes the technical aspects and engineering basics, which constitute the inner workings of the field. Second, on a more fundamental level, Hansen believes that engineers and their environments are central to understanding the relationships of even the nontechnical factors in the field. The unique engineering features of aircraft, unlike other technologies, Hansen asserts, have been the critical element in shaping many of the social relations making up the world of aeronautics — the formation of university departments, the structure of industry, and relationships among business, academia, and the government. Hence, the aircraft as device is the natural focus for the historian, serving the needs of literacy as well as ordering the contextual study of aeronautics. In this sense, Hansen calls not only for a public reeducation in aeronautic history, but for what might be termed an "anthropology" of the engineer, centered on his work and products.

Virginia Dawson looks at the world of engineers, with a focus not on the technical elements of their work, but the ways in which individual research initiatives are affected by the large institutional structures that have come to dominate space science. More specifically, she examines the impact on such initiatives of a pronounced shift in institutional values as Lewis Research Center moves from the quiet world of the National Advisory Committee on Aeronautics (NACA) to the fast-paced, highly visible National Aeronautics and Space Administration (NASA). Dawson centers her analysis on the laboratory's engineers and their work on emerging propulsion technologies from 1945 through the early 1960s. She counters one view that basic research was prescribed and carefully controlled by a cautious and deliberate leadership in NACA headquarters. Instead, Dawson offers a glimpse of innovative research — especially on electric propulsion — fostered at Lewis through the creative efforts and drive of individual engineers. But, as Lewis made the transition from research and applied engineering in service of industry and the military under NACA to a NASA organization built around the management of contract research and development, this creative research activity waned. And as NASA grew more complex and its goals became more narrowly directed toward a lunar landing, this research was completely redirected to the immediate development needs of Apollo.

In part, this is a familiar cautionary tale on the nurturing of research in an organization built around research *and* development: research suffers and is expendable in the face of institutional and political pressures to get a job done, in this case the completion of key elements of Apollo. The peril was compromising the future (losing the fruits of research) to meet immediate needs. More fundamentally, Dawson argues, Lewis lost a special part of its institutional identity when the value of research was diminished and supplanted by new values associated with the *management* of research and development. Although her narrative focuses on the fate and disappointments of a capable and enterprising group of Lewis engineers, perhaps her most useful insight is the way in which the central direction of large technical projects can quickly reshape local research institutions to serve new goals. The result is not only an altered work environment for Lewis engineers, but a new set of relations with the laboratory's clientele, primarily industry, through management of contracts. In addition, the events at Lewis highlight the difficulties in understanding the work of the laboratory and its relation to its environment through terms such as "basic" or "applied," or "research" and "development." The dynamic character of the workplace given the close and complex interrelationships among engineers, institutions, and their sponsors seems to require a different descriptive framework — or at least critical attention to the uses and functions of such terminology in its historical context.[4]

These two papers in their somewhat complementary approaches, as well as other papers in this volume, illustrate the diversity of current perspectives in the history of air and space. The commentary by Richard Hallion indicates that these papers are not without controversy. And as opportunities for historical analysis become even more diverse — from the study of particular devices to broad social investigations — these controversies will provide the substance of new debates and add to our understanding of the role of air and space development in twentieth-century American history.

## NOTES

1. These methodological issues have been frequently analyzed and often surveyed. One of the more useful overviews is Paul T. Durbin, *The Culture of Science and Technology* (New York: Free Press, 1980).

2. The result was to shift methodological attention to a new challenge: how to develop clear, sophisticated approaches for identifying and elucidating the interconnections between the content of science and technology and its context. For a useful review and discussion of this point see Thomas P. Hughes, "The Seamless Web: Technology, Science, Etcetera, Etcetera," *Social Studies of Science* 16 (1986): 281–292.

3. Recalling the proceedings of the seminar's second session, it should be noted that these developments coincided with a "boom" in the sociology of science where studies on community and the genesis of disciplines and professions had effects on the historian of science.

4. The degree to which such descriptive terms complicate the task of understanding the activities and operations of laboratories is addressed in Michael A. Dennis, "Accounting for Research: New Histories of Corporate Laboratories and the Social History of American Science," *Social Studies of Science* 17 (1987): 479–518. Although this study focuses on industrial laboratories, there are clear parallels to the NASA situation—most notably that the direction and agenda of the laboratories are strongly affected by parent organizations.

*James R. Hansen*

# Demystifying the History of Aeronautics

The history of aeronautics is a unique, and some might even say strange, field of modern history. What makes it unique and perhaps even strange is the attention paid by its disciples to a single thing, to one particular type of device. For most aviation historians, the aircraft per se has always been the center of attention. Without the flying machine in the spotlight, these historians have felt, why bother? All that would be left for study are the diverse aspects of aviation that deal largely with other things: laboratory research, with scientific theories and experimental equipment; manufacturing, with production techniques and labor; airlines, with corporate structure, finance, and law; airports, with civil engineering and urban planning issues; air power, with tactics, strategies, and logistics.

These subjects that concern the infrastructure of aviation are not what "take off" into the clouds, and because they are not, they have been much ignored traditionally by those who have claimed to do the history of aeronautics. That is unfortunate, because aviation could not get very far without its infrastructure. Those airplanes had to come from somewhere; their requirements had to be created by someone; and that someone almost always had some mission or use in mind for the airplanes.

But fascination with aircraft has not in itself constituted the main problem in the history of aeronautics. Enthusiasm of this sort does not have to preclude analysis, interpretation, and integration of the diverse subjects that are essential to the overall performance of the aeronautical enterprise. The most important scholarly work in aeronautical history has in fact been done by people who, in different ways, feel strongly about aircraft. Enthusiasm for flight, although it has certainly produced more than its share of "gee-whiz" histories written by and for "buffs," has also stimulated the best and most evocative treatments of aeronautical history that we have or are likely to get in the future.

The real problem with aircraft being the principal subject of aeronautical history has been the "magic" with which aircraft have been endowed. Unlike sparrows and robins who do, in fact, have little hearts pounding inside their breasts, the airplane is a machine. Nevertheless, the literature of aviation treats it as if it were alive, and as if each type of airplane, like a species of bird, possesses its own distinct vital force and its own nesting habits.

As a result, too much of aviation history resembles the literature of ornithologists. As far as most ornithologists are concerned, birds may as well slither along the ground. Rather than concentrating on how or why a bird flies, their obsession is with such things as the color of feathers, how many feathers, the texture of the feathers, the characteristics of the beak and claw, the speckles on the egg, the sound of the mating calls, and how many twigs are in the nest.

In one sense, of course, the aircraft should be understood as an organism that is more than the sum of its mechanical parts. As the late Nevil Shute, British aeronautical engineer and best-selling novelist, once wrote: "A beautiful aircraft is the expression of the genius of a great engineer who is also a great artist."[1] Many experts consider the North American P-51 to represent "the highest level of technical refinement ever achieved in a propeller driven fighter."[2] But that accomplishment was not simply the result of applying scientific principles. The designers of the famous Mustang also used practical skills and an innate sense of aesthetics. As Eugene S. Ferguson has underscored many times in his writings about the history of technology, unless one understands and appreciates the contributions of the human imagination and the mind's eye to the creation of technological devices, including aircraft, a vital factor in successful engineering will be neglected.[3]

Up to now, though, historians of aeronautics have only scratched the surface in terms of researching the creativity that goes into making aeronautical progress. What we need in order to comment more intelligently on aeronautical progress is more biographical work on the designers. We need to know where their ideas came from, and then we need to see how those ideas moved from the individual mind through social and political processes to a technological application.[4] At the same time it is worth looking into how *bad* ideas were weeded out or otherwise failed to make it to a successful design.

Compromise is an essential part of aeronautical engineering. Most of the time, for technical reasons, a price has to be paid in the outward beauty or attractiveness of a flying machine. A case in point is the design of the McDonnell F-4 Phantom, a plane that saw a lot of action in the Vietnam War. The F-4 is not a pretty plane; some, in fact, would say it is ugly. At best it is a sinister-looking machine. One of my friends in aviation thinks it looks like someone dropped it from a height of 100 feet onto a hard surface.

But the F-4 is a highly successful plane. In terms of numbers, the Phantom has been "the most successful supersonic fighter ever produced in the United States."[5] Its success has depended not on cosmetic beauty, but on the way its aerodynamic shaping has met demanding performance objectives. Or, as the adage in the architecture textbooks says, "form follows function."

The story of the Phantom suggests a basic standard by which to judge the success of an aircraft: "How well does it do the things it was designed to do?" And contrary to what many historians have suggested, the achievement of this goal depends on a lot more than just the vision and talent of the designer. It depends largely on the extent to which those who write the requirements, plus those whose job it is to meet the requirements — that is, the manufacturer who employs the designers — understand the state of the art. If one side or the other fails in this equation, then the aircraft might easily prove a failure.

Historians tend to forget, if they think about it at all, that (1) the airplane is a product, (2) the airplane is built to be sold, (3) most airplane builders have to cater to buyers, and (4) as often as not, it is the buyer, not the builder, who establishes the "requirements."

There was only one period of history when the designers themselves established the requirements: this was the period when the airplane was being invented. In the years 1896 to 1908, the Wright brothers established their own requirements, in the sense of having to design a fundamental control system. But when the Wrights wanted to sell their finished product to the War Department (and history should not forget that even the Wrights insisted on a monetary return), it was the Army that established the first real requirements as we understand such today.

Initially these requirements were so rough and general that the Wrights could claim rights over nearly all of them. If a designer could get his contraption to fly, that was about all that was expected. Not until the start of the First World War did the ideas of definitive aircraft configuration and mission types begin to germinate. Then, the demands of combat aviation, together with the international struggle for air superiority, transformed the airplane from a useless freak into an increasingly practical and versatile vehicle whose every detail had to be designed rigorously if the total configuration was to prove successful.

From that time on, as both civilian and, especially, military aviation requirements grew in number and severity,[6] the airplane developed into what is arguably the most complicated and unforgiving piece of machinery ever built. And the specialized field of aeronautical engineering, at first just a branch or option within a few mechanical engineering programs, grew up in American and European universities to meet the challenges.

As it grew, aeronautical engineering matured into an autonomous field, and with good reasons. Along with naval architecture, aeronautical engineering proved to be exceptional or anomalous in that it was the only major field of engineering devoted to the progress of a particular kind of device.[7] As a result, it became the field where the nature of one device went the farthest toward defining all of the engineering that was done in that field.

People realized that the device in question was a very unique and especially vexing machine that had to operate in three dimensions while totally "submerged" in its supporting medium. In this environment, which was quasi-unpredictable, there were hazards like gusts, shears, and microbursts that could not always be seen. This meant that in creating different versions of the airplane, engineers had to be very concerned with such dangers as gust loads and maneuver loads. Civil engineers also had to worry about critical loads, of course, but as a rule they did not have as many of them to worry about, and usually most of them were static rather than dynamic ones. The orientation of all of the other fields of modern engineering was much broader than that of aeronautical engineering, because work in those fields was less specific to any particular device.

From time to time engineering schools attempted to alter this situation by assimilating "aero" into their engineering departments. Many did this on the grounds that all of the basic principles of the field could be learned by taking a proper combination of mechanical, civil, and electrical engineering courses. Almost always, though, the attempts failed. They failed because the schools involved were convinced that the requirements of aeronautical education were special enough to justify autonomy.[8]

The purpose of an autonomous aeronautical education, after all, was the effective design and operation of aircraft that could meet the ever-more-difficult requirements being created by aviation's ever-more-demanding customers. To meet these requirements, aeronautical engineers had to place an especially strong emphasis on compromise. "Tradeoffs" were an essential part of all engineering. But because aircraft had to satisfy performance requirements that were widely diverse and even conflicting, aeronautical engineers had to learn to place a higher premium on compromise than did other types of engineers. Every step taken by an aeronautical engineer in designing a flying machine became a compromise. For every improvement there was a corresponding loss. If a designer wanted a machine with a considerable amount of inherent stability—say for the purpose of creating a safe and easy-to-fly general aviation airplane for the private owner—he had to surrender something in terms of that airplane's responsiveness to controls. If a designer wanted a very high speed machine, he often had to accept a landing speed that was higher than desirable.

In other words, aircraft could not be designed just to do one thing well, such as to go fast. They had to be designed to do several things well: to take off, cruise, turn, dive, accelerate, decelerate, deliver projectiles, and many other things. For example, according to United States Air Force specifications, one of the requirements for the design of the F-15 fighter that McDonnell Douglas eventually built in the 1970s was that it had to be able to make and withstand a violent turn in which its gravitational weight was multiplied by a factor of six (i.e., a 6 G turn). This had to be done at 30,000 feet at a speed of just less than 700 miles per hour (Mach .90). These kinds of extreme "energy maneuverability" or "specific excess power" requirements imposed on designers of military aircraft exceeded by a wide margin any load, safety, or performance considerations that were imposed on the designers of other transportation technologies.

Time and again this difference has eluded some aircraft builders, and has caused some sorry results. For example, the relatively dismal records of Ford and General Motors in aircraft manufacturing illus-

trate the enormous difficulties of transferring mass-production techniques learned in making automobiles to the building of aircraft.[9]
Another example of an unsuccessful transfer involves British ship-
builders in the 1920s and early 1930s who tried branching off into
the aircraft industry. As Nevil Shute relates in his aeronautical autobiography *Slide Rule,* the shipbuilding magnates simply could not
fathom how a cruiser 700 feet long could be designed in only eight
weeks when the design of a much smaller airplane could take many
weeks more, or how the cruiser could be delivered complete with all
details in twenty-seven months when it could take several months
more for the aircraft to be delivered. They learned too late that a different set of rules governed the aircraft industry. Unless those rules
were followed, by corporate officers and engineers alike who were
both specially trained to understand aircraft requirements, failure was
the only guarantee.[10]

It was at this point, sometime in the 1930s, that aeronautical engineering became one field of engineering where "almost" was not
good enough. It was as if the leaders of the aviation industry understood the vital importance of the airplane's salient qualities for the
first time, and then influenced the basic training of aeronautical engineers to meet the challenge. One might say that from this time on,
aeronautical engineers were educated to believe that they did the
same things as other types of engineers, "they just had to do them
better."[11]

Whether they subsequently did do the same things better is impossible to prove. But given the rapid progress of aeronautical technology from the 1930s to the present, one might accept the following
conjecture: perhaps the *belief* of the aeronautical engineers in having
to do the same things better became a self-fulfilling prophecy. Because they were trained to believe that work on flying machines required superior efforts, maybe the aeronautical engineers worked
harder to live up to that requirement, and in striving to do so actually did do the same things better. As historian David S. Noble might
assert, the thrust of aeronautical engineering education could hardly
have been more to the point of industrial applications.[12]

It should be clear from the preceding discussion that an understanding of requirements is fundamental both to aeronautical engineering and to aviation history. As stated earlier, if one side or the
other fails in the equation that sets out the requirements, then the
aircraft might easily fail. It is tempting to claim that this seems to

be what happened with the C-5, the giant cargo transport built for the Air Force in the 1960s by Lockheed. We know that the wing of the C-5 had a rather serious "structural fatigue" problem, and that eventually the plane had to be given new wings. Since then, the C-5A has done an outstanding job. Still, there are questions, nearly twenty years later now, as to *why* and *who* was responsible for the original problem. Did the manufacturer deliver a plane that lived up to all the requirements that the Air Force specified? Did the Air Force accept a weak wing in order to reduce structural weight and thereby meet payload requirements?[13]

Answering these questions is beyond the scope of this essay, but one of the lessons to be learned from the answering is surely that one has to be just as careful in writing the requirements as in carrying them out through the actual design. But how many historians of aeronautics have paid much attention to the ways in which the military services or commercial airlines have arrived at the requirements for their aircraft?

A few historians have paid attention. One of the best of them is Walter G. Vincenti, professor emeritus of Aeronautics and Astronautics at Stanford University and a former researcher with the National Advisory Committee for Aeronautics, NASA's predecessor.[14] In the early days of aviation, as Vincenti points out in one chapter of a projected book on the epistemology of engineering, flying-quality specifications were derived almost solely from subjective pilot impressions of how their airplanes handled or reacted to different stimuli such as turbulence, engine stalls, high-speed turns or other difficult maneuvers, and so forth. As a result of this professional practice, aircraft designers were "hard pressed to know" just what the pilots meant when they spoke of "tail heaviness" or "lightness of controls." All that the Army Air Corps or Navy Bureau of Aeronautics could tell the aircraft manufacturing companies was to make the military airplanes "perfect in all respects."[15] This was a terrible oversimplification, of course, not to mention an impossibility. It was then left up to the contractor to guess what the client wanted in terms of stability and control, maneuverability, and handling qualities. But of course the client had no clear idea of what they wanted; they only knew that their pilots would complain in no uncertain terms if that "magical" feeling was not there.

Beginning in the middle of the 1930s, aeronautical engineers learned to relate flying qualities in quantitative terms. This made meaningful communication among pilots, military and civilian aviation bureaus, and aircraft manufacturers much easier. In the early 1940s, at the conclusion of a comprehensive NACA flight test program involving several different airplanes, engineers knew for the first time what flying qualities pilots actually desired, and they had a numerical means by which to specify those flying qualities for future design competitions.[16] In other words, aeronautical engineering had matured to the point where its practitioners wanted to demystify the primary device that defined what they did. They desired to understand what it really was about the airplane that up to that time had passed for magic.

Ever since then, evaluating an airplane has meant *measuring* it, and much about aeronautical development has been shaped by the improved methods for doing so. For aeronautical engineers, the famous remark of Lord Kelvin became the gospel: "If you can measure that of which you speak you may know something of your subject, but if you cannot measure it your knowledge will be unsatisfactory." For this reason, test pilots who were also professionally trained engineers (the fame of Chuck Yeager notwithstanding) were from this time on worth their weight in gold.

Compared with engineers, historians have had a much harder time integrating rigorous quantitative measurements into their evaluations of aeronautical developments. Some of the standard aeronautical measures have been integrated, such as: How fast and high could the aircraft fly? What was its payload? How many passengers did it hold? These are measurements that historians and other nonengineers have readily appreciated.

But many of the design and performance measures that have been most critical to engineers over the years have been, and still are, too abstruse for the average lay person: wing loading (in pounds per square foot), power loading (in pounds per horsepower), maximum lift coefficient, maximum lift-drag ratio, the skin friction parameter. These measures of an aircraft's physical and performance characteristics, although integral to the aircraft's engineering, are beyond the pale of most aeronautical history.

But should they be? For a former director of aeronautics at NASA Langley Research Center, the entire evolution of modern aircraft is best summed up by the ability of aeronautical engineers to achieve lower and lower values of one of these esoteric parameters. In his 1985 book *Quest for Performance: The Evolution of Modern*

*Aircraft,* Laurence K. Loftin Jr. argues that, in engineering terms, the progressive reduction of the zero-lift drag coefficient, a nondimensional number that expresses the aerodynamic "cleanness" or refinement of an aircraft design, exemplifies the aeronautical progress that has been made since the Wright *Flyer* better than anything else.[17]

Between the Fokker E-III of World War I and the P-51 Mustang of World War II, Loftin relates, there was a difference in zero-lift drag coefficient that amounted to a "whopping" value of 0.0610. Unfortunately for Loftin's book—an outstanding contribution to our understanding of the history of aeronautical engineering, which deserves a wider reading among aviation historians than it will probably get—the mentioning of this seemingly minuscule reduction in the value of one aerodynamic coefficient will not impress the public with the rapid aeronautical progress that took place between the two world wars.

I say that with some confidence because when I mentioned the fact to my history of technology students—it barely caused a ripple. My students did seem to appreciate the fact, however, that in the same time span (1915–1940) the price of the average fighter plane increased from about $5,000 to about $50,000. The dollar, unlike the zero-lift drag coefficient, is a unit of measurement that everyone appreciates.

What everyone does not appreciate is the vital importance of aerodynamic considerations, even minor ones like smashed bugs on a wing surface, in aeronautical engineering. Aerodynamics have been, and have had to be, much more important in airplane design than in any other field of design. In some famous cases outside of aeronautics, such as the failure of the Tacoma Narrows Bridge over Puget Sound in 1940, this lack of concern for aerodynamic considerations has resulted in disasters. In most cases, though, the lack of concern for aerodynamics has not been all that crucial. If an automobile runs out of fuel because, contrary to external appearances, it is aerodynamically unrefined and possesses less than an optimum fuel efficiency, the situation is not life threatening. The driver simply pulls off to the side of the road and walks to the nearest filling station.

Moreover, the fuel efficiency of land transportation vehicles has not made as much difference to their corporate profitability as has the fuel efficiency of aircraft. Just ask an executive of any airplane company whether a 1 percent reduction of the company's annual fuel consumption will make any difference to the profit margin. This is not simply a matter of paying for less fuel, as it is with a fleet of trucks. By being able to operate with less fuel, the airplane can carry a greater payload. Airplane operators buy fuel by the gallon, but in pumping it aboard their airplanes they measure it by the pound.

One might make the counter-argument that meeting certain mileage goals has been crucial for automobile companies, with the introduction of CAFE (Corporate Average Fuel Efficiency) and other federal regulations in the late 1970s. Or one might point to the trend in racing-car design in which cars are now literally stuck to the track by a partial vacuum in a plenum beneath the car, and airfoils are used for fine-tuning the chassis to different conditions. But both of these developments are very recent. Historically, aerodynamic refinement has been far more crucial to the design of aircraft than to the design of any other vehicular device.

With this information in mind, our appreciation for Loftin's point of view increases. His emphasis on the zero-lift drag coefficient as the best quantitative indication of progress in aircraft design then makes more sense. In fact, it suggests to us three important messages or guiding principles. Together, they suggest a good way by which to demystify the history of aeronautics.

The first message is to appreciate, as Lord Kelvin did, the precise measures with which scientists and engineers themselves are often most concerned in their daily exercises. As soon as aeronautical historians do this, they will begin to move, as the aeronautical engineers of the 1930s and 1940s did, to a more mature understanding of their subject.

The second message is to integrate these esoteric measures as intelligently as possible into the aviation literature. Do not neglect these measures. They are too important.

The third and most important message is to accomplish this integration in such a way as to make the measures, as well as the details that are being measured, less esoteric. In other words, translate the meaning of the privileged technical information into historical knowledge that the educated public can better understand and use. Do not just say that the difference in zero-lift drag coefficient between the Fokker E-III and the P-51 is a whopping 0.0610, but show how and why that number is significant. Explain how the drag of the Fokker equates to a flat plate having an area of 12.5 square feet, while the drag of the P-51 equates to a flat plate having an area of only 3.8 square feet. Point out that this difference of some 9 square feet in drag area corresponds to roughly a factor of four, or 300 percent—a much larger number than 0.0610, so it will make the appropriate impression on the nonengineer. Use the analogy of the two plates flying through the air; that way the layman will be able to see in his mind's eye how much more aerodynamically efficient the Mustang is than the Fokker. One might even want to tell him to imagine sticking his flat hand out the window of a moving car, and then imagine the greater wind resistance his hand would encounter if it were in a baseball catcher's glove used to catch knuckle-ball pitches.

Anyone who really understands fluid mechanics will have some problems with such analogies because, among other things, they leave out such complicating factors as the flow separation caused by the edges of the plates. But even aerodynamicists deal sometimes with "ideal" conditions, and the analogy would be about 80 percent true at any rate. Moreover, it would do so much to help the nontechnical person understand why Loftin's zero-lift drag coefficient is important.

Historians can help to explain why such details are so important to aeronautical engineers. They can help to explain why it is in aeronautical engineering, for example, that the design of every last detail— every last percent—counts more than in any other engineering field. The basic reason for this is the matter of weight. Remind the public that the function of any vehicle of transportation is to move a weight from "here" to "there" with all practical speed. Then remind them that among all of the different types of transportation vehicles only the airplane must also lift its own weight while doing so.

In the design of a railway locomotive, it might be explained, there has not been any particular need to place a premium on weight, especially after iron and steel rails were developed in the nineteenth century capable of carrying tremendously heavier loads than the older wooden ones. Weight has really only been a concern relative to the structures that must ultimately carry it, for example, the rails and the bridges. Otherwise, it has just been a matter of distributing the locomotive's weight on its wheels and establishing tractive effort by ensuring that the locomotive is heavy enough to sustain traction where load and track meet.[18] This has led to the paradox that a powerful but lightweight railway locomotive has rarely been successful unless it has been pulling a light-weight train—which is the major reason why the railroad industry has had such a difficult time trying to adapt the light-weight gas turbine as a prime mover.

The historian could also point out that in contrast to all other transportation devices, the airplane is a device—and in fact maybe the *first* device in human history—in which engineers could not solve problems by simply making things heavier. In aeronautical engineering, weight and weight-to-power ratios have been crucial considerations from the beginning. If such things had not been considered carefully, nothing of any appreciable size or capacity would have ever lifted off the ground and carried itself to a destination at a reasonable speed.[19]

Unless such information basic to a good understanding of aeronautical engineering is emphasized, and unless such esoteric things as the value of the zero-lift drag coefficient are explained in the aviation history books—and explained verbally rather than just numerically—many basic things about aeronautics will remain unknown or meaningless to most of the public. The flight of an airplane will remain magic, and the aviation museums will continue to exhibit all of the most "charmed" airplanes but show little about the infrastructure that built and used them.

Some people have advised that this appeal is like barking up a tree: it will do no good because no one really wants this demystification to take place. The world is too machinelike as it is. People like mystery. The public does not care to understand the nuts and bolts; they like to see magic in their machines. How do computers work? Who cares, so long as they get the telephone bill correct and do not spit out our name for an IRS audit. How do airplanes fly? Who cares, so long as they land safely.

Some have even suggested that the engineers themselves would not want this demystification to take place either. Did the cathedral builders share their precious building secrets with just anyone? Did the medieval alchemists or Renaissance astrologers advertise their secret techniques and rituals? Of course not. If they had, their identity as a privileged brotherhood, one closer to God because of the special knowledge its members possessed, might have collapsed. So, too, it might also be with modern engineers. Maybe they want the public to think that technology is magic; that way they can retain their status as an elite group.

As a teacher of technical history, however, I opt for a more widespread literacy, and I suspect that many engineers would opt for that, too—especially when they read and see how the mass media sensationalizes the threat of airline accidents, for instance. In demystifying aeronautics, historians can go a long way toward demonstrating how an engineering product is actually achieved, how a series of those products form an organic system, and how the whole cannot function as expected unless every detail of that system is properly on hand. When humankind understands these things better, our appreciation of all technological endeavors will not only be greater, it will be deeper and more genuine.

## NOTES

1. See Chapter 2 of Nevil Shute's 1952 novel, *No Highway.*

2. Laurence K. Loftin Jr., *Quest For Performance: The Evolution of Modern Aircraft* (Washington, D.C.: NASA SP-468, 1985), 128.

3. See Ferguson's essay, "The Mind's Eye: Nonverbal Thought in Technology," *Science* 197 (August 26, 1977): 827–836. On the sources of technological creativity in aircraft design, I recommend John McPhee's *The Deltoid Pumpkin Seed* (New York: Farrar, Strauss, and Giroux, 1973).

4. Alex Roland made this point in his essay, "Defining Aeronautical Progress," unpublished manuscript, NASA History Office, June 24, 1980.

5. Loftin, *Quest For Performance,* 316–319.

6. A 1972 study by the United States Air Force on the contributions of research and development to aviation progress began by pointing out that more than eight out of ten of the commercial jet airliners then operating in the "free world" were designed and built in the United States, and that one of every four of those American-built craft traced its lineage to a single military bomber program. U.S. Air Force, *Research and Development Contributions to Aviation Progress (RADCAP): Executive Summary, August 1972,* available as NASA CR-129574.

7. Walter G. Vincenti, emeritus professor of Aeronautics and Astronautics at Stanford University, pointed out the "anomalous" character of aeronautical engineering to me in a telephone conversation on 25 May 1987.

8. On the state of aeronautical engineering education in America during the 1920s and 1930s, see Richard P. Hallion, *Legacy of Flight: The Guggenheim Contribution to American Aviation* (Seattle, 1977).

9. For a case study of an automobile company's problems in mass producing an aircraft, see I. B. Holley's recent essay, "A Detroit Dream of Mass-produced Aircraft: The XP-75 Fiasco," *Technology and Culture* 28 (July 1987): 578–593.

10. Nevil Shute, *Slide Rule* (New York: Ballantine Books, 1954), 209.

11. Telephone conversation with Mark Levinson, an aeronautical engineer who is a professor of mechanical engineering at the University of Maine, Orono, May 4, 1987.

12. See Noble's *America by Design: Science, Technology and the Rise of Corporate Capitalism* (New York, 1977).

13. Wilfred C. Garrard, *The Lockheed C-5 Case Study in Aircraft Design* (New York: AIAA Aircraft Series, 1977).

14. Another historian who has explored the importance of aircraft requirements is I. B. Holley. See in particular Holley's *Buying Aircraft: Material Procurement for the Army Air Forces, United States Army in World War II, Special Studies* (Washington, D.C.: Office of the Chief of Military History, Department of the Army, 1964).

15. Walter G. Vincenti, "The Formulation of Design Requirements: Flying-Quality Specifications for American Aircraft, 1918–1943," unpublished manuscript (subject to revision), January 1987. I am grateful to Mr. Vincenti for permitting me to mention his unpublished work.

16. James R. Hansen, *Engineer in Charge: A History of the Langley Aeronautical Laboratory, 1917–1958* (Washington, D.C.: NASA SP-4305, 1987), 182–183.

17. Loftin, *Quest for Performance,* 4–5, 158–160.

18. This point is made by G. Gabrieli and Theodore Von Karman in their classic essay, "What Price Speed? Specific Power Required for Propulsion of Vehicles," which appeared in *Mechanical Engineering* (October 1950): 777–778.

19. For a historical analysis of the importance of weight in aircraft design, see Richard K. Smith's "The Intercontinental Airliner and the Essence of Airplane Performance, 1929–1939," *Technology and Culture* 24 (July 1983): 428–449. Smith is also the author of an article entitled "The Weight Envelope," which was published during 1986 in *Aerospace Historian.* I am grateful to Dr. Smith for reading an early draft of this paper and for offering several very helpful suggestions.

*Virginia P. Dawson*

# The Push from Within

## Lewis Research Center's Transition to Space

Although it is often stated that the National Advisory Committee for Aeronautics (NACA) became the nucleus for the National Aeronautics and Space Administration (NASA), the word nucleus is misleading because it implies that the hereditary material contained in this nucleus provided the blueprint for the subsequent organization of NASA. Although at first the NACA seemed destined to play a leading role in the new organization, equally divided between research, the NACA's forte, and development, to be focused in a new arm of the agency, as events in the organizational life of NASA unfolded, the influence of the NACA waned. The early effort on the part of Hugh Dryden, the former director of the NACA, and T. Keith Glennan, the new administrator, to maintain a balance between research and development could not be sustained under the pressure of the Apollo program.[1] The NACA research philosophy that encouraged technical innovation and individual initiative yielded to the prerogatives of a professional manager like James Webb, who attempted to curb the autonomy of the research centers. In the 1960s the old NACA laboratories, Langley, Ames, and Lewis, became multipurpose laboratories engaged in a mix of research and development activities. By the 1970s the diversity of programs earned for the centers the epithet of "hobby shops." Two of the three original NACA laboratories, Ames and Lewis, risked closing.[2] The transition from an autonomous research laboratory during the NACA era to a dispensable appendage was particularly painful for Lewis Research Center. The single most

This essay won the Dr. Robert H. Goddard Historical Essay Award, March 18, 1988, sponsored by the National Space Club.

**167**

traumatic event in its corporate memory is the reduction in force of nearly 500 engineers at the termination of its nuclear research program in 1972.

The later difficulties of all three of the original NACA laboratories may be related to the external perceptions of the NACA after Sputnik. The prevailing opinion, expressed by the members of the nation's scientific community was that the NACA was too conservative to lead the exploration of space. Presumably, what made the NACA conservative was that it did "applied research" rather than unfettered basic scientific research, and it had no experience in the management of a large-scale organization with a big budget. Historians have concluded that the NACA was selected, not for its positive qualities as a research organization, but to avoid having the new space agency become an instrument for the militarization of space and a stimulus to greater Cold War competition. They emphasize that Eisenhower favored building NASA around the NACA, not because of the Committee's perceived strengths but because of his desire that a civilian agency direct the conquest of space. "Such reasoning," according to Walter McDougall, "made elevation of the innocuous NACA an attractive answer to the question of what to do about outer space."[3]

This presumed conservatism of the NACA bears scrutiny. NACA-trained engineers did not view themselves as technically conservative. Headquarters, however, had to project a practical, responsible image to the Congress in order to assure continued funding. Political conservatism was necessary if the NACA was to survive as an independent aeronautical research organization. In the political climate of the 1950s, which was either indifferent or hostile to science and technology unless tied to the nation's defense, Hugh Dryden, the director of the NACA from 1947, never went to Congress without a carefully conceived, down-to-earth program. The NACA had to account for every penny to a budget-conscious Congress, while the military could request funds for research within a large budget justified on national security grounds. This had enabled the Air Force to build new research facilities at Wright Field and an array of the latest in wind tunnels at Arnold Engineering Center in Tullahoma. From the point of view of one NACA-trained engineer, until Sputnik took space out of the realm of science fiction and made it part of the Cold War, the NACA "would have stood as much chance of injecting itself into space activities in any real way as an icicle in a rocket combustion chamber."[4]

Nevertheless, during the so-called lean years between 1952 and 1957, the organizational structure of the NACA allowed its three laboratories, Langley, Ames, and Lewis, considerable autonomy, and the technical and scientific problems that the laboratories tackled during these years belie the label of conservative. Obviously, each laboratory had to respond to the needs of the military and industry, but the NACA considered that part of its role should also be to anticipate the future technical needs of the nation by laying a base of knowledge on which industry could build future development.[5]

Although it was understood that all NACA research would ultimately be applied to advance the state of the art of the airplane, projects whose immediate commercial applications were not clear attracted considerable interest. Examples of research that pushed the frontiers of existing knowledge are found at all three laboratories. Ames Laboratory's long and sustained interest in the problem of aerodynamic heating culminated in Harvey Allen's blunt body theory, later applied to the shape of the Mercury reentry capsule. James Hansen, in discussing aeronautical research in the 1950s at Langley, demonstrated the audacious reach of the X-15 to the edge of space.[6] The X-series of research aircraft demonstrated the technical feasibility of high speed flight. Although the joint program with the Air Force and the Navy involved building aircraft prototypes and therefore came close to the line separating research from development, the program yielded technical and scientific data that could be gained in no other way. Thus, the program satisfied the criteria for what the NACA called fundamental research.

Between 1945 and 1957 at Lewis Flight Propulsion Research Laboratory, research focused on the improvement of the turbojet from a bulky, roaring, fuel-thirsty engine to a quiet, dependable, commercially viable propulsion system for aircraft. This was also considered fundamental research because it involved the analysis of problems common to all turbojet engines. But in addition to this research in support of existing technology, there was sufficient autonomy and flexibility within the program of research for projects to grow organically from within the laboratory, rather than in response to specific requests from industry or the military. It was possible to devote some research to less conventional projects in a few well-chosen areas.[7] At

Lewis, if a particular project won the attention of Abe Silverstein, who became chief of Research in 1949, it received support. Generally, problems whose technical feasibility had not yet been demonstrated attracted the greatest enthusiasm among both Silverstein and his staff. Silverstein's "pet projects" may have had only a small percentage of the total budget of the laboratory, but he assigned some of his most talented staff to these projects and watched over their progress with an attentiveness that the more routine projects did not receive. Three areas of research to be briefly discussed here, high-energy propellants for rockets, nuclear propulsion, and electric rocket propulsion became important and visible only after the formation of NASA. Nevertheless, all three had deep roots in the early postwar NACA period. Because of the momentum that these space-related projects had developed prior to the launching of Sputnik in October 1957, the transition to space related research was not as dramatic as the transition from the piston engine to jet propulsion. Lewis was already primed for space. Because Sputnik only took the lid off the pent-up desire for more funding and recognition for areas that were already receiving considerable research interest at Lewis, much of the early leadership of NASA at headquarters came from Lewis.

## INVESTIGATION OF LIQUID HYDROGEN

In 1962 NASA decided to transfer the management of the Centaur program from Marshall Space Flight Center to Lewis. The decision was based on the Center's prior experience with liquid hydrogen and its belief in its feasibility as an upper stage for the large conventional kerosene-fueled boosters under development by von Braun's group at Marshall. The possibility of an oxygen-hydrogen combination to fuel a rocket had long been considered by rocket pioneers, but there were enormous technical problems to be surmounted. First suggested by Konstantin Tsiolkovskiy, the possibility of the high-energy fuel caught the imagination of Krafft Ehricke, one of von Braun's V-2 team at Peenemünde. Ehricke moved with the von Braun group to Huntsville, where he reputedly grew impatient with the sultry climate, but more important, with von Braun's cautious engineering attitudes. Although the von Braun group could be visionary in proposing various schemes for space exploration, as engineers they were extremely conservative. They preferred heavy, solid structures to con-

tain the rocket's propellant, which Ehricke derisively referred to as
the "Brooklyn Bridge" approach. As John Sloop has pointed out in
his book *Liquid Hydrogen as a Propulsion Fuel:* "This conservative
design philosophy mitigated against the use of liquid hydrogen
which, more than conventional fuels, depended upon very light structures to help offset the handicap of low density."[8] Ehricke tried to
convince the Air Force to back his proposal for a liquid-hydrogen
upper stage on an Atlas intercontinental ballistic missile, but it was
only after Sputnik that the Advanced Research Projects Agency
(ARPA) contracted with General Dynamics and Pratt & Whitney
(RL-10 engine) to develop Ehricke's brainchild. Part of Ehricke's final
success was due to the strong backing that his idea received from
Abe Silverstein, then in charge of Space Flight Development for
NASA. In July 1958 Silverstein set up and chaired a technical committee to consider NASA's launch vehicle needs. Silverstein did not
have the same engineering conservatism that characterized the von
Braun team and his commitment to liquid hydrogen was a product
of long experience with liquid hydrogen at Lewis Flight Propulsion
Laboratory.

The laboratory's involvement in rocketry had begun as early as
1944, although liquid hydrogen did not emerge as the fuel of choice
until 1948. During the war, members of the Fuels and Lubricants Division carried out tests of solid propellants in four primitive rocket
test stands. In 1945 this work was officially terminated. However, it
is not easy to snuff out the pursuit of intriguing technical issues in
a research laboratory. The implications of the V-2 had been quickly
grasped by the staff. In addition to German work, Lewis chemists
also studied the papers of the group at the Jet Propulsion Laboratory.[9]

At first the laboratory's rocket program had to be disguised
from headquarters as "high-pressure combustion" because Jerome
Hunsaker, chair of the NACA's Main Committee, regarded rockets as
artillery and therefore an inappropriate area for aeronautical research.[10] Despite the lack of official sanction, between 1947 and
1949 work on rocket fuels slowly increased, pushed by the technical
interests of the group rather than any external demands or specific
applications.

In 1949 Silverstein allowed the rocket group more responsibility
and visibility. As John Sloop, then head of the rocket section, recalled, "It was moved up one level in the organizational hierarchy,
named for what it was, and given more personnel."[11] Silverstein was

particularly interested in establishing the criteria for propellant selection and encouraged the group to undertake analytic studies to lay a base of knowledge that would be available should it be needed in the future. Nevertheless, without formal support for facilities, the experimental side of their research suffered. At last, in 1951, possibly in response to intelligence reports of Russian advances in rocketry, the NACA authorized a formal Subcommittee on Rocket Engines within the Power Plants Committee. That same year Lewis received its first appropriation for rocket research, although the number of personnel assigned to the rocket section was still small, less than 3 percent. The group was disappointed at the relative lack of support for its work compared to that of ramjets, and they paid close attention to Army missile policy, which in 1952 was beginning to swing away from air-breathing propulsion systems.[12]

Pushed by the momentum of their technical interests in liquid propellants, they chafed at the lack of attention on the part of NACA policy makers to the investigation of problems they felt were worthy of sustained support. As early as 1948, they had concluded through analysis that among liquid propellants worthy of experimental study, liquid hydrogen, because of its high specific impulse and low density, showed greatest promise.[13] Although liquid hydrogen was a cryogenic fuel, dangerous to handle and difficult to store, they concluded that these technical problems were not insurmountable. By the early 1950s they had convinced Silverstein of the worthiness of liquid hydrogen as a focus of research.

What application, if any, Silverstein had in mind is not clear, but the attraction of this particular fuel may have been related to a 1947 secret report by physicists at the Applied Physics Laboratory at the Johns Hopkins University who had proposed hydrogen as the preferred propellant for a nuclear rocket.[14] This interest in hydrogen-fueled rockets may thus have dovetailed with the increasing emphasis on nuclear aircraft and rocket propulsion on the part of the Air Force. Moreover, liquid hydrogen also had possibilities as a fuel for high-altitude aircraft such as the U-2.

Lewis lacked adequate facilities for production, storage, and testing of liquid-hydrogen rockets. Although they had no financial support from headquarters, Silverstein allowed the group to design four additional rocket cells, which were built by an ad hoc laboratory construction group using operating funds. However, with encouragement from the new NACA rocket engine subcommittee, they began to plan an additional large rocket test facility for a remote location in the West, later scaled down so that it could be built at Lewis. Although authorized by Congress in 1953, the frustrated researchers had to wait until 1957 for the new high-energy rocket propellant test facility to be ready for operation.

In July 1956, Dryden at last took the belated initiative to canvass the opinion of the NACA rocket subcommittee on the future role of rocket research in the NACA's long-term agenda. This approach to policy was typical of headquarters when entering a new area of research. As the head of the rocket section described Dryden's cautious *modus operandi,* it was to "solicit opinions and build a broad base of national support so that it would appear the agency was practically pushed into the new work."[15] On the behalf of frustrated members of the NACA rocket subcommittee, Richard Canright, then employed by Douglas Aircraft, wrote in July of 1957:

> We have constantly spurred the NACA on to tests on a larger scale. We have urged them to become familiar with complete engines rather than work only on component R&D. We have tried to emphasize the importance of rocket technology to this country's defense effort and urged that the NACA devote a greater portion of its personnel and funding to this important field.[16]

Nothing would have pleased the rocket group more than to have the opportunity to work on complete engines and they obviously chafed at the failure of headquarters to respond more resolutely even at this late date to the urgings of its own subcommittee. No doubt Doolittle and Dryden shared the rocket group's frustration. Although Eisenhower waited until his farewell address to articulate fully his views on the potential risk to the nation's values from the rising prominence of the military-industrial complex ruled by a technical elite, they could not have missed these attitudes reflected in the tight-fisted mood of the Congress. Rather than technical timidity, political realism prevented them from taking a more aggressive approach to funding. For example, Doolittle wrote in the NACA's *Annual Report* for 1957, several days before Sputnik, that compared to the Russians, America's commitment to aviation was deteriorating, and he urged greater support for research.[17] Increased funding for the NACA's work on liquid hydrogen would only come after NASA was created in response to Sputnik.

## NUCLEAR PROPULSION

The initiative from within the laboratory can also be seen in the evolution of nuclear propulsion research. Like the assignment of the Centaur program to Lewis, the setting up in 1960 of NASA's joint program with the Atomic Energy Commission to develop a nuclear rocket grew out of the prior commitment of the Lewis laboratory to nuclear propulsion. During the NACA era, the attraction of a nuclear power plant for aircraft was its potential for long-range flight without refueling. If the feasibility of the new propulsion system could be demonstrated, it would represent a "breakthrough" in propulsion similar to that of jet propulsion during the war. As early as July 1945, one month prior to the bombing of Hiroshima and Nagasaki, two Cleveland physicists, completely unaware of the Manhattan project but certain of the technical feasibility of splitting the atom, urged headquarters to allow them to begin exploration of the potential of a nuclear energy source for aircraft propulsion.[18] Days after the President's announcement that the United States had dropped two nuclear bombs on Japan, laboratory personnel suggested to headquarters that four or five NACA scientists ought to be sent to the "inner sanctum" of Los Alamos.[19] Six months later, a Cleveland memo warned headquarters that "unless the Committee sets up an active and farsighted group in this field, we will be 'left at the post.'"[20] While the Cleveland laboratory enthusiastically formulated its plans to tap into the mainstream of nuclear propulsion research, in May 1946 the Air Force initiated its project, Nuclear Energy Propulsion for Aircraft (NEPA).[21]

The Cleveland laboratory staff persevered in their pursuit of a piece of the nuclear propulsion program and succeeded in winning the support of Farrington Daniels, head of the metallurgical laboratory at the University of Chicago. However, in 1947 the NACA's role in nuclear propulsion had no official sanction from headquarters although this did not deter the laboratory staff from initiating basic studies in heat transfer and materials. The following year, a secret study for the Air Force by Massachusetts Institute of Technology concluded that aircraft nuclear propulsion was feasible. The Air Force and the NACA initiated a joint research program. Various Lewis personnel were assigned to Oak Ridge for training, and the laboratory acquired a cyclotron.[22]

Unlike its difficulties in obtaining adequate support for facilities for the study of high-energy propellants, it appears that because nuclear research was tied to the Air Force program, in 1955 Lewis obtained funds authorizing the construction of a nuclear reactor. The reactor was intended to be a research facility in the same way that wind tunnels were used to test inlets, nozzles, and other components for conventional aircraft engines. Research on materials to withstand embrittlement by radiation and basic studies in heat transfer would become its primary focus. The following August, the Atomic Energy Commission approved plans for Lewis's nuclear reactor at Plum Brook, about 50 miles from Lewis. At the time of the groundbreaking for the new facility in September, Silverstein called nuclear propulsion "the 'shining hope' for increasing the range of aircraft at high speeds and for increasing aircraft ranges to values unobtainable with conventional or special chemical fuels."[23]

The high hopes for aircraft nuclear propulsion were never fulfilled and the program was cancelled in 1961 after fifteen years and a cost of $880 million failed to produce the anticipated breakthrough. Nevertheless, belief in the feasibility of a nuclear rocket continued through the Apollo decade.[24] The cancellation of the Rover program in 1972 brought to a close over twenty-five years of research in various facets of nuclear propulsion at Lewis.

## ELECTRIC ROCKET PROPULSION

The sustained interest in nuclear propulsion from the early postwar years at Lewis is directly connected to the development of electric rocket propulsion, one of Lewis Research Center's pioneering areas of space research and my third example of space-related research begun prior to Sputnik. What it demonstrates is that research can grow organically from within a laboratory and, like the research on high-energy propellants, in its early stages can flourish without external demand and large-scale support.

In the case of electric propulsion, interest can be traced to the influence of a single individual. About 1949, Wolfgang Moeckel, one of the laboratory's theoreticians, dusted off Herman Oberth's book, *Wege zur Raumschiffahrt*, published in 1929. He was particularly intrigued by a chapter devoted to the electric rocket that suggested that for space travel, rocket thrust could be produced by the flow of electrically charged particles. The chemical rocket was limited by the enormous amounts of propellant required to be carried into space for flight to distant planets. Although relative to chemical rockets, the amount of thrust was small, the attraction of electrically propelled rockets was that with a power source in space they would continue to be able to produce thrust over long periods of time. This suggested to Oberth, as it had to Robert Goddard in 1906, that electric rockets might be useful for long-distance travel between planets. Although Oberth explored the concept of electric propulsion, he had no idea of what power source to use. Thus, the electric rocket was confined to the nether region of intriguing but impractical technical ideas.[25]

In 1956, with national planning for the International Geophysical Year underway, as well as increased emphasis on intercontinental ballistic missiles, Moeckel, along with other colleagues at Lewis, began to think more seriously about space. Moeckel recalled that during that year he was asked to present a lecture on Earth Satellites and Interplanetary Travel as part of an in-house course on hypersonics. His colleagues at Lewis received his lecture with considerable interest.

Expanding these lectures later the same year, he came across two papers by Ernst Stuhlinger, one of the scientists who had worked on the V-2 at Peenemünde and who accompanied Werner von Braun's rocket group to the United States.[26] Moeckel may have heard about Stuhlinger's work at the semiannual meeting of the American Rocket Society held in Cleveland in 1956 where Krafft Ehricke, also once part of the Peenemünde group, lectured on "The Solar Powered Space Ship."[27]

Stuhlinger had become intrigued with the possibilities of electric propulsion as early as 1947 when, at the Army Camp at Fort Bliss, von Braun had asked him to restudy Oberth's rocket work. Like Moeckel somewhat later, Stuhlinger immediately grasped the potential advantages of electric over chemical propulsion. In Stuhlinger's first paper, published in 1954, he tackled the question that Oberth had left unanswered: how to generate the necessary electric power in space. He suggested a solar turbogenerator that consisted of a system of mirrors and boilers. In his second paper, published in 1955, he took a more radical approach. Stuhlinger suggested a nuclear fission reactor as the power source. He reasoned that "a vehicle designed for a Mars mission would be lighter and somewhat faster if powered by a nuclear reactor than if it were powered by solar energy."[28]

Stuhlinger's papers impressed Moeckel because they were "much more concrete, comprehensive and realistic than previous work." Once Stuhlinger had placed electric propulsion within the realm of technical feasibility, Moeckel set enthusiastically to work. "I immediately began a study of low-thrust trajectories, and the capabilities of such low-thrust systems for interplanetary travel."[29] If headquarters had been apprised of Moeckel's work, it might have discouraged it as "space-cadet" enthusiasm. However, like the analytic work on propellants, which was done before large experimental facilities were authorized, there was no need to inform Washington at this point. Moeckel received the strong support of his division chief, John Evvard, then head of the Supersonic Propulsion Division, who gave him the necessary freedom to think through his ideas. Evvard himself began a study of the feasibility of a manned flight to Mars.

The point of looking at these three examples of advanced research at Lewis is to show that within the overall research program whose focus was on the incremental improvement of existing turbojet engines, there was freedom to explore less conventional areas of propulsion in anticipation of the nation's future technical needs. The timidity of headquarters, a response to the difficulty of obtaining adequate funding for research, can be contrasted with the bold technical thinking that was possible at Lewis. Because Silverstein, who became assistant director in 1952, had considerable freedom to allocate resources and personnel within his overall budget, technical creativity could be nurtured without incurring the wrath of headquarters.

## TRANSITION TO SPACE

Late in 1956, Silverstein, his finger on the changing national technical pulse, became convinced that the problems of the turbojet engine were routine enough to leave to industry to solve. He began to consider a major reorganization of the magnitude of the one that accompanied the switch from the aircraft reciprocating engine to jet propulsion in 1945. There is no indication that Dryden or James H. Doolittle, who was appointed chairman of the NACA that year, specifically suggested the critical reassessment of the research priorities that began at Lewis at this time.

With plans to abolish the compressor and turbine division, Silverstein selected some of the compressor and turbine division's most versatile engineers and scientists to attend a "nuclear school." Eight additional engineers were plucked from other divisions of the laboratory and invited to drop their current projects and to prepare for leadership in the anticipated reorganization by learning the principles of nuclear physics from the small core of researchers who had been engaged in nuclear work for almost a decade. Although the subject matter was new, the need for continuing technical education had long been recognized. The laboratory had instituted an in-house training program in the late 1940s after the transition to jet propulsion. In all, twenty-four engineers had no duties other than to attend the school for six months. The rationale for the nuclear school appears to have been to single out individuals with leadership qualities to teach them the fundamentals of the new areas that Silverstein believed would become the division and branch chiefs after the reorganization.

In January of 1957, six engineers chose not to continue in the nuclear field. The remaining eighteen were divided into three groups. Harold Finger headed a group to work on a nuclear rocket, and in 1960 would be selected by Silverstein to become project director of the joint AEC-NASA nuclear projects at headquarters. Eldon Hall formed a group to study aircraft nuclear propulsion. He would also go to Washington with Silverstein after NASA was organized. Robert English focused the energies of his group on a design study for a nuclear space power system. With the imagined goal of sending eight people to Mars, they proposed a nuclear reactor with the potential to act as the power source for an electric rocket similar to the one that Moeckel was considering.[30]

In March, Silverstein's first act in moving the laboratory toward a comprehensive shift in research priorities was to establish a research planning council. At about the same time he abolished the compressor and turbine division, long one of the premier divisions of the laboratory because of its contributions to the design of the axial compressor for turbojet engines. Many of the aerodynamicists who had worked on the aerodynamics of the compressor were assigned to a new fluid systems division to study the mechanics of flow within rocket systems. At the same time Silverstein created a nuclear reactor division to be responsible for research in connection with the new re-actor nearing completion at Plum Brook.

Meanwhile, other streams leading to space research were con-verging. In the spring of 1957 plans were underway at Lewis for a conference on the evaluation of propulsion systems to be held the following fall. During the meeting to organize the conference, propo-nents of space-related research urged Silverstein to allow them to in-clude sessions on space flight and rocket propulsion systems among the more conventional subjects, such as turbojets and ramjets. Never one to avoid considering daring technical concepts if there was a possibility that they might ultimately prove feasible, Silverstein agreed. With the imagination of many staff now sparked, the re-search groups to study liquid hydrogen and nuclear rockets and space power systems expanded. The rocket branch began to organize a ses-sion on high-energy propellants and Moeckel took a small group under his wing. As Moeckel recalled, "The studies for this conference formed the foundation for the rapid expansion of our research in the fields of electric propulsion, power generation and nuclear rockets."[31]

As preparations for the Propulsion Conference moved into high gear in September 1957, Silverstein called a meeting of the Research Planning Council. He expressed what appears to have been the con-sensus of the planning council that "existing problems on the air-breathing turbojet engine were not of sufficient laboratory interest for the continuation of a large scale program."[32] His proposal that rocket research be expanded, while proportionally reducing turbojet engine research, effectively marked Lewis's transition to space.

## RESPONSE TO SPUTNIK

The tension between the conservatism of headquarters and the gath-ering momentum of the Cleveland laboratory toward space-related research mounted in September when representatives from headquar-ters visited Lewis to critique its rehearsal for the finely orchestrated NACA Triennial Inspection. Unlike the anticipated more specialized propulsion conference to be directed toward a technical audience, politicians and industry executives attended these inspections, which were intended to convey the work of the laboratory in layman's terms. John Victory, always on the lookout for anything that might offend potential congressional sponsors, ordered references to space removed from the presentations. As one member of the rocket group explained: "The climate in Washington in the fall of 1957 was very negative toward space. It was all right to talk about the slow-paced scientific Vanguard satellite, part of the International Geophysical Year, but anything beyond it was considered 'space-cadet' enthusiasm."[33] However, on October 4, between the rehearsal and the inspection, the Russians launched Sputnik. When the inspection began several days later, Lewis engineers proudly unveiled their work on space flight propulsion systems and high-energy rocket propellants.

However, the most detailed consideration of Lewis's work in space propulsion was reserved for the classified NACA-Industry Conference, held November 22, 1957. It reflected a distillation of the current thinking of the laboratory. Industry representatives were "anxious to get advice on how to move forward in this new area."[34] Although its major focus was on the potential of liquid-hydrogen as a rocket fuel, the paper that the group working with Moeckel submitted on "Satellite and Space Propulsion Systems" showed how far the thinking of the laboratory had advanced. It contained a detailed discussion of flights to the Moon and Mars with particular focus on electric propulsion systems and the types of generators required.[35]

As national debate over the implications of the Russian triumph in space raged, Lewis, like the rest of the NACA, was divided over what role it should play in the changed political and technical environment. The laboratory was divided between those who were reluctant to give up their work on air-breathing engines and those who were eager to push on to the problems of engines in zero-gravity. Bruce Lundin, later director of Lewis (1969–1977), recalled that about half of the staff were afraid that they would get swept up in space research and half were afraid that they might get left out.[36] This division could also be found at Ames and Langley where many older researchers were reluctant to leave the familiar territory of aeronautics. However, many of the Lewis staff had begun to prepare themselves for the transition when Silverstein abolished the compressor and turbine division. As *Business Week* later reported, Lewis Laboratory "leaped over to space" because it had begun its jump well before Sputnik.[37]

To many of the Lewis staff, the issue that had far greater implications was whether research would be threatened if the NACA became an agency responsible, in addition to research, for both development and missions. The need to keep research as a separate government function had been a cornerstone of postwar planning. In 1945 Vannevar Bush had warned of the dangers of combining research and development in the same organization. In *Science, the Endless Frontier* he had written, "Research will always suffer when put in competition with operations."[38] Lewis researchers asked themselves, would the developmental and operating activities let the proverbial camel into the tent to push out its regular inhabitants? Would large-scale missions swallow up this carefully built, if underfunded, research organization?

As the discussion of the NACA's role in space dragged on at Lewis through meeting after meeting of the research planning council and in the informal debates at the lunch table in the cafeteria, Bruce Lundin sat down one Sunday afternoon in early December and put his own thoughts into writing. The document that he produced, "Some Remarks on a Future Policy and Course of Action for the NACA" summarized the views of the two pro-space factions at Lewis: those who thought that the NACA should select one "dramatic" space project around which to organize its activities, such as a manned space station or placing a dye marker on the Moon, and those who argued that the NACA should aim at nothing less than leadership of a national space program. Lundin argued for the more ambitious course of action. He advocated a program that would be "bold, imaginative, aggressive, and visionary" and he warned of the dangers of settling for less. If the NACA focused its energies on a specific project, this might "dangerously limit our goals, restrict the range of our thinking, and give us nothing to grow on." Aeronautical research, not directly controlled by the military and directed to national goals, had been the traditional role of the NACA. Space research seemed a logical extension of that role. Calling upon Cold War rhetoric, Lundin declared that space research was a matter of national survival.

> In our technological age, it will be the country that advances in science that will have the greatest impact on the emotions and imagination of men, that will command respect (or at least allegiance) and that will gradually assume world leadership. If Russia does this, eventually their way will be *the* way and we will have lost the struggle without knowing just when and how it occurred. The final victory in the struggle may well go to the country that offers mankind the greatest scientific achievements.[39]

Central to Lundin's views was the role of the NACA as the coordinator of all American space-related research, both within the government and by industry. To have a successful space program, in
Lundin's view, new knowledge had to be generated. "In practically
all areas, there is a great deal of new knowledge that must be found
and new principles that must be established. It is a time for research—
fundamental and applied—in many fields." Lundin did not tackle the
question of development or a mission role for the new agency.

Finally, taking a shot at the traditional conservatism of headquarters, Lundin wrote:

> It is easy and probably correct to argue that this approach is idealistic
> and not practical enough for down-to-earth and skeptical Congressmen
> and budget keepers. It seems, however, that it is time for a little more
> idealism, vision and courage in our approach.[40]

No sooner had Lundin put the finishing touches on his memo than
Dryden called a meeting of the directors and associate directors of
the laboratories to discuss the future role of the NACA in space.
Henry Reid and Floyd Thompson of Langley were unenthusiastic
about changing the traditional aeronautical emphasis of NACA research. Smith DeFrance of the Ames Laboratory reputedly opposed
a NACA space initiative, "fearing that it would destroy the whole
concept on which the NACA was based."[41] Silverstein, last to speak,
pulled Lundin's memo from his briefcase. He had changed Lundin's
"I" to "we" and read the memo as "Lewis Laboratory Opinion of
a Future Policy and Course of Action for the NACA." This swung
the opinion of the meeting in favor of space research. The "Lewis
Laboratory Opinion" was "accepted with little modification as the
official NACA opinion."[42] What became known as the "Dryden
Plan" contained many of Lundin's ideas. Silverstein's timely advocacy
of a strong NACA initiative in establishing a new agency tagged him
for a leadership position in the new space agency.

That evening Dryden and Doolittle hosted the famous "Young
Turks Dinner," intended to give the middle management of the three
laboratories a chance to express their views on redirecting the goals
of their venerable research organization. The sober Dryden gracefully
accepted the barbs flung at him by some of the spirited staff who
called him too cautious, a criticism that he would soon encounter as
he testified in the House of Representatives. The consensus of the

stormy meeting was that a NACA space initiative had strong support from the future leaders of the laboratories.[43]

Two days later the Research Planning Council at Lewis met to appoint a seven-member committee to plan the new Space Flight Research Laboratory recommended in Lundin's document. On February 10 they submitted "A Program for Expansion of NACA Research in Space Flight Technology." Not surprisingly, given the fact that it was conceived at Lewis, the main focus of the new facility was to be on the research to support the development of launch vehicles—a stable of chemical, nuclear, and electric rockets. Notably absent from this early planning document was a consideration of the mechanics of how missions would actually be carried out. As first conceived, the new laboratory would continue to operate in the NACA tradition. It would generate the knowledge, the technical know-how, necessary to make manned and unmanned space flight missions feasible. The development of the actual hardware to be sent into space and the operation of those missions would be left as it had been in the past, respectively to industry and to the military.[44]

These plans might have been appropriate if the conquest of space had not been viewed as a national crisis. Firm centralized control of all three elements of the space program—research, development, and operations—seemed to be required. Research would ultimately suffer.

## FROM THE NACA TO NASA

On March 5, President Eisenhower announced his decision to organize the new space agency around the NACA. In his memo justifying the decision in favor of a civilian agency, he cited three documents that indicated the interest and competence of the NACA for leadership of the space program: the so-called Dryden Plan based on the ideas found in the Lundin-Silverstein "Lewis Opinion," the February 10 plan for the new Space Flight Laboratory generated at Lewis with input from the other two centers, and the January 16 resolution of the Main Committee that endorsed the idea in "Lewis Opinion" that the NACA assume the role as coordinator of research.[45] However, between March and July when the Space Act authorizing the National Aeronautics and Space Administration became law, a very different organization than the one envisioned by Lewis planners took shape.

Although they had proposed a role for the NACA that they considered radical, it was not sweeping enough to satisfy the various competing forces in Washington. After considerable debate within the Congress, the new agency was given extensive responsibility for development and operations, in addition to research.[46]

Once development and operations were added to NASA's mandate, the old NACA laboratories, now called research centers, were vulnerable—how vulnerable was not clear until much later. Initially, Dryden insisted that research be kept separate from development to protect the NACA centers from the "encroachment" of the development and mission orientation of the new agency.[47]

This idea of keeping the research centers "pure," was clearly also shared by Abe Silverstein, whom Dryden called to Washington in March to take responsibility for the other side of NASA, the emerging space flight development program. Among the leaders of the NACA, Silverstein was probably best suited to assume the problems of pulling together the diverse elements of the new development program because, of the three centers, the work at Lewis on full-scale engines came closest to development. Because of Silverstein's technical competence, the force of his personality, and the quality of the staff he selected to serve under him, a disproportionate amount of power at headquarters was concentrated in his hands until headquarters was reorganized in mid-1961.[48] Not only did Silverstein's province include the Space Task Group at Langley, which he managed through his deputy George Low (also from Lewis), who shuttled between Robert Gilruth at Langley and headquarters, but also he was in charge of the initial planning of what would become Goddard. N. Phillip Miller, who had worked on the February 10 NACA plan, could be counted on as Chief of the Plant and Facilities Construction Program.[49]

When President Eisenhower named T. Keith Glennan the first administrator in August, Glennan accepted an organizational structure in the process of being implemented by the "NACA boys" as sound, although one of his first priorities was to reduce the "in-house" emphasis that had characterized the NACA. Good Republican that he was, he was determined to avoid "excessive additions" in terms of added civil servants.

Since our basic organizational structure was to be erected on the NACA staff, and since their operation had been conducted almost wholly 'in house,' I knew that I would be faced with demands on the part of the technical staff to add substantially to that in-house capacity. Indeed, approval had been given in the then-current budget to initiate the construction of a so-called "space control center" laboratory at Beltsville, Maryland, an action of which I approved. But I was convinced that the major portion of our added funds must be spent with industry, education and other non-profit institutions.[50]

This was a key decision that affected the future of the former NACA laboratories. During the NACA era, almost all of the research had been done "in-house." The technical competence of the staff was nurtured in part through work on selected projects initiated and sustained by the staff rather than external demands. This had made possible the pioneering work on liquid hydrogen, and the exploration of the potential of nuclear and electric propulsion at Lewis. At first, contracting was confined to the Space Flight Development Program and the research centers were allowed to continue to operate much as they had in the past. The "proper balance," however, between the work done by the laboratories and by contract became a thorny issue. Glennan disapproved of the policy of "farming out to industry only the repetitive and straight production items" saving the more challenging and creative projects for the "in-house" staff.[51] This was an inversion of the traditional NACA priority of nurturing technically challenging projects from within the laboratory. Routine development activities had traditionally been left to industry.

By 1960, Lewis Research Center was beginning to struggle with the implications of the new organizational structure. In a talk to the staff, the acting director, Eugene Manganiello, pointed out that the so-called developmental centers did development as well as research because the two could no longer be neatly separated the way they had in the past. Dealing with the new aerospace industry required new definitions. "Applied research" and "advanced development" had become indistinguishable in current practice, and the development centers were doing both. The net result was that Lewis Research Center would need to rethink its place in the propulsion community. If the difference between research and development had become murky, nevertheless, Manganiello argued, the research character of the laboratory could be preserved if NASA recognized the distinction between short-term and long-term research and development:

> We at Lewis have no desire or intention to engage in the short-range ac-
> tivity or get into the problems of the construction of flight hardware. We
> are not particularly intrigued with the battle of the 'O' rings but we are,
> on the other hand, intensely interested in the advanced research and de-
> velopment end of the business, the nuclear rocket, electric propulsion and
> power generation, high energy chemical rockets — their systems and
> components — where the scientific and engineering technology needs to
> be established before useful and reliable propulsion can be created. . . .
> We cannot afford to permit our basic research or our conceptual re-
> search into new and better ideas to become submerged or deemphasized
> so that we have nothing left to grow on.[52]

As long as the space program could proceed at the deliberate pace
set by Glennan, Lewis could continue to concentrate on contributing
to the base of knowledge out of which advanced propulsion systems
might later be developed. However, in May 1961, when President
Kennedy announced the national goal to land a man on the Moon
within a decade, the research centers were forced to fall into the pace
set by the development side of NASA.[53] With objectives more and
more closely identified with development and increasing pressure to
meet tight deadlines, advanced technology research did not have a
high priority with headquarters personnel, especially after the November 1961 reorganization that left fewer NACA representatives in
top positions. The Apollo program was to be accomplished with existing technology, and Lewis, to the extent that it attempted to nurture advanced technology research, was pushed out of the mainstream of NASA. Nevertheless, the three programs that marked
Lewis's transition to space are a tribute to the NACA's philosophy
that had permitted the nurturing of advanced concepts within an
overall structure that met the more immediate demands of industry
and the military. Perhaps former engineers at Lewis, who embraced
the new space initiative so enthusiastically and put their mark on the
early space program, still recall the arguments of those who were
against letting the camel's head into the research tent.

## NOTES

1. For the early administrative history of NASA, see Robert Rosholt's *An Administrative History of NASA, 1958–1963*, especially 178, 202 for the idea of keeping a balance between research and development. A more detailed account of the early debates prior to the formation of NASA is provided by Enid Curtis Bok Schoettle in her article, "The Establishment of NASA," Chapter 5, *Knowledge and Power*, ed. Sanford A. Lakoff (New York: The Free Press, 1966).

2. For information on the threat of Ames closing, see Elizabeth Muenger, *Searching the Horizon: A History of Ames Research Center, 1940–1976* (NASA SP-4304, 1985), 148.

3. Walter A. McDougall, . . . *The Heavens and the Earth: A Political History of the Space Age* (New York: Basic Books, Inc., 1985), 166. See also Homer E. Newell, *Beyond the Atmosphere* (NASA SP-4211), 90–91.

4. Ira H. Abbott, "A Review and Commentary of a Thesis by Arthur L. Levine entitled 'U.S. Aeronautical Research Policy, 1915–1958,'" 197. Alex Roland has explored the conservatism of NACA headquarters in *Model Research* (NASA SP-4103, 1985).

5. National aeronautical policy decreed that fundamental research was the province of the NACA; development was to be left to industry, operations to the military. For the postwar statement of "National Aeronautical Research Policy," approved 21 March 1946, see Alex Roland, *Model Research,* vol. 2, doc. 36, 693–95. For distinctions between fundamental or basic, applied, and specific developmental research, see Abbott, "A Review and Commentary," 5–6, 186.

6. James R. Hansen, *Engineer in Charge: A History of Langley Aeronautical Laboratory, 1917–1958* (NASA SP-4305, 1987).

7. Arthur L. Levine placed this so-called fundamental or basic research at about 10 percent of total NACA research. "United States Aeronautical Research Policy 1915–1958: A Study of the Major Policy Decisions of the National Advisory Committee for Aeronautics" (Columbia University, Ph.D. dissertation, 1963), 97–98. As noted above, note 5, in principle all NACA research was fundamental.

8. John Sloop, *Liquid Hydrogen as a Propulsion Fuel, 1945–1959* (NASA SP-4404, 1978), 208.

9. Interview by author with Walter Olson, 16 July 1984. The papers by Richard Canright may have been particularly influential.

10. Sloop, *Liquid Hydrogen,* 74.

11. Sloop, *Liquid Hydrogen,* 75.

12. Sloop, *Liquid Hydrogen,* 81.

13. See R. O. Miller and P. M. Ordin, "Theoretical Performance of Rocket Propellants Containing Hydrogen, Nitrogen, and Oxygen," RM E8A30, 1948, cited by Sloop, *Liquid Hydrogen,* 80.

14. R. W. Bussard and R. D. DeLauer, *Fundamentals of Nuclear Flight* (New York: McGraw Hill, 1965), 2.

15. Sloop, *Liquid Hydrogen,* 84.

16. Quoted by Sloop, *Liquid Hydrogen,* 85.

17. James H. Doolittle, letter of submittal, 1 October 1957, *43rd Annual Report of the NACA, 1957* (Washington, 1958) quoted by Muenger, *Searching the Horizon,* 81.

18. Hicks and Simon to Acting Executive Engineer, "Nature of AERL Research on Nuclear Energy Fuels," 11 June 1945, NASA-Lewis Research Center Records, Cleveland, Ohio 34/17112.

19. Evvard to Acting Engineer, 9 August 1945, NASA-Lewis Research Center Records, Cleveland, Ohio 34/17112.

20. Cleveland to NACA, "Recommendations Concerning the Application of Nuclear Energy to Aircraft Power Plants," 24 May 1946, NASA-Lewis Research Center Records, Cleveland, Ohio 34/17112.

21. Under NEPA the Air Force studied both nuclear aircraft and rocket propulsion between 1946 and 1951, when it became a joint project with the AEC, called the Aircraft Nuclear Propulsion (ANP) program. See Bussard and DeLauer, *Fundamentals of Nuclear Flight,* 2 ff.

22. See Roland, *Model Research,* 255 and notes 54–55, 383; See also Richard Hewlett, *Atomic Shield, 1947/1952,* vol. 2, in *A History of the United States Atomic Energy Commission,* 420. Correspondence between NACA and AEC on nuclear propulsion can be found in National Archives, Record Group 255, Transactions/Communications 63A 250 Box 14, C-2-8. From this rather spotty collection of letters it appears that A. Katalinsky, chief engineer, Nuclear Energy Propulsion for Aircraft (NEPA) Fairchild, was anxious to be able to use NACA research data. After a meeting with Cleveland laboratory engineers, he wrote on October 1, 1947: "In the course of these discussions it became apparent that the analytical and experimental heat transfer studies now under way at Cleveland may be of great immediate value to NEPA. In the analytical studies, a method of calculating heat transfer and pressure drop has been devised which appears to be far simpler and more accurate than anything we now have available." Cooperation was formalized between AEC and NACA, July 15, 1948. The NACA cyclotron was scheduled for delivery from General Electric September 1949. It is hoped that greater light will be shed on the relationship between NACA and AEC after the Rothrock files at the National Archives, Suitland, have been declassified.

23. Press Release, September 26, 1956, NASA-Lewis Research Center Records, Cleveland, Ohio 298/116.1-42.

24. See "Remarks of Melvin Price," *Congressional Record-Appendix,* 26 August 1960, A6420. Nuclear rocket development (Rover) started in 1955. A joint AEC-NASA office was established in 1960 with Harold Finger as its head. The program was cancelled in 1972.

25. Moeckel to Stuhlinger, 2 June 1964, personal papers of Moeckel. See also Ernst Stuhlinger, *Ion Propulsion for Space Flight* (New York: McGraw-Hill Book Co., 1964), 6.

26. Moeckel to Stuhlinger, ibid.

27. K. A. Ehricke, "The Solar Powered Space Ship," ARS Paper No. 310-56.

28. Ernst Stuhlinger, *Ion Propulsion for Space Flight,* 6.

29. Moeckel to Stuhlinger, 2 June 1964, personal papers of Moeckel.

30. Interview with Robert English, 11 July 1986. Unfortunately, I was unable

to find the curriculum of the nuclear school among what has survived of Lewis administrative records.

31. Moeckel to Stuhlinger, ibid.

32. "Research Planning Council," 6 September 1957, NASA-Lewis Research Center Archives, Cleveland, Ohio 298/117. Members of the Research Planning Council, established 8 March 1957, were: Eugene Manganiello, John Evvard, Bruce Lundin, Walter Olson, Irving Pinkel, and Newell Sanders.

33. Sloop, *Liquid Hydrogen,* 91.

34. Evvard to author, February 1987.

35. Wolfgang Moeckel, L. V. Baldwin, Robert English, Bernard Lubarsky, and Steve Maslen, "Satellite and Space Propulsion Systems" NASA TN D-285, June 1960. Unclassified version of material presented at NACA Flight Propulsion Conference, November 22, 1957. The previously classified papers of the conference were published in 1972 as "NACA 1957 Flight Propulsion Conference," NASA TMX 61622. It includes Paul G. Johnson, James W. Miser, and Roger L. Smith, "Nuclear Logistic Carrier," and Frank E. Rom, Eldon W. Sams, and Robert E. Hyland, "Nuclear Rockets."

36. Sloop, *Liquid Hydrogen,* 180.

37. See "How an Aircraft Lab Leaped Over to Space," *Business Week* (June 4, 1960): 98–102.

38. Quoted in Levine, "U.S. Aeronautical Research Policy 1915–1958," 90.

39. A copy of the memo, dated December 9, 1957, was obtained from Lundin, with Silverstein's handwritten comments. The typed Silverstein version was found in NASA-Lewis Research Center Records, Cleveland, Ohio 221/115.1-71 "Lewis Laboratory Opinion of a Future Policy and Course of Action for the NACA." The first Lewis memo, "Suggested Policy and Course of Action for NACA on Space Flight," December 2, 1957, by Walter T. Olson can be found in the NASA History Office, Washington, D.C.

40. Ibid. Lundin memo.

41. Sloop, *Liquid Hydrogen,* 180.

42. "Minutes of December 20, 1957 Meeting of Committee on Space Flight Laboratory Opinion" was the original document that, with modifications and input from the other two laboratories, became "A Staff Study of the NACA," dated January 14, 1958. This then was further refined into a four-page document called "A National Research Program for Space Technology," referred to by later commentators as the "Dryden Plan."

43. Sloop, *Liquid Hydrogen,* 181 and Hugh L. Dryden to Eugene Emme, "The NACA-NASA Transition," 8 September 1965. NASA History Office.

44. Members of the Lewis Special Committee on Space Flight Laboratory were: J. Howard Childs, Chairman, E. M. Cortright, R. E. English, E. R. Jonash, B. Lubarsky, P. N. Miller, and I. Warshawsky. William Mickelson served as secretary and Silverstein attended meetings on January 6 and January 27. They were given one month to produce the plan. From the personal papers of I. Warshawsky, I obtained the complete Minutes of the meetings. This document is reproduced *in toto* by Alex Roland, *Model Research,* vol. 2, document 46, p. 732 ff. The final version, somewhat condensed and called "Summary of a Program for Expansion of NACA Research in Space Flight Technology," was found in NASA-Lewis Re-

search Center Archives 295/117.71. From the 27 January 1958 Minutes, it is clear that Langley and Ames offered similar proposals, but headquarters decided to use the Lewis proposal for a brochure to be presented to the NACA Special Committee on Space Technology (Stever Committee). The final version is also attributed to Lewis senior staff by L. Swenson Jr. et al., *This New Ocean* (NASA SP-4201, 1966), 76 and 533, note 7. This is presumably the earliest plan for what became Goddard.

45. Rosholt, *An Administrative History of NASA*, 35, states that the March 5 memo to President Eisenhower from his Advisory Committee on Government Organization cited three documents as justification for the decision to organize the new space agency around the NACA: the "Dryden Plan," the January 16 Resolution of the Main Committee, and the February 10 "A Program for Expansion of NACA Research in Space Flight Technology." As my discussion below indicates, the initial planning for the third document was also done at Lewis and was submitted to the NACA "Stever Committee," probably by Silverstein who served on the committee. Although set up in November 1957, the Stever Committee did not actually meet until January. It seems that by this time most of the NACA policy had been formulated and the committee merely ratified the already formulated NACA plans.

46. For the metamorphosis of the NACA into NASA see especially Schoettle, "The Establishment of NASA;" Rosholt, *Administrative History of NASA*, 37–70; Swenson et al., *This New World*, 75–106.

47. Homer E. Newell, *Beyond the Atmosphere*, 102–103.

48. Rosholt, *Administrative History of NASA*, 206–207.

49. From Lewis, Silverstein selected: DeMarquis D. Wyatt, assistant to the director of Space Flight Development; Edgar M. Cortright, chief of Advanced Technology Program; Harold B. Finger, chief of Nuclear Engines Program; Eldon W. Hall, chief of Analysis and Requirements Program; N. Philip Miller, chief of Plant and Facilities Construction Program, Space Flight Program. Also George M. Low, chief of Manned Space Flight Program; Warren J. North, chief of Manned Satellite Program; Adelbert O. Tischler, chief of Liquid Fuel Rocket Engines Program; Francis C. Schwenk, Nuclear Program (title unknown); Newell Sanders, assistant director of Advanced Technology; William Fleming, head of Project Review Division, chaired task group to prepare "Fleming Report," first study of feasibility of manned flight to the Moon.

Of the approximately 40 members of the Space Task Group (became Mercury program), 10 were from Lewis: Elmer Buller, A. M. Busch, W. R. Dennis, M. J. Krasnican, Glynn S. Lunney, Andre J. Meyer, W. R. Meyer, W. J. Nesbitt, Gerard J. Pesman, Leonard Robb. Commuters to Langley from Lewis: John Disher, Kenneth Weston.

50. T. Keith Glennan, "The First Years of the National Aeronautics and Space Administration," unpublished manuscript, The Dwight D. Eisenhower Library, Abilene, Kansas, vol. 1, 7.

51. Ibid., 141.

52. E. J. Manganiello Address to Staff, "The Changing Trends in our Activities," 4 November 1960. Address to Lewis Research Center Staff, RG 255 73A32, 116/1-52, FARC, Chicago, Illinois.

53. Rosholt, *Administrative History of NASA*, 259.

# Commentary

I am struck by the way in which Dr. Hansen and Dr. Dawson present internalist perspectives on aviation and aerospace history, inasmuch as I consider myself an internalist, who takes an external perspective as required. I believe one of the problems in aviation history, as distinct from space history, is that we have very few good *internalist* studies. When Walter McDougall wrote his monumental book on the space program, . . . *The Heavens and the Earth,* I think he was able to do such a good *externalist* work in part because there were a number of high quality *internalist* histories upon which to draw. For example, we have Frank Winter's work in early rocketry, and we have the notable series of studies that have come out under the sponsorship of the NASA history program. We need more of the same if we intend to look at the aviation field in depth.

I begin by commenting on Dr. Dawson's paper. The most important point she raises sounds trivial, unless one is familiar with the nature of works on the National Advisory Committee for Aeronautics. Dr. Dawson points out that in the 1950s the National Advisory Committee for Aeronautics was an agency in a bit of a muddle. There was a conservative headquarters staff, but a field staff that was anything *but* conservative. She has focused on the least known of the NACA centers, the Lewis Center, largely neglected until now because flight propulsion fails to excite the imagination in the way that aerodynamics or even structures do. Very little has been written about the Lewis Center and its activities. But the examples she uses in which Lewis was interested, could very well be matched by Dr. Hansen with reference to Langley, or by Dr. Elizabeth Muenger with reference to Ames, or in my own work with reference to the Dryden Center. The larger point is that the NACA's workers in the field were *very* venturesome, despite greater conservatism in headquarters. They had a spirit of adventure as they pursued their work. Thus, many of the projects that we perceive to be space projects in the 1960s were projects that really owed their origins to the work of the NACA during the early 1950s to late 1950s—when the NACA as a whole was allegedly blind to space and instead was concentrating "just" on winged vehicles. For example, there were NACA concepts that were bridge-gappers (transcending flight within the atmosphere and flight in space) and overt space concepts—such as the X-15 and X-20 technology demonstration programs, lifting body conceptualizations for returning from orbit, the basic blunt body re-entry principle (which was developed at Ames in 1951), early Shuttle studies, hydrogen fuel, supersonic combustion ramjet work, electric propulsion, and even the notion of nuclear propulsion studies. It's very nice with 20-20 hindsight to look at the nuclear propulsion programs of the 1950s for aircraft and rockets, and to wonder sometimes what these people were smoking. I'm reminded of a comment that General Curtis LeMay allegedly said in 1963, cancelling the Air Force nuclear propulsion program; he remarked that a nuclear airplane was great, if you wanted to cruise at about 600 feet at 200 miles an hour for the rest of your life. Going beyond that, there were some aspects of nuclear propulsion that *were* rather intriguing and which did have great potential. Project Orion by Ted Taylor was one of these; there's an example of an Orion development vehicle in the collections of the National Air and Space Museum. It would really be a worthwhile cultural study of technology to examine nuclear propulsion and ideas such as the Atoms for Peace proposals and the proposal to build a new canal across the Isthmus using strategically placed nuclear devices in the ground in the vicinity of Nicaragua. (I'm sure some people look back on that with nostalgia today!) In any case, I am pleased that Dr. Dawson focused on the NACA as an agency that really cannot be characterized as *either* conservative *or* advanced, except insofar as one breaks out what component, branch, and project of the agency one is talking about.

When examining the NACA, it is necessary to recognize an agency that tended to be dominated by its centers. The centers ran the NACA in a way that NASA centers today wish they could run NASA. For that reason, I would suggest not classifying NACA as "conservative" or "non-conservative," but rather recognizing it as an agency somewhat confused in its orientation. On the one hand, there were pragmatic headquarters people such as John Victory, who, having to run up to the Hill to get funding support, was very conscious of the environment he was dealing with and of the way political winds blow in Washington. On the other hand, there were hard-chargers and fast-movers in the field, entranced (to speak of that mysterious quality in technology) with their research and the pursuit of technology.

Dr. Hansen's paper intrigued me; I think it is a fabulous paper because it stimulates a great deal of thought on the methodology and goals of aviation history. Basically, when we talk about *aeronautical* engineering as distinct from what we term *aerospace* engineering today, we are really talking about the *process* of aircraft design. If we look at contemporary aeronautical engineering, we find that it is an area where we *can not* afford to put in the amount of attention required to get that very last bit of performance, that last 1 percent—a slight quibble with what Jim Hansen has said. In today's development of high performance aircraft, both for commercial purposes and particularly for military purposes, we find we would have to spend an exorbitant amount of time, money, and effort to get that dubious "last" 1 percent of performance. Typically speaking, major aeronautical projects today consume a twelve to fifteen-year development time—from the time of framing an operational requirement to the time of achieving an Initial Operational Capability (IOC). This IOC, of course, is when the *first* vehicle enters service. I'm fond of saying that (especially in military affairs) IOC is *not* the important milestone to shoot for. Rather, it's when the *last* vehicle is delivered—that's important. For example, the l'Armee de l'air (the French Air Force) found itself in May/June of 1940, at the time of its collapse, with a few good aircraft entering service, but with a very large number of mediocre machines in service. Consequently, France's airmen lost their war in part due to critical acquisition failures.

If we consider the nature of aeronautical design, we see that it's really a process of *integration*—integrating diverse technologies, particularly in four key areas: structures, propulsion, controls, and aerodynamics. This is done to meet specific mission requirements and necessarily involves selective trade-offs and compromises, as Dr. Hansen has pointed out. Requirements tend to be formed on the basis of needs. For the military, other "drivers" are the nature of the

threat that services perceive themselves confronting and also the nature of doctrine. Services formulate doctrine to govern their force
structure, based on their anticipation of how they wish to go to war.

Depending on the vehicle being designed, operating costs may or
may not be a serious concern. I mention this because one aspect of
contemporary studies within the history of technology that distresses
me is the overemphasis on cost. Historians always seem to be looking for an economic "bottom line," and I think it's because, in many
cases, they tend to be less comfortable dealing with the kinds of parametric nuances that Dr. Hansen has mentioned. Historians are less
comfortable dealing with measures of merit concerning performance
and capability, and, instead, they are much more comfortable dealing
with dollars and cents, even though that may not be an appropriate
measure to evaluate technology in every case. Operating cost is a
very appropriate measure if one is dealing with commercial aircraft:
for example, seat costs per mile. But to the military, understandably,
operating cost is much less significant than performance. For example, the only cost matters that are really significant to the military
tend to be acquisition, maintainability, and support costs: what are
termed life-cycle costs. The military has to be concerned by a basic
noneconomic fact of life: staying alive to the point where an aircrew
can complete a mission, or at least staying alive to the point where
the crew facilitates the purposes of the mission.

Because aircraft design is a broad field, and because it is a process whereby we produce numerous types of designs for many different and often contradictory missions, it is dangerous to focus on a
few key parameters as a means of evaluating aeronautical development. Rather, one must focus on the particular parameters that are
relevant to the vehicle or the technology. For example, seat costs per
mile is a very appropriate measure to evaluate the development of
commercial air transport. But if one examines fighter aircraft technology, qualities such as sustained turn rate are what is important.
For the development of re-entry vehicles, there are factors such as
lift-to-drag ratio and ablation cooling measures. Significant and
meaningful history will have to include addressing technological development in these terms, using incisive scholarship that recognizes
the relevancy of parametric analysis, particularly for comparative
purposes. When one examines trend curves, relating such quantities
as horsepower to weight ratios, or values for the Breguet range equa-

tion, one gets a feeling for what has taken place and what has driven the development of technology.

We should recognize that flight is an inherently dynamic process and that there is more to aviation merely than lifting weight and carrying it a certain distance. Indeed, this preoccupation with studying aviation in the sense of lift alone doomed many early pioneers of flight in the era of experimentation before the Wright brothers. Instead, we should concern ourselves with the revolutions that have and are taking place and that have transformed the nature of aerospace engineering. For example, looking within the fields of aerodynamics, propulsion, structures, and controls, a few of these revolutions are the structures and aerodynamics revolution of the 1920s and 1930s, including the streamline impulse; the progression from the wooden airplane to the wooden and metal tube airplane, and, finally, to the all metal aircraft; the turbojet revolution of the 1930s and 1940s; and then the space flight revolution itself from the 1950s to the present. Today we are in the midst of two revolutions that are having profound effects for both commercial and military vehicles. These are the *avionics revolution* (the electronics revolution) and the *revolution in flight structures*. Aerospace science is moving beyond the basic structure we have dealt with—the all-metal airplane—to what I call "Tupperware airplanes" with composite structures. I would particularly like to emphasize two fields that I think are too often neglected in aviation study. The first of these is aeropropulsion. Engines have always been the classic pacing factor constraining what designers have sought to do with aircraft. The second is control systems technology. The most significant contribution of the Wright brothers was their emphasis on doing something with the airplane once it got into the air: they stressed the controllability of the vehicle.

What distinguishes aeronautical engineering from most other engineering disciplines? My own "guesstimate" would be that it involves designing machinery to routinely undertake tremendous transient excursions in speed, loads, distance, and pressure (altitude). In commercial aircraft, these involve "cycling" performances. An airliner takes off, climbs to a very high altitude, goes through a complete change of environment that in itself is extremely demanding, and does this on a constant repetitive basis, many times in a single day. In military fighters, this may involve repeated maneuvering up to 9 G, and sustained routine maneuvering between 3 and 6 G. I was happy to hear Dr. Hansen's mention of what has been a largely un-known and certainly unappreciated factor present in the design proc-ess: the role of the test pilot and flight test engineer. We tend to be conditioned by the images from Tom Wolfe's book, *The Right Stuff:* the notion of the test pilot as a sort of reckless daredevil who will do anything in an airplane at least once. That image predates Wolfe by forty years, starting with an influential motion picture made in the 1930s entitled *Test Pilot,* starring Clark Gable, Myrna Loy, and Spencer Tracy. It has one fantastic line. Spencer Tracy turns to Myrna Loy and says "You little fool, don't you know it's dangerous just to look at an airplane?" In any case, since the time of Sir George Cayley at the beginning of the nineteenth century, flight re-searchers have *always* operated as professionally as their knowledge base permitted them. By the end of the First World War, notably in Great Britain and then in the United States, formalized training had begun for test pilots who even then were usually trained engineers, something not generally appreciated. In the 1920s, in contrast to his reckless daredevil image, test pilot James H. "Jimmy" Doolittle was one of the first people in this country to earn a doctorate in science from MIT. He did so in 1925 under the guidance of Professor Wil-liam Brown at MIT, on the basis of flight testing and flight research work with the Army Air Service at McCook Field, Ohio. The test pilot and the designer, as one British test pilot stated, have always spoken the same language, though not necessarily the same dialect. The test pilot pursues his work from the perspective of the aircraft operator, and thus Dr. Hansen's emphasis upon the evolution of han-dling qualities criteria in aircraft is most significant, for it is in this area that the test pilot has been most influential. If we trace the de-velopment of handling qualities criteria for a wide range of machines—commercial aircraft, fighter aircraft, and so forth—we find that it was test pilots who generated those handling criteria, not merely the qualitative "The airplane feels all right to me" analysis, but the actual quantitative measures—for example, the Cooper-Harper rating system of the 1950s, which is still in use today.

The statement was made that if one took aircraft away, we re-ally would not have aeronautical engineering. But that is also true of most other fields. Take ships away and you really wouldn't have naval architecture. Take concrete away and you wouldn't have civil engineering. It's a chicken-and-egg question, and I would merely sug-gest that since the time of George Cayley, aeronautical engineering has necessarily preceded the flight process—that is, preceded the pursuit of vehicles.

In turn, that leads to the question "What *is* aerospace history?" Is it the history of individual aircraft, or is it the story of people? To me, it's the story of people, people who design, build, fly, maintain, and utilize flight vehicles. And in this regard, it is like other fields of technology or the history of science. I have a fascination with individual aircraft myself, but only because of what they tell us of their "parents," the designers—the Jack Northrops, the Kelly Johnsons, the Ed Heinemanns, the Burt Rutans. One of our colleagues, Colonel Donald Baucom, USAF, made a provocative comment on the undesirability of "demystifying" the airplane. Aircraft *do* have idiosyncratic tendencies. Anyone who has flown them will recognize that immediately. And while I wouldn't consider these tendencies "magical," there is, nevertheless, an element of mystery. What really excites me about aircraft design is that the aesthetics of these vehicles are dictated by functional questions. Truly this is a case of "form following function." Antoine de Saint-Exupery, trained as an engineer, became an early French airline pilot, and evolved into a philosopher of flight. He compared the design of an airplane to a sculptor freeing an imprisoned image from stone. Le Corbusier, one of the great founders of the modern school of architecture, stated in 1923 that "We may then affirm that the airplane mobilized invention, intelligence, and daring: *imagination* and *cold reason*. It is the same spirit that built the Parthenon."[1] So, faced then with the elegance of a Concorde (irrespective of the Concorde's operating economics) or the purposeful look at an F-4 Phantom II, one might say, "pretty is as pretty does," or "beauty is in the eye of the mission."

Finally, I think design *is* inherently romantic, and it is certainly seen so by the people who engage in it. I have found no other form of technology that so dominates the lives of its participants. If you talk to the technologists involved in aviation, or to pilots, you find that it permeates their entire existence. Their after-hours activities, their circle of friends, their casual bar conversations, all tend to be very closely related to aviation. I believe trying to demystify aviation is somewhat like sex education without romance. Take the romance and the mystery away, and we're left with basic physics and plumbing and a nagging question whether it was all worth it.

Like Dr. Hansen, I'm fascinated by the question of requirements and requirements-framing. I would argue, wearing my Air Force hat for a bit, on the judgment passed upon Lockheed's C-5 Galaxy transport. My argument there would be that Lockheed basically built an overly compromised airplane and that questionable requirements for the C-5 invariably led to some of the difficulties experienced in placing this transport in service. But, despite all of this, we must not lose sight of the fact that the C-5's problems *were* eventually made right and that it has served with distinction. The state of Israel, in large measure, owes its continued existence to the C-5 airlift during the Yom Kippur War. Had it not been for C-5s resupplying Israeli forces with critically needed items, I think we would have a very different picture in the Middle East today. A better example of policy failure, and one that is certainly more intriguing to me, is the story of Robert McNamara's F-111, because the story of the F-111 (the so-called TFX—Tactical Fighter Experimental—of the early 1960s) is a classic case of what happens when the design process is constrained, where external forces operate to limit the freedom designers have to pursue their fulfillment of requirements, and where other requirements themselves are badly drawn.

Interestingly, if we look at the difficulties that this program experienced, we find that these difficulties did not stem from the *uniformed* service community, but instead they stemmed from the activities of the *civilian* community operating with the Department of Defense. These were highly placed individuals obsessed with cost. In the interests of commonality and cost reduction, they combined two widely differing performance requirements—one for a Navy fighter emphasizing high altitude, long endurance, and agility, and another for an Air Force strike aircraft emphasizing low altitude and long-range supersonic penetration. Without recognizing the historical evidence that one should not proceed in such fashion, they brutally merged these two together and tried to force the military services to live with the result. Consequently, the F-111 program cost the Navy ten years of fighter development time, and the Air Force aircraft ultimately produced was so compromised that it required a very long time to be made into a worthwhile machine.

There are some interesting ways in which to regard how the research, development, and acquisition process takes place in the light of the F-111 story. There have been two F-111 studies: one of these, Robert Art's, *The TFX Decision,* came out just after the airplane had flown, and simplistically concluded that the controversy revolved around the traditional issue of civilian-military relations.[2] Art concluded the reason the military opposed merging the two requirements was because they were uncomfortable with the notion of civilians running the Department of Defense, proving that Art had fallen victim to the very same mind-set that afflicted the Kennedy Administration, particularly when McNamara and his staff were confronted with opposition to their plans. A subsequent history of the F-111 program by Robert F. Coulam entitled *Illusions of Choice* is a much more thoughtful work.[3]

At the risk of stirring even greater controversy, I'll offer a modest thought on the relationship between the science community and the engineering community within the aircraft design process. I was compelled to do this on reading a quote from Lord Kelvin in the contributions. When scientists have assessed the state of aeronautical development or attempted aeronautical development themselves, their efforts have almost always been marked by failure or disappointment. For example, Kelvin in 1896 wrote that he had "not the smallest molecule of faith in aerial navigation other than ballooning . . ."[4] This was, of course, within a decade of the first successful flight at Kitty Hawk. And he is not a singular case. There is the astronomer Simon Newcomb and Samuel Langley (who tried to develop a flying machine and met with total failure). There is Lord Cherwell (Churchill's scientific advisor, who totally missed the nature and significance of Nazi weapons development), and, lastly, there is Vannevar Bush, Cherwell's American equivalent with regard to the Soviet Union in the postwar years. I would like to suggest that this is because when scientists and engineers confront technical challenges—we can think of many of them, two of the current ones, for example, are SDI and the National Aerospace Plane—the scientists are conditioned by their training to see *complexity* and *problems,* whereas the engineers are conditioned to see *potentialities* and *capabilities.* In closing, I would like to echo Dr. Hansen's call for more biographies of key figures, for it is by studying these people that I believe we will learn more about the nature of engineering and the engineering process.

## NOTES

1. Le Corbusier, *Towards a New Architecture* (New York: Praeger Publishers, 1970), 102.

2. Robert Art, *The TFX Decision: McNamara and the Military* (Boston: Little Brown, 1968).

3. Robert F. Coulam, *Illusions of Choice: The F-111 and the Problem of Weapons Acquisition* (Princeton, New Jersey: Princeton University Press, 1977).

4. C. H. Gibbs-Smith, *The Aeroplane: An Historical Survey of Its Origins and Development* (London: HMSO, 1960), 35.

# Part 4. Civilian and Military Remote Sensing and Reconnaissance

**Sylvia D. Fries**

# Introduction

A constant of the American approach to technological development has been a philosophical and policy distinction between the appropriate roles of the public and the private sectors in stimulating innovation and the actual manufacture and marketing (or distribution) of technological goods and services. For example, with the exception of the "armory system" through which the U.S. Army manufactured its own weapons, even in the national emergencies of wartime the U.S. government has turned to the private sector for the materials, hardware, and finished goods it required. The experience of World War II, when the command of advanced technologies appeared critical to the war's outcome, left as one of its legacies the assumption that social progress and national security required the promotion of scientific research and technological innovation, which were thus too important to be left to the uncertainties of the marketplace.

A related assumption — that scientific research would perforce lead to technological progress — obscured the fact that the relationship of research to technological innovation, and of innovation to the dissemination of new technologies ("technology transfer") was perhaps less well understood than the workings of the marketplace. The U.S. government ventured into uncharted territory as it attempted in the postwar era to command new space technologies (along with nuclear energy) for peaceful as well as national security purposes. Both the civilian and military space programs offer exemplary opportunities to explore the larger issues not only of national technology policy, but of the extent to which, and how, governments can actually "command" technological innovation *and* the most effective use of advancing technologies.

The two papers that follow reflect the complexity of this problem, one where public policy interests converge with those of the historian of technology. Once the processes described by Robert W. Smith and Howard E. McCurdy (see Part 1) have produced the political and budgetary commitments for an agency like NASA to go forward with a program, what becomes of the technologies developed by the program? In her essay, Pamela Mack describes how the conflicting missions and roles of federal bureaucracies complicated and prolonged the use of satellite technology for the improved knowledge of changing global climatic and geophysical conditions. The bureaucratic players were many: NASA, an agency authorized by statute and organizationally committed to innovation and the protracted process of research and development, was reluctant to accede to pressures to develop a simple, operational satellite that would then necessarily become the "property" of another agency. Surrounding NASA were other agencies like the Department of the Weather Bureau, the U.S. Geological Survey, the Navy Oceanographic Office, and the Agency for International Development. Had the "unavoidable tensions between the developers and users" of satellite technology for earth observations been more creatively managed, Mack argues, that new technology may have received earlier and more effective use by the public that might benefit from it.

Toward the end of her paper, Dr. Mack alludes to the Department of Defense's interest in the outcome of the Earth Resources Observation Satellite, or EROS, proposal. (EROS was the Department of the Interior's name for the satellite that finally evolved into Landsat, the first of which was launched in 1972.) But historians wishing to ask the same kinds of questions that Dr. Mack has asked of the military "users" and developers of space technologies, soon encounter the secrecy that surrounds military space programs. Until 1982 the NASA portion of the United States' space budget was larger than the defense department's budget. Beginning in 1982, the Department of Defense's share of the country's space budget surpassed NASA's until, after 1985, it was between 60 percent and 65 percent of the U.S. space budget. Some of the Department of Defense's share went to reconnaissance satellites, which also came under the purview of the Central Intelligence Agency.

The growth of the military space program has posed a serious problem for historians, for there is little unclassified information about military space activities and, about military reconnaissance satellites, there is virtually no unclassified information. The information that is available is largely conjectural, pieced together by journalists often relying on "unnamed" sources and unlikely to be confirmed by anyone in a position to know whether or not the journalist's account is accurate. But the professional historian shares with scientists and jurists a canon that includes the notion of verifiability of evidence as the basis for "valid" conclusions. It can be argued that classified military programs can have no true history precisely because it is impossible to develop a literature about them that can be subjected to the same critical scrutiny that other forms of historical research and writing are normally exposed.

This dilemma is interwoven in the second of these two papers, an account by journalist William E. Burrows of the methods he used to gather information for his 1986 book *Deep Black: Space Espionage and National Security*. Burrows's paper illustrates the difficulty of gathering reliable information about this country's "black" programs (an unofficial term for highly classified military activities) when those programs are shrouded in secrecy and making public any of their details can be seen as compromising national security.[1] Jeffrey T. Richelson's commentary that follows reveals the deep divisions possible over the extent of classification and the true purposes it serves.[2]

Those divisions are not readily overcome by academic debate, for they are part of a larger public issue in an ostensibly open and democratic society, namely, how much secrecy can a free society tolerate and remain free? On this issue the historian's interest coincides with the ordinary citizen's. But the historian's interest goes further, for until historians can not only gather, but confirm and verify, information about military space programs, we are unlikely to acquire the same level of understanding of those programs that we are beginning to acquire about civilian space programs.

## NOTES

1. The general outlines of U.S. reconnaissance satellite programs have been detailed in the *Congressional Record* and such open sources as *Aviation Week and Technology Review* and *The New York Times,* causing a reviewer of *Deep Black*

in the *Friday Review of Defense Literature* to write, "one wonders what the fuss is all about." See "National Technical Means—Imaging Reconnaissance Satellites," *Congressional Record—Senate* (April 14, 1983) S 4617; "International Cooperation in Space: Enhancing the World's Common Security," *Congressional Record* (March 31, 1987) H 1706; James Bamford, "America's Supersecret Eyes in Space," *The New York Times Magazine,* January 13, 1985; and Herb Coleman, review of *Deep Black: Space Espionage and National Security* (New York, 1986) in *The Friday Review of Defense Literature* (April 24, 1987), a publication "prepared by the Air Force as executive agent for the Department of Defense to bring to the attention of key DoD personnel current literature of interest to them in their official capacities. Opinions expressed in this publication do not reflect official views."

2. Publication of William Burrows's paper and Jeffrey Richelson's commentary in no way represents official government views on the information contained therein.

*Pamela Mack*

# Research and Development for Whose Benefit?
## The Relationship Between NASA and the Users of Earth Resources Data

Landsat satellites provide new information about our world by collecting data in the form of sophisticated images of the surface of Earth. These can be utilized for geology, agriculture, land-use mapping, and other resources management fields. Yet the U.S. Earth Resources Satellite Program has developed slowly, with much opposition. Five Landsat satellites have been launched since 1972, and the project has been officially declared operational and turned over to private industry. Yet today, more than twenty years after the origins of the program, its future is still uncertain. Many of the key difficulties for Landsat have arisen in the relationship between research and development and the practical use of the satellite data.

## THEMES

The central question for the study of government development of technology should be: what determines whether new technology will be effectively used? Effective or ineffective use of a technology has often been explained simply by technical faults or organizational problems. Rather than using just one of these factors to explain effectiveness, this study will seek to explain it on the basis of the interaction of the process of technological change with the needs and organizations that form a context for that change. The central focus is thus on how the government context affects the relationship between research and development and the use of technology.

Landsat is a particularly interesting case for such an examina-

tion of the transition from research and development to application
and diffusion because the development and the use of Earth resources
satellites were divided among NASA and a variety of different government agencies and other institutions. Research and development
were assigned to NASA, while other agencies and organizations were
the ultimate users of the technology. Landsat, like weather and communications satellites, but unlike most other space projects, required
NASA to deal with users outside the agency who would put the
space technology to practical use. NASA had the responsibility for
research and development of space applications, but it was generally
assumed that the space agency would turn over operational programs
(those ready for routine use) to the agency concerned with the related application (for example, the weather bureau would take over
weather satellites). Many of the controversies of the Landsat project
grew out of disagreements over what voice the users should have in
the development of the project and at what point it should be turned
over to the users.

This division between research and development and use raised
a variety of challenges. It meant that the transition from development
to use could not be handled as informally as in a single institution,
making it easier for the historian to examine. It also made interagency politics the major tool for mediating between the interests of
the research and development team and the interests of the users.
Such interagency politics can be either creative or destructive; in the
case of Landsat it became destructive with the addition of pressures
resulting from general political opposition to the space program in
the late 1960s and 1970s. The government context thus at times
meshed with the process of technological change in ways that increased
the difficulty of technological innovation. Yet it is by no means clear
that Landsat could have been better handled by private industry;
NASA had the opportunity to develop the Landsat program to bring
the most benefits rather than the most profit.

How can the interaction between technological change and the
government context be broken down into more manageable pieces
for analysis? Let us first look at these two elements in isolation, and
then try to put the matrix together to see the interaction. For the
Landsat case, technological change can be divided roughly into four
stages: research and development of the satellite and of equipment on
the ground to process the data coming from the satellite, testing the

resulting system and developing ways of applying the new data, persuading people to use the applications, and creating a truly operational permanent system. My larger study of Landsat is concerned only with the first three stages; this paper examines in detail part of the first stage, analyzing cooperation between developers and users during the development process.[1]

The strength and weakness of a research and development agency like NASA lies in its freedom to innovate boldly. As a government agency, NASA could seek to develop a satellite system that would bring broad benefits from improved resource management, even though it was clearly not going to be quickly profitable. More specifically, because NASA was an independent research and development agency, NASA engineers had the freedom to investigate the potential of various technologies before worrying about the requirements of the users. The space agency had an interest in developing the best possible system, rather than throwing something together to meet user demands that might reflect only current expectations rather than the true potential of the technology. At its best, this approach can bring unexpected benefits from technological breakthroughs. At its worst, an independent research and development organization can end up pursuing technological sophistication for its own sake when a simpler, less expensive, system would better meet the needs of the users.

The process of bringing the technology into use can be divided into two tasks: developing applications and cultivating users. NASA had to help develop methods of applying Landsat data, in cooperation with the research and development branches of the agencies that would ultimately use the operational satellite. Some of these agencies wanted a larger role in Landsat, but NASA tended to want to keep control of the project and the design, and limit the users to the development of applications. Later on, in seeking to encourage use of the data, NASA managers learned the hard way that publicizing a new technology and funding scientific research to show its potential were not sufficient to convince organizations to adopt it for everyday use. NASA had little experience with selling new technology, and it showed. It is often assumed that this is an area where private industry would have an advantage. However, some government agencies have developed impressive skill in encouraging innovation, most notably the extension program of the Department of Agriculture. Therefore, the problem lay not in government agencies per se, but in NASA's role as a research and development agency without a clearly developed relationship with a constituency.

To look at the same story from a different perspective, it is crucial to recognize that the government context is far from monolithic; it can be viewed on a variety of levels, from philosophies of government to management policies within an agency. The word "politics" often includes not only electoral politics but also the relationships between branches and agencies of the government. Using that broad definition, there are many types of politics that affect government projects. None of these can be examined in isolation, but the emphasis of my work is on the relationships between agencies. Other studies have concentrated on other levels: a deeper treatment of the Presidential politics of the space program can be found in John M. Logsdon's *The Decision to Go to the Moon* and W. Henry Lambright's *Presidential Management of Science and Technology: The Johnson Presidency.*[2]

The broadest level of analysis shows competing philosophies of government. One nagging controversy in the Landsat project was whether the whole thing was properly a government enterprise or whether it should be left to private industry. Ideally, the government sponsored technological development for the public good when the benefits were too diffuse or too far in the future for private industry to be willing to sponsor the new technology.[3] Opinions about what fell within this definition depended on attitudes toward the relative roles of government and private industry.

The highest stage of the government hierarchy played a much smaller role in Landsat than in more expensive and popular space projects. Landsat cost only about $32 million through the launch of the first satellite, so it was too small to get much attention from the highest levels of government. What little authority was exerted over Landsat from above NASA came mostly from the President through the Office of Management and Budget, which negotiates with federal agencies their share of the budget the President proposes to Congress. The Office of Management and Budget opposed Landsat both because of a presidential policy of seeking to cut government spending and because of specific opposition at the budget bureau to Earth resources satellites. Landsat received occasional support from the presidential level when NASA appealed to Presidents Nixon and Carter to prevent devastating budget cuts. But each President who gave the project support also expected it to serve his own policy interests, whether they were improving international cooperation or diminishing the size of big government. Congress, particularly the House Subcommittee on Space Science and Applications under the leadership of Congressman Karth, gave the project more consistent support. However, Congress could not oversee the project in as much detail as could the Office of Management and Budget. Congress occasionally reversed a damaging budget cut, but NASA's top policymakers could not appeal directly for such a change because they had to be loyal to the administration that had appointed them.

Because Landsat received little attention from political decisionmakers, decisions had to be thrashed out between the interested agencies, with NASA taking a dominant role as lead agency for the project. Landsat was shaped by two kinds of interagency politics. One of the functions of government bureaucracy is to make decisions on grounds of the good of the nation, rather than just profit or technological feasibility. The process of interagency politics at its best is a process for negotiating decisions among competing priorities that use scarce resources. Because of the many interests involved, the Landsat project required a large amount of this kind of decisionmaking.

But Landsat was also influenced by another kind of interagency politics. Government agencies seek to increase their own importance by increasing their budgets and the number of projects they control (they may have to do this simply to obtain the influence necessary to achieve their broader missions), and a project can be hurt or helped by this competition for power for reasons independent of the merit of the project.[4] In an interagency project, each agency is monitored by its branch of the Office of Management and Budget and its congressional committee to determine how well that agency uses its funds to meet its own objectives. Few mechanisms exist for rewarding agencies that work together effectively toward larger goals. In the Landsat case, NASA had to deal with the different interests of the Departments of Defense, the Interior, and Agriculture, and the Office of Management and Budget. Agencies had interests both in whether stress was put on the experimental or operational nature of the project and in specific technologies. For example, the Department of Defense did not want reconnaissance satellite technology revealed by civilian use; the Department of Agriculture wanted the satellite to carry the sensor most useful for agricultural research and survey. Interagency politics caused special problems for Landsat because NASA managers had little experience in working cooperatively with other agencies on practical projects.

In the Landsat project, NASA had to deal not only with other government agencies but also with a variety of organizations that the space agency hoped would eventually make practical use of Landsat data. NASA had little experience in dealing with constituencies and clients other than politicians, scientists, and the aerospace industry. NASA sponsored a variety of programs to encourage the use of Landsat data, but the agency was disappointed by the results. The interactions of technology and context are particularly clear in the case of NASA's attempt to encourage the use of Landsat data by state and local governments. Such users could give NASA valuable political support, but they were hard to convince to use Landsat data because they were particularly inexperienced with and suspicious of advanced technology. The importance of skillful technology transfer and early involvement of the users is one of the most important lessons to be learned from Landsat.

The interaction of technological change and the government context depends on historical circumstances, so the Landsat case study can only raise questions, not prove a model. It does raise two issues in particular that provide good examples of the interaction of the various stages and levels discussed above. As seen above, one central theme of the Landsat case was what influence the needs of the users had on the design of the technology. NASA was not strongly bound to user requirements by either its institutional framework or its prior experience. The interaction between the government context and technological change can be examined by asking how effectively NASA's relationship with the users provided the coordination needed for beneficial technological change.

The second issue is a related question that came up repeatedly during the Landsat project: the timing of the transition from experimental to operational Earth resources satellite programs. Research groups and users not only had different priorities but also had different concepts of the process of technological change. Because NASA had responsibility for research and development but turned operational programs over to the appropriate user, the space agency had an interest in prolonging the experimental phase of a project as long as possible while the agencies that would take a project over had an interest in defining the project as operational as soon as possible. But this was not the only use to which definitions of experimental and operational phases were put. The Bureau of the Budget used a narrow definition of an experimental project to constrain Landsat by requiring that the system built be adequate only to test the concept, not for routine use. In addition, the definition of the project as experimental for more than ten years scared away potential operational users and reduced the pressure to bring it into effective use. The definition of the phases of technological change thus became a tool of the conflicting interests of the organizations involved.

These issues suggest that one of the most important factors in determining the effectiveness of a new technology is how closely the goals of the developers and the definition of the stages of technological change are integrated with the needs of the users. To prove this whole proposition requires a much broader examination of the history of Landsat than is possible here. This paper will examine only one facet of the story: the relationship between the user agencies and NASA in the definition of Landsat.

## USER AGENCIES AND THE ORIGINS OF LANDSAT

Although NASA involved potential users of Earth resources satellites in the Landsat program only to the extent of supporting research at a few federal agencies, those agencies attempted, with limited success, to play a major role in the program. While the space agency depended on the user agencies for some scientific research, it did not always agree with them about what their role in the overall program should be. NASA-funded experiments generated so much enthusiasm among groups of scientists at the Department of Agriculture and the Department of the Interior about the potential of satellite data for agricultural and geological studies that the user agencies became strong lobbyists for an accelerated satellite program. The Department of the Interior took the lead in an attempt to pressure NASA to speed up the program that reflected interagency power-playing, different ideas than those held by NASA and the Department of Defense about what an Earth resources satellite should do and what technology it should use, and a sensitivity to the needs of at least a small part of the potential user community for Landsat data. Not surprisingly, NASA managers wanted to design the program with as little interference from outside as possible, but the process of interagency politics enabled some compromises to be made among conflicting interests. The question addressed here is not whether interagency politics reflected or subverted national policy, but how interagency negotiations shaped the developing Landsat project and the technology used for Landsat.

In 1963, a NASA geologist working on background work for Apollo, Peter Badgley, received authorization to investigate the use of space for Earth resources research. One of his first steps was to fund research at the agencies that could potentially use Landsat data to help fulfill their assigned missions. He transferred NASA research funds to the Departments of Agriculture and the Interior for agricultural and geological research and provided funds to the Naval Oceanographic Office to investigate using a satellite for oceanography. This last area of research was transferred from the Naval Oceanographic Office to the National Oceanic and Atmospheric Administration when that agency was created in 1970. It led eventually to Seasat, a satellite designed for oceanographic research, launched in 1978.

Contracting with other agencies for research was standard NASA procedure. The Army Corps of Engineers and the U.S. Geological Survey had already contributed special skills to the Apollo program and had been reimbursed by NASA, so it seemed logical to call on the Departments of Agriculture and the Interior for scientific expertise in the field of Earth resources.[5] That NASA paid the departments for their services rather than bringing them in as partners in the enterprise shows that NASA considered itself solely responsible for space research and development. The departments found this arrangement useful because as operating agencies, they had difficulty funding their own advanced research. NASA's other goal was to enlist the political support of these potential beneficiaries for NASA's new applications program to help persuade the Bureau of the Budget and Congress of the value of the program.

Most of the funding provided by NASA to the Department of the Interior for Earth resources research went to one of its branches, the U.S. Geological Survey. The U.S. Geological Survey used this funding to assign a group of scientists to investigate potential applications of remote sensing from space and to determine specifications for an Earth resources satellite and additional experiments on Apollo Applications missions. In 1966 Badgley asked the Geological Survey to prepare a summary evaluation of the potential value of an Earth resources satellite for geology, cartography, and hydrology. The Geological Survey scientists reported that remote sensing from space would be very valuable in these fields and should be developed quickly.[6]

By mid-1966 the group at the Department of the Interior became impatient with NASA's lack of progress toward defining a satellite system. The leaders of this discontent were a geologist in the Geologic Division of the Geological Survey, William Fischer, and hydrologist Charles J. Robinove. NASA had been discussing Earth resources experiments for the human spaceflight program and small, medium, and large orbiting Earth resources observatories for at least a year without actually approving any project. The scientists at the Geological Survey believed that the experiments under consideration at NASA were too diverse and sophisticated; the Geological Survey group wanted a simple, useful satellite as soon as possible.

NASA managers, in the meantime, had many reasons to proceed slowly with an Earth resources satellite. Earth resources experiments for the Apollo Applications program also had to be developed, taking time and energy away from work toward an automated satellite. More importantly, NASA may have had a secret agreement with the Department of Defense or the National Security Council to go slowly on Earth resources satellites.[7] The details of this policy, if it existed, will not be available until information on reconnaissance satellites is declassified. There is, however, evidence of much discussion in late 1965 and early 1966 of what resolution could be used without classification problems.[8] This suggests that the relationship between reconnaissance satellites and Earth resources satellites was an issue at that time.

Despite this policy problem, Badgley and Leonard Jaffe, head of NASA's applications programs, were sensitive to the demand for the speedy development of an Earth resources satellite. They continued the Earth resources research program and tried to speed things up by arguing to their superiors that NASA needed to reorient itself toward practical missions.[9] By 1966 the program had a good foothold in NASA, although not a great deal of support from the agency's policy makers, and NASA scientists were aware of growing interest outside the agency. In an August 1966 memo pushing for authorization to develop a small orbiting Earth resources observatory, Badgley pointed out that the user agencies wanted an operational satellite in 1970 instead of in 1974–1975 as NASA officials intended. Badgley stressed that NASA should take a leading role in the program, including providing research funds to other agencies, because strong

leadership was particularly important for a satellite that would collect data for many agencies. He pointed out that the benefits of
studying Earth resources from space could help justify the space program if Earth resources experiments lived up to their promise, and
that application "is an area which NASA is holding up to Congress
as very promising, and one which needs strong support."[10] The same
memo mentioned a fact that was to come as a shock a month later:
the Geological Survey was considering asking Congress for money in
fiscal year 1968 for construction of a small satellite, for a launch
possibly as early as 1969. The Survey, according to Badgley, considered photographic and television sensors and the necessary communications system "to be already operational for space use" for needs
in the fields of geology, hydrology, cartography, and geography.[11] Officials in the higher levels of NASA did not absorb Badgley's warning.

An August 1966 meeting of representatives from NASA (including Jaffe), the Geological Survey (including Fischer and Robinove),
the Agency for International Development, the Department of Agriculture, and the Naval Oceanographic Office clearly brought out the
Survey's concerns. The Geological Survey and the Agency for International Development expressed enthusiasm about using data collected from space for resources studies in Latin America. This discussion had been partially motivated by a State Department paper that
suggested studying the feasibility of using a spacecraft to collect
Earth resources data over South America.[12] Jaffe, with caution typical
both of NASA's position and his own personality, warned "about
overenthusiasm on [the] part of underdeveloped nations for new and
exotic techniques, with concomitant exclusion of proven methods."[13]
Fischer discussed the idea of a Department of the Interior Earth Resources Observation Satellite, based on an RCA proposal using a
newly developed very-fine resolution television camera. In a memo on
the meeting, Jaffe concluded that "USGS would like to budget for an
'operational' satellite as soon as possible to establish jurisdiction."[14]
In other words, he suspected that the Geological Survey was making
a move to insure that it would control the eventual operational satellite system. In the meeting, Jaffe suggested that the user agencies
should develop data requirements; NASA would consider what sort
of satellite would meet those requirements after "certain decisions"
were made. Those decisions, presumably classified, were expected in
September.[15] Jaffe's remarks implied a lengthy experimental phase

under NASA's control, very different from the quick development of an operational satellite that the Department of the Interior wanted.

The Department of the Interior wanted to control an Earth resources satellite program both because it believed that data from such a satellite would help the agency fulfill its mission and because, like most agencies, it sought to increase its own areas of responsibility, and thus its size and power. By mid-1966 Fischer and Robinove at the Geological Survey had a good idea of what an Earth resources satellite could do and who could use it. They were frustrated by NASA's rapidly changing ideas for a variety of Earth resources satellites, without any approved project in progress. Fischer and Robinove wanted to force NASA to commit itself to building the small satellite they believed would be most useful.[16] Their first step was to go to William D. Pecora, director of the Geological Survey, with the idea that the Department of the Interior might develop its own operational Earth resources satellite. In an interview, Robinove described why Pecora liked this idea:

> Now Bill Pecora . . . recognized that this concept technically was one that, if it worked, there would be a very, very large payoff. It would be very worthwhile doing and something that would be good for the country to have this information. . . . And also being a very astute politician he recognized that if we took the leadership, the Geological Survey and the Department of the Interior stood to gain simply by being a good forward-looking agency.[17]

Fischer, Robinove, and Pecora presented the idea to the Secretary of the Interior, Stewart L. Udall, arguing that the satellite would be useful to other branches of the Department of the Interior in addition to the Geological Survey. They quickly convinced Udall of the merits of an Interior satellite program. According to Fischer, Udall may have liked the idea in part because he resented the amount of government money going to military and space programs rather than to the preservation of natural resources and undeveloped areas that he valued so highly.[18]

The enthusiasts at the Department of the Interior prepared a plan in secret, and most observers were shocked when Udall unilaterally announced on September 21, 1966, that the Department of the Interior planned a program of Earth Resources Observation Satellites (EROS). At a news conference, Pecora described EROS as a evolutionary program beginning in 1969 "with television cameras flown in an orbit that will cover the entire surface of the earth repeatedly."[19] While the proposed satellite had many of the features eventually incorporated in Landsat, the announcement appears to have been largely a political move designed to accelerate NASA's program. In fact, as William Fischer remembered one reaction to the announcement: "Pecora had no more resources than the Prince of Liechtenstein with which to launch that satellite."[20]

NASA leaders were upset over Udall's announcement, nonetheless.[21] The threat they saw was typical of interagency conflict; the Department of the Interior appeared to be attempting to take over a function that clearly belonged to NASA, the development of a new satellite system. NASA's only mission was research and development; if other agencies developed their own space systems they would take away NASA's reason for being. Fischer remembered one NASA official telling an Interior official: "If you so much as used a nickel of NASA's money to write that press release I'll see you in jail."[22] The negative reaction was not limited to NASA. Willis H. Shapley, who had moved from the Bureau of the Budget to NASA in September 1965, reported that Udall was nearly fired because the Department of the Interior announcement was in conflict with national policy so secret that Udall had not been informed of it.[23] Pecora said a few years later that he, too, had feared he would lose his job.[24] At least in retrospect, however, the reaction was not entirely hostile. Many people at NASA remembered the EROS announcement as a "good friendly bureaucratic maneuver to get the guys moving and doing something instead of just talking."[25]

NASA responded through official channels. Peter Badgley's office received the Department of the Interior announcement a few days before its release, and immediately sent it up the hierarchy to NASA Administrator James E. Webb, who discussed it with President Lyndon B. Johnson on September 20.[26] An announcement by the Secretary of the Interior required a response from a high level in NASA. Deputy Administrator Robert C. Seamans Jr. wrote to Udall on September 22, presenting what appears to be a decision from above about which agency would control the program:

> At this time, I believe that all affected agencies are fully aware of the potential value of such a program as EROS and of the enthusiasm with which the Department of the Interior has approached the applications

of space technology to the hard problems of natural resources measurement. NASA is anxious to work closely and effectively with your Department in developing and testing this exciting application of technology prior to the decision to establish an operational system. Since many agencies are interested in pursuing similar efforts, and since there are a number of critical considerations involved (especially in the area of international relations), NASA is being assigned "lead agency" responsibility in *experimental* space applications for civil functions.[27]

NASA was allowed to define Earth resource satellites as experimental, even though the Department of the Interior claimed that some sensors were ready for operational use. Seamans's letter stressed the experimental nature of the project, cautioning that a "careful research and development effort must precede operational systems decisions if we are to assure that performance lives up to promise."[28] Thus NASA kept control of Earth resources satellites for an experimental phase of unspecified length.

The Department of the Interior continued to press NASA for a commitment to an operational satellite as soon as possible. After a meeting with Webb, Seamans, and Jaffe, Under Secretary of the Interior Charles F. Luce wrote to Seamans:

> Our staff people are quite optimistic that the state of the art has advanced to the point that we are ready for an operational system which we have called the EROS program. In staff discussions with Mr. Jaffe and his people we should be able to established whether our optimism is justified.[29]

On October 21, 1966, Luce transmitted to Seamans performance specifications titled "Operational Requirements for Global Resource Surveys by Earth Orbital Satellites," calling for an operational system by the end of 1969.[30] These specifications were reasonable; in fact, they closely resemble those for the experimental satellite that was eventually developed. When NASA provided no immediate reply, Pecora and Fischer continued to discuss an operational satellite to be launched in 1969. When Pecora led a discussion of Earth resources satellites at a November 1966 meeting with officials from the Organization of American States, Jaffe (the NASA representative at the meeting) worried that Pecora was promising too much. Jaffe's memo on the meeting states:

> We agree on all points except whether anyone had the authority to hold

out promise of an operational earth resources survey satellite as early as
1968 or 1969. Pecora took the position that since after the EROS public announcement no one specifically told them to stop, that they had
every right to pursue and talk about EROS. We agreed that a policy
clarification is required.[31]

The operational satellite that Pecora hoped to have in 1969 indeed
turned out to be an elusive goal that has still not fully been realized
today.

NASA's response to the Department of the Interior's October
data specifications was written in January and officially transmitted
to the department in April in the form of a letter from Seamans to
Luce. It stressed the need for an experimental program, stating that:
"orderly development and flight qualification and testing of subsystems and sensors in an experimental development program permit as-
surances that the technology base exists on which to build the operational systems."[32] The comments attached to the letter described a
system that could meet the requirements, but saw the need for significant development of sensor, data storage, and data transmission
technologies before they would be ready for a satellite.[33] Thus NASA
defined a long research and development program.

The announcement of the EROS program caused NASA to accelerate its Earth resources research and development program. Although NASA officials were slow to respond to the requirements provided by the Department of the Interior in October, Interior's
announcement generated wide interest in the press, forcing the space
agency to show at least steady progress. For example, an article in
*Technology Week* in February 1967, headlined "Earth Resources Satellite Far From Reality," pointed out that since NASA had not yet
asked for any development funds, an experimental satellite could not
be launched until the early 1970s.[34] Negative articles continued to
appear for months. Jaffe explained to NASA Associate Administrator
Homer Newell that an October 1967 article in *Aerospace Technology* "is obviously based on partial information resulting from the aftermath of the Department of Interior's EROS press release" and
stated that relations with the Department of the Interior "are extremely good at the moment."[35] A draft memo from Pecora to Luce
in June also stressed good relations, but explained:

The ungracious reception by Administrator Webb of the Secretary's announcement hindered full cooperative efforts for several months. The

visit to Houston by the Secretary has helped measurably to alter Mr. Webb's views. Until some helpful statement by NASA appears, the technical press will continue to refer to NASA's earlier unfavorable position.[36]

By mid-1967, the Department of the Interior and NASA had officially agreed on policy, but not necessarily on how they construed it. An Interior offer to participate in funding was met with the response that it would be discussed further "if it proves desirable to proceed with an experimental satellite system."[37] In June, Pecora wrote, "We continue to speak in terms of 'experimental system,' leaving the concept of 'operational system' for some distant time schedule."[38] The Department of the Interior described the project as a joint research and development effort. NASA simply assumed lead agency status and went ahead with the development of a satellite proposal.[39]

The group of enthusiasts at the Geological Survey felt that they had lost the battle but won the war. That is, their announcement had resulted in the acceleration of activities at NASA. They had also established the EROS program, which continued to serve as an institutional base for satellite studies at the Department of the Interior even when NASA was given responsibility for all satellite projects. However, they had also crystallized the opposing interests of some of the other agencies potentially involved by pushing for control of an operational Earth resources satellite. The Department of Agriculture had an equally valid interest in the program. This point became significant quickly, particularly when the time came to choose the sensors for the satellite.

## CONCLUSIONS

The conflicting interests of the participating agencies were a fundamental problem visible from the beginning of the Landsat project. NASA defined its interest as control of the experimental phase of the project and tended to see this phase as a long, incremental process of development. The user agencies wanted an operational satellite as soon as possible, so that they could justify their interest by using the data in the routine execution of the missions they had been given by Congress. Even the Department of Defense was apparently involved, struggling behind the scenes to protect its interests by keeping the reconnaissance satellite program free from controversy. Obviously, an understanding of the relationship between NASA and the user agencies requires a broader examination of the Landsat project than space has allowed here. But this portion of the story can suggest that the Landsat project suffered from lack of creative management of the unavoidable tensions between developers and users of technology.[40] In various forms those tensions have caused many of the problems that have reduced the effective use of Earth resources satellite technology in the United States.

## NOTES

1. This paper is based on my larger study, *Viewing the Earth: The Social Construction of the Landsat Satellite System* (Cambridge: MIT Press, 1990).

2. John M. Logsdon, *The Decision to Go to the Moon: Project Apollo and the National Interest* (Cambridge: MIT Press, 1970); W. Henry Lambright, *Presidential Management of Science and Technology: The Johnson Presidency* (Austin: University of Texas Press, 1985). For more general information on NASA management, not focused on the highest political level, see Arnold S. Levine, *Managing NASA in the Apollo Era* (Washington, D.C.: NASA SP-4102, 1982).

3. The classic example is weather forecasts, which are subsidized by the government because they provide widespread benefits. Those benefits are diffuse in the sense that they are difficult to measure and it would be impossible to fund the weather bureau by charging fees to the individuals who benefit from better forecasts. More formally, the concept of public good has many different definitions, as illustrated in Glendon Schubert, *The Public Interest: A Critique of the Theory of a Political Concept* (Glencoe: The Free Press, 1960). My working definition, which I think follows the most common usage at NASA, is that the public good is the long-range benefit of the society, balancing the interests of organized and unorganized interest groups, as opposed to the short-range benefit of industry or other individual interest groups. (Professor Schubert would probably characterize this definition as somewhere between social engineering and psychological realism.)

4. A strongly stated and useful discussion of the effect of agency self-interest on Landsat can be found in W. Henry Lambright, "ERTS: Notes on a 'Leisurely' Technology," *Public Science* (August/September 1973): 1–8.

5. Homer E. Newell to Dr. Thomas B. Nolan, Jan. 19, 1975; "SM Reading file" folder, box 52, accession 74-663, record group 255, Washington National Records Center.

6. Interview with Charles J. Robinove, EROS Program Office, Reston, VA, July 31, 1978. "EROS Program—Issue Paper," attachment to David S. Black to James E. Webb, November 21, 1967; "Related Sciences 3, ERTS/EROS, NASA/ Interior Collaboration," 77-0677 (33), RG 255, WNRC.

7. Interview with Willis H. Shapley, American Association for the Advance-

ment of Science, Washington, D.C., August 13, 1979.

8. Edward Z. Gray to Director, Manned Space Science, "Pete Badgley's White Paper on Remote Sensing," October 18, 1965; Peter C. Badgley to Deputy Director, Space Applications Programs and Director of Meteorology, "Guidelines for Meeting with DOD Relative to Geography Program," March 30, 1966; "Response to Supplementary Questions Raised by Associate Deputy Administrator in Connection with Schultze (BoB) Letter to Webb Re FY '68 Budget Backup Materials," March 30, 1966; all in "Documentation—Earth Resources" folder, History Office, NASA Headquarters.

9. Leonard Jaffe to the record, "Commentary Delivered by Mr. Leonard Jaffe at the Airlie House Planning Seminar, June 1966," July 8, 1966; biography file on Leonard Jaffe, History Office, NASA Headquarters; Peter C. Badgley to the record, "Relative Funding Support by NASA and the Earth Resources User Agencies Over the Next Several Years," August 10, 1966; "Documentation—Earth Resources" folder, History Office, NASA Headquarters.

10. Badgley, "Relative Funding Support . . . " August 10, 1966.

11. Ibid.

12. "Space Applications Program, May 23, 1967," program review document; Donald P. Rogers's files, NASA Headquarters.

13. Robert G. Reeves to the Record, "Meeting at the U.S. Geological Survey (USGS), 10 am, August 25, 1966," August 31, 1966; "Documentation—Earth Resources" folder, History Office, NASA Headquarters.

14. Leonard Jaffe to the Deputy Administrator, "Meeting at the U.S. Geological Survey, August 25, 1966, Regarding Remote Sensing and South America," September 6, 1966; "Documentation—Earth Resources" folder, History Office, NASA Headquarters.

15. Reeves, "Meeting at the U.S. Geological Survey . . . " August 31, 1966.

16. Robinove interview. Interview with William Fischer, EROS Program Office, Reston, Virginia, August 8, 1978.

17. Robinove interview.

18. Fischer interview.

19. Office of the Secretary, U.S. Department of the Interior, News Release, "Earth's Resources to be Studied from Space," September 21, 1966; "EROS Program—Creation" folder, EROS Program Office files.

20. Fischer interview.

21. Ibid.

22. Ibid.

23. Shapley interview.

24. Charles P. Boyle to John F. Clark, "Highlights of NASA Hearing Before the House Subcommittee on Space Science and Applications, March 19, 1969," March 20, 1969; "ERS, ERTS" folder, Information Processing Division Files, Goddard Space Flight Center.

25. Interview with Marvin Holter, ERIM, Ann Arbor, Michigan, May 15, 1981.

26. Peter C. Badgley to the record, "Interior Department News Release on Earth Resources Observation Satellite (EROS)," September 29, 1966; "Documentation—Earth Resources" folder, History Office, NASA Headquarters.

27. Robert C. Seamans Jr. to Stewart L. Udall, September 22, 1966; "Related

Sciences 3, ERTS/EROS, NASA/Interior Collaboration" folder, History Office, NASA Headquarters.

28. Ibid.

29. Charles F. Luce to Robert C. Seamans Jr., October 7, 1966; "Related Sciences 3, ERTS/EROS, NASA/Interior Collaboration" folder, 77-0677 (33), RG 255, WNRC.

30. Charles F. Luce to Robert C. Seamans Jr., October 21, 1966, with attachment "Operational Requirements for Global Resource Surveys by Earth-Orbital Satellites: EROS Program," "Related Sciences 3, ERTS/EROS, NASA/Interior Collaboration" folder, 77-0677 (33), RG 255, WNRC.

31. Leonard Jaffe to the record, "Meeting at Organization of American States (OAS) on Applicability of Remote Sensor Satellite Programs for Latin America, November 3, 1966," November 15, 1966; "Landsat 1 Documentation" folder, History Office, NASA Headquarters.

32. Robert C. Seamans Jr., to Charles F. Luce, April 7, 1967; "Landsat 1 Documentation" folder, History Office, NASA Headquarters.

33. "Specific Comments on October 21 Letter From C. F. Luce to R. C. Seamans," January 14, 1967, attachment to Robert C. Seamans Jr. to Charles F. Luce, April 7, 1967; "Landsat 1 Documentation" folder, History Office, NASA Headquarters.

34. John Rhea, "Earth Resources Satellite Far From Reality," *Technology Week* 20 (February 13, 1967): 34–37.

35. L. Jaffe to Dr. Newell, "Article on the Earth Resources Satellite in *Aerospace Technology,* October 9 Issue," October 13, 1967; "Related Sciences 3, ERTS/EROS, NASA/Interior Collaboration" folder, 77-0677(33), RG 255, WNRC.

36. W. T. Pecora to the Under Secretary, "Status of EROS Program," June 15, 1967; William Fischer's Significant Documents file, EROS Program Office.

37. Charles F. Luce to Robert C. Seamans Jr., April 24, 1967; "Related Sciences 3, ERTS/EROS, NASA/Interior Collaboration" folder, 277-0677(33), RG 255, WNRC. Robert C. Seamans to Charles F. Luce, June 1, 1967; William Fischer's Significant Documents file, EROS Program Office.

38. Pecora, "Status of EROS Program," June 15, 1967.

39. Stewart L. Udall to James E. Webb, September 9, 1967; James E. Webb to Stewart L. Udall, December 1, 1967; both in "Landsat 1 Documentation" folder, History Office, NASA Headquarters.

40. For a comparison of Landsat with communications and weather satellites see Pamela E. Mack, "Satellites and Politics: Weather, Communications, and Earth Resources," in *A Spacefaring People: Perspectives on Early Space Flight,* ed. Alex Roland (Washington, D.C.: NASA SP-4405, 1985).

*William E. Burrows*

# A Study of Space Reconnaissance
## Methodology for Researching
## a Classified System

Two events occurred in August 1960 that both literally and figuratively added a new dimension to the way the United States collects strategic intelligence: a reconnaissance surveillance[1] satellite was successfully orbited and retrieved for the first time and an organization, the National Reconnaissance Office, was created to manage the development and operation of succeeding generations of such spacecraft. Although events observed by reconnaissance satellites have been publicized in varying degrees almost incessantly through the years since then (the Cuban missile crisis being an obvious example), details about the spacecraft themselves, their "product," and the governmental and industrial infrastructure that designs them, builds them, operates them, and exploits what they gather have remained among the nation's most stringently classified, or "blackest," systems. Indeed, the various technical collection systems are taken to be so secret that they have been placed on a classification strata above even top secret—that of Sensitive Compartmented Information, which theoretically allows those working within the vast and complex system to know only what they need to know in order to do their jobs and not a whit more. There are severe penalties for anyone inside this labyrinthine system who reveals its workings to outsiders. Mere mention of the National Reconnaissance Office, the Joint Reconnaissance Center, or any of the various satellites brings almost certain recrimination and censure. It should also be noted that in my

The study referred to in this paper is William E. Burrows, *Deep Black: Space Espionage and National Security* (New York: Random House, 1987).

experience, the overwhelming majority of those who keep the secrets do so on patriotic grounds, not primarily because they fear punishment for betraying their country. Whatever the motivation, however, such pervasive secrecy raises formidable obstacles for the would-be chronicler of the nation's space reconnaissance system. This paper seeks to explain why the system is secret, what goals were set for its study before research began, and how an adequate overview of the system was assembled through a variety of reportorial techniques.

There are at least five reasons for keeping the space reconnaissance program secret.

1. There is a need to maintain the essential integrity of the system. Space reconnaissance serves the dual purpose of providing hard intelligence data on much of the world while monitoring arms control compliance at the same time (and with the same equipment). If the first task is to uncover as many strategically important secrets as possible, and the second is to make cheating as difficult as possible, then providing the nation's adversaries with information about how the system works, and therefore with the wherewithal to fool it, is counterproductive and potentially dangerous.

2. It has been unvarying policy going back at least to the Kennedy presidency to avoid humiliating the Soviet Union either by publicizing hard strategic intelligence data or by unduly trumpeting the space reconnaissance program's considerable capability.[2] "Rubbing the Russians' noses in it" could provoke an attack on one or more U.S. assets, an act that would, in turn, send a spasmodic shudder through the whole technical collection system, very possibly leading to retaliation followed by escalation. It has therefore been concluded that the risks of blatant bragging in the form of revealing information about the satellites and what they collect far outweigh the benefits that might accrue from displaying the espionage establishment's crown jewels to the taxpayers.

3. Secrecy helps protect the space reconnaissance budget, the great preponderance of which goes to the National Reconnaissance Office for the satellites and all of the related equipment that keeps them healthy and productive. It is probably inevitable that such a system, which is on the very edge of technology and applied science, suffers some extremely costly mistakes. As a consequence, managers can hide mistakes made by over-optimistic engineers that result in severe cost overruns in otherwise innocuous Air Force and Navy budget categories. In addition, funding levels and allocation can provide

clues to what is being produced, both qualitatively and quantitatively, thereby further threatening the security of the system.

4. Deference to the sensibilities of underdeveloped (later less developed, and eventually Third World) nations was and remains another motivating factor, though not an extremely important one, where maintaining the secrecy of the system is concerned. Neither the Kennedy Administration nor its successors wanted to give the appearance of using the nation's highly advanced technology to scrutinize—spy on—countries that had recently emerged from colonialism with a dark appreciation of some of western industrialism's excesses. It was therefore no accident that in 1972, when military reconnaissance satellites in the Keyhole series had resolutions on the order of 3 inches, the first Landsat Earth resources satellite was restricted to a resolution of about 80 meters from a nominal altitude of 917 kilometers.[3]

Finally, and in my judgment most important, it has been felt over the years that opening the system—and especially making public some of the imagery collected in orbit—would restrict the President's political options by, in effect, allowing the media to look over his shoulder as he weighed the various choices for formulating foreign policy. The Central Intelligence Agency and other organizations in the business of collecting technical intelligence take it for granted that the sanctioned release of even one space reconnaissance photograph would open a floodgate of Freedom of Information Act requests for still more imagery. Staving off such requests would consume enormous resources, while having to succumb to them would seriously compromise space-based technical collection capability and so intrude on the deliberations of the National Security Council that the result would almost be paralytic. It is, therefore, a matter of longstanding doctrine that events photographed by satellite that are to be made public are rephotographed by U-2 or, when they were in service, SR-71 aircraft before they are released, however expensive, time-consuming, and hazardous such operations may be.[4] And although not strictly germane, it might be noted in this context that possession of the capability to define the President's options through the National Security Council—that is, to be able to set events in a particular perspective based on the kind of intelligence that is collected and the manner in which it is processed, analyzed, and distributed—has been a primary cause of the tribal warfare that has taken place over the years between the various organizations involved in technical collection, notably the Air Force and the CIA, with each trying to control the system because of the immense influence such control engenders.

The depth and breadth of the secrecy attending the space reconnaissance was a decisive factor in both defining the project's goals and establishing its research methodology. The goal was to provide the educated, general public and members of the nation's policy-making infrastructure, within the government and outside of it, with a political and technical understanding of the system and how it simultaneously collects militarily useful information while monitoring compliance with arms control agreements. (The issue of whether space-borne national technical means of verification are adequate has prompted a great deal of discussion, some of it thunderously polemical, but very little of it having the benefit of a factual frame of reference regarding what, exactly, the reconnaissance systems can and cannot accomplish. This has left the electorate to take the respective arguments merely as matters of faith, which is a politically dubious situation in a democracy, and one that seemed to require rectification.)

Since the operational heart of technical intelligence collection is technology in its many relevant forms, the barriers that have been put in place by the security apparatus become progressively more difficult to surmount as the researcher moves from the general to the specific; from broad categories of equipment to particular, highly specialized, forms of it. It is not difficult to establish that imaging satellites like the KH-11 and KH-12 use large reflecting telescopes, for example, but determining the size of the telescopes and the manner in which they produce real-time imagery are quite a bit more difficult because such details are more secure in that they are more easily compartmented. Yet, as we will see, there are ways to put much of the mosaic together.

The question of how much technology to put into a project like this resolved itself at a very early stage of planning because of three basic factors: first, because I wanted to reach a general audience, overemphasis on technology would have been counterproductive and undoubtedly would have had the effect of intimidating the very audience I wanted to reach. Conversely, deemphasizing technology for the sake of making the book utterly painless to read for even the least competent in the potential audience would have been equally counterproductive, since so much of the book's meaning would necessarily have been lost that I would have missed those on the other end of the scale (the ones I most wanted). There was never any question but that I would opt for quality over quantity. As a consequence, I set myself to provide as much technology as was required to make sense of the subject, and not a bit more, thereby striking a suitable balance. In addition, technical data was softened whenever possible by the use of analogy or metaphor. Thus, a 640,000 pixel charge-coupled device (CCD) was likened to a similar number of buckets collecting various amounts of rain in a field (Philip Morrison has called CCDs mechanical retinas, which is not only more accurate, but shorter as well).

Second, given the fact that the more detailed the technology, the more difficult it is to uncover, the going becomes so progressively tough as one moves deeper into the thicket of secrecy that at some point the costs begin to outweigh the benefits in terms of time and energy. This, too, necessarily defines the scope of the work by limiting detail that, while potentially interesting, is simply not worth pursuing.

Third, there are the national security considerations (as they are narrowly defined by the Department of Defense and the various intelligence organizations). The line that separates educating the citizenry of the United States from supplying the nation's enemies with useful information is often not clear in relatively accessible areas (at scholarly meetings concerned with computer technology or aeronautical engineering, for example), and the problem, of course, becomes infinitely more difficult when one is groping along inside the security thicket where, by definition, everything is classified. A paradox soon becomes apparent. Those who are cleared into one or more compartments, and who therefore probably understand how sensitive the various components of a given system are—that is, which information can really be helpful to the other side, and which is either already known or unimportant—are strictly prohibited from making their knowledge public. Those who are unencumbered by clearances, and who are therefore able to write freely about subjects such as space reconnaissance, are least qualified to make such judgments (again, according to the narrow definition).

No responsible writer wants to inflict damage on the very nation whose liberty has provided him with the license and the wherewithal to freely practice his craft in the first place. Some rules were therefore set in the beginning. One rule had it that only material directly related to the subject would be included, thereby eliminating a substan-

tial amount of classified information that fell through the cracks in
the course of chasing down the other stuff. Another prohibited the
use of material that could be life-threatening (as might be the case
where U-2, SR-71, and RC-135 aircrews are concerned). Finally, as
familiarity with the subject increases—as the researcher's expertise
grows—he begins to develop an instinctive understanding that alerts
him to the fact that he is occasionally edging into areas in which the
potential damage that could be done by exposure outweighs the need
to inform. It is a matter of public record, for example, that the Satellite Data System spacecraft relays imagery from the KH-11. But a
chance remark by a source indicated that the 595 is not the only satellite performing that function. An effort to pursue the matter, either
by questioning sources about that subject, or else by making my own
calculations and then exercising conjecture based on published orbital data, such as can be found in *The R.A.E. Table of Earth Satellites,* was not undertaken.[5] Had the information been incorrect, the
reader would have been poorly served. Had it been correct, it would
have been the nation that was poorly served. Either way, the risk
seemed to be unacceptable.

By far the greater problem, however, had to do with the extrica-
tion of information, purely historical as well as technological, which
properly belonged on the public record but which was officially inaccessible because of needless, and often confusing, security constraints.
While an Air Force general assigned to the North American Aerospace Defense Command in Colorado Springs was patently refusing
to so much as utter the name KH-11 (while in almost the same
breath, warning that the surrounding community was fairly teeming
with enemy agents intent on prying out all manner of secrets), Ad-
miral Stansfield Turner was preparing to publish a memoir that had
cleared rigorous CIA censorship and that mentioned the K-11 quite
explicitly.[6] As another example, James T. Killian's Technological Capabilities Panel produced a report for President Eisenhower in 1955
that laid the basis for the U-2 program and for the introduction of
satellite reconnaissance. Despite the fact that the Soviet Union obtained a U-2, together with its cameras and exposed film, in 1960,
and also despite there having been a spate of publicity about both
of our first generation reconnaissance satellites (the Air Force's
SAMOS and the CIA's Discoverer) as soon as they appeared during
the final years of the Eisenhower Administration, the TCP report remains substantially classified.

Even the success of efforts to set the historical record straight and sort out the major government organizations that have been responsible for reconnaissance activity in its many guises, some going back to 1960, depended heavily upon the particular source being interviewed. It became clear by the time research was complete that however rigid the security system, the degree to which it is able to constrain the flow of information rests squarely on whether the individuals who operate, or who have operated, within it believe it to be appropriate or excessive. In that regard, the politics of the security system closely reflects that of the reconnaissance system it was designed to protect. That is, insiders with a more liberal outlook tended to want to share some information that their more conservative colleagues were adamant in not sharing because it was classified.

Six basic kinds of sources were used. There was an official source, namely the United States Air Force.[7] I was given access to Beale Air Force Base in California, the home of the Strategic Air Command's 9th Strategic Reconnaissance Wing, which operated U-2R, SR-71A, and KC-135Q aircraft on worldwide strategic reconnaissance operations. I spent two days at Beale, during which time I flew in one of the tankers during a refueling exercise, photographed reconnaissance aircraft in the air and on the ground, and questioned aircrews at some length. It should be noted that the visit to Beale was on condition that I submitted general questions in writing in advance (a practice ordinarily opposed by reporters), and that a noncommissioned officer from the base's public affairs office was present at nearly all of the interviews, occasionally interceding to tell a pilot or a reconnaissance systems officer that a particular question touched on a sensitive area. The rule, which the pilots appeared to understand and mention themselves, was that information that had been "published" was all right to discuss, but that unpublished information could not be discussed. During one interview with a pilot, the squadron's commanding officer appeared and, visibly agitated, said that no one had ever asked the kinds of questions I was asking (which concerned the SR-71's performance envelope at altitude). I was permitted to examine an SR-71 on static display but was not allowed to get into one. Although I pointed out that SLAR and IR[8] were painted in red on the aircraft's chines, questions about its sensors were not answered.

I was also given access to NORAD's Space Defense Operations Center in Cheyenne Mountain, outside of Colorado Springs, where

Air Force officers gave me a standard briefing on the facility and answered questions, also without getting into specifics and, again, in the presence of a public affairs representative. The Space Defense Operations Center is a command post that is responsible for assessing threats to U.S. spacecraft and for providing warning in the event of an attack. As such, it very closely monitors all space activity, and particularly anything resembling a Soviet anti-satellite operation. As was the case at Beale, those who responded to my questions were careful to keep their answers within the bounds of previously released information. Opaque plastic covers had been placed over some objects in the room prior to my arrival, though a blue looseleaf entitled the Space Threat Environment Description, which I later learned from another source lists hundreds of possible attack scenarios against U.S. space assets that have been assessed through war gaming, had been left uncovered in an apparent error.

Brigadier General Paul D. Wagoner, who headed NORAD's combat operations, spent close to an hour discussing the overall subject of my project, again in the presence of a public affairs official. General Wagoner not only steadfastly refused to answer all questions about specific systems (one of them being the ubiquitous KH-11), but at the very mention of electro-optical, real-time sensors, grew quite alarmed. "You throw around terms that scare the shit out of me," General Wagoner said, adding, "I'm not trying to discourage you, but I'm telling you that what you're treading on is very, very dangerous to national security." The General went on to say with unbridled anger that the nation was in peril, that the Soviets could in no sense be trusted, and that arms control is futile and dangerous. At the close of the interview General Wagoner, clearly pleased that he had divulged no secrets, bragged to the public affairs officer that he led me "around the bush." To the contrary, though, General Wagoner provided one of the best interviews. I had decided at the outset of the project that partisan politics in its many ramifications was central to the story, so I sought to emphasize the "human angle" whenever it was appropriate.[9] Thus, in exploding as he did, General Wagoner betrayed his deep-felt feelings and articulated in a forceful way the vehemence attending national security considerations that is shared by many of his colleagues in the technical intelligence community, both civilian and military.

The open literature provided what was by far the most bountiful source of information. This included newspaper accounts of political

events, trade magazines, journals containing highly specialized articles (on U.S. satellite reconnaissance during the Falklands war, for
example, or one about the role of the Space Transportation System
as a support operation for reconnaissance satellites), and books. It is
important to note that the aforementioned *The R.A.E. Table of
Earth Satellites,* annually updated by the Royal Aircraft Establishment at Farnborough, England, lists all satellite launchings and includes invaluable data on the launch date and time, the shape,
weight, and size of the spacecraft, its booster, the date of orbital de-
termination, inclination, period, semimajor axis, perigee, apogee, ec-
centricity, and the argument of perigee. It doesn't take long for the
practiced eye to be able to tell that a Titan 3D carrying a maneuver-
able, 29,000-pound spacecraft to an orbit whose inclination is 96.46
degrees, and which has a perigee and apogee of 169 and 265 kilometers, is on a Keyhole mission. Similarly, an Atlas that disgorges four
very small satellites into an almost circular orbit just over 1,000 kilometers high and having an inclination on the order of 63 degrees
is pretty obviously engaged in ocean surveillance. But such work is
not without its dangers. If there was a single serious distraction that
went with researching the reconnaissance project, it had to do with
the unproductive hours I spent wandering across the pages of *The
R.A.E. Table of Earth Satellites,* trying to track more elusive game
that was as tantalizing as it was irrelevant to the task at hand; of
pondering the missions of some of the mysterious highly elliptical orbiters and those parked way out at geosynchronous.

Individuals who either were not in the security loop, or whose
clearances were unrelated to the level at which I worked, and who
were highly knowledgeable in the area of technical intelligence or the
militarization of space, constituted a third resource. These individuals, who spend their working lives engaged in researching the details
of which are beyond the capacity of the newcomer who is merely
passing through their well-mined terrain, are invaluable in at least
two regards: as sources of information about the systems themselves,
and as repositories of the names of other people who might be of
help. I should add that, with one exception, I did not use journalists
as sources, since I consider doing so professionally unsound. In the
first place, journalists are by definition secondary sources, and as
such have incomplete knowledge, their own distinct perceptions, and
occasionally faulty memories. Information from them, unless it is
confined to merely citing other sources, is automatically distorted,

perhaps drastically, and is therefore suspect. Second, studies like mine, no less than some kinds of news stories, are competitive endeavors. And as is the case with news stories, the journalist who provides information fully expects information in return, which can result in one's being "scooped."

Given the fact that there is a commonality of applied science and technology within both the classified and unclassified systems, in that scientists and engineers in both camps share a common educational experience, read and write for the same journals, attend many of the same meetings, and otherwise try to stay abreast of developments in their fields, it seemed appropriate to go to the scientists in the "white" programs in order to get at least some measure of what was happening in the black ones. These became a fourth resource, and an exceedingly valuable one.

Although they were obviously not able to tell me with certainty about what was taking place within the black systems, some extremely well educated guesses were made and several technological possibilities were narrowed. Asked whether it is likely that the KH-11's imaging system uses charge-coupled devices as the basis for its real-time operation, a CCD specialist at the Jet Propulsion Laboratory answered simply and directly: "They'd have to be crazy to use anything else." An astrophysicist at Berkeley who designs telescopes provided a fascinating, short tutorial on active optics—so-called rubber mirrors—and estimated the type of telescope that the KH-11 would have to carry in order to perform its mission optimally based on current advanced technology. Then, using his pocket calculator, he estimated the telescope's field of view and theoretical resolution, based on the KH-11's typical perigee, in about one minute. The telescope, which he figured as having a 2-meter aperture, has a theoretical resolution in the visible light spectrum of 2 inches. This could be checked out by referring to the SALT II agreement, which is verifiable by national technical means, and which prohibits altering the size of an existing missile by more than 5 percent. The smallest known Soviet ballistic missile (ICBM) at the time the treaty was signed was the 55-11, a pencil-shaped weapon that was 64 feet long and 6 feet in diameter. Five percent of 6 feet is 3.6 inches. The two numbers coincide so nicely (particularly since the arms controllers would have factored in a resolution somewhat short of the theoretical limit) that they make the calculation compelling.

Individuals who at one time played important roles in overhead reconnaissance constituted another key research element. In addition to General Keegan and Mr. Colby, they included Herbert Scoville Jr., Richard M. Bissell Jr., Amrom Katz, Merton E. Davies, McGeorge Bundy, Hans Mark, James R. Killian Jr., Edwin Land, George Kistiakowsky, E. Henry Knoche, and Clarence L. "Kelly" Johnson.

Although I sought to gain some technological details from some of the interviews I had with these men, my primary purpose was to fill in important historical gaps and acquire a feel for the politics of overhead reconnaissance, particularly as it existed between the Air Force and the CIA. When the subject of recording historical aspects of the program arose, each respondent agreed that such a task was eminently worthwhile, yet ranks were broken on whether it could be done, given security constraints. Hans Mark, who at one time was Under Secretary of the U.S. Air Force, which is responsible for the design, production, and operation of U.S. reconnaissance satellites, adamantly refused to discuss any element of the program. In response to a letter I wrote after a short interview, Mark replied: "I am aware of the fact that you possess classified information. In spite of my personal feelings, it is important for the integrity of the system that this information not be repeated publicly or revealed in more detail. The decisions of those who have the responsibility for classification must be respected. Doing otherwise would, I believe, give direct aid and comfort to our adversaries around the world. Accordingly, I hope very much that you will delay publication of your manuscript until such a time as a decision to declassify the information is reached by the appropriately constituted authorities."[10] Richard M. Bissell Jr., who headed the U-2 program until Francis Powers was shot down, and who was intimately involved in the development of the early CIA reconnaissance satellites, had no such problem. "I should say that, at this fairly late date, I have few inhibitions on security grounds," he wrote.[11] Neither did "Pete" Scoville or George Kistiakowsky who, with Bissell, provided extremely valuable historical material relevant to the early days of the program, especially regarding circumstances leading to the creation of the International Reconnaissance Office.

The rivalry between the Air Force and the CIA, which started at the dawn of the postwar overhead reconnaissance program and continued, unabated, throughout the 1970s and into this decade, had many causes. There was sharp disagreement over which organization was to procure and operate the spacecraft, which targets were to be

tasked and how frequently they were to be rephotographed (with the
Air Force giving priority to targeting for retaliatory strikes, especially
in the 1960s, while the Agency preferred to collect a wide array of
weapons data), and how distribution of the "product" was to be
handled: who was going to get to see what. At bottom, however, the
discord resulted from differing institutional philosophies on the nature of the threat. And those differences most obviously manifested
themselves in the interpretation of the intelligence, and particularly
imagery.

The saga of the TU-26, or Backfire, is a fine example of how
the interpretation of raw intelligence can be affected as it passes
through the political prism. Backfire, which went into service with
the U.S.S.R.'s Long Range Aviation section in the mid-1970s, is a
twin-engine, swinging, turbo-fan-powered bomber capable of carrying either free-fall bombs or cruise missiles. Prior to the negotiation
of the SALT II treaty, a disagreement developed between the Pentagon and the CIA over whether Backfire was a heavy bomber.
"Heavy" is shorthand for long-range, a subject that was of more
than esoteric interest, since Backfire would have to be classed as a
strategic weapon if its range was sufficient to get it to the United
States and then to a landing at a friendly base.

The Defense Intelligence Agency (DIA), representing the Pentagon and relying on Air Force interpreters, concluded after sifting the
evidence that Backfire was heavy. Langley decided after examining
the same evidence that it was not heavy at all, and that it could not
make a bombing attack on the continental United States except as a
suicide mission, since it did not have sufficient fuel, given its 12,000-
pound-plus bomb load, to make the round trip. The DIA countered
that Backfire would not necessarily have to return to Soviet bases,
but could instead continue on to Cuba. Further, air-to-air refueling
probes could extend Backfire's range. The CIA responded by pointing
out that the imagery showed that Backfire had no refueling probe.
That does not mean they can't be put on, answered the DIA. Even
if probes were added, the CIA countered, Long Range Aviation does
not have enough tanker aircraft to service all of those thirsty bomb-
ers. Apparently not wanting the matter to end there, the DIA made
the further observation that Backfire's range could be lengthened
without the use of tankers simply by flying it at high altitude, where
there is less of a fuel penalty, for most of the mission and then coming in low for the attack. One can almost imagine knuckles turning

white at Langley as a response was drafted pointing out that strategic bombing doctrine dating back to the early 1960s called for extended low-level attack precisely because aircraft trying to nurse fuel at high altitude were extremely vulnerable to radar tracking and attack by fighter-interceptors. The CIA's analysis prevailed and Backfire was not counted as a strategic bomber in the SALT II negotiations, though it was not until 1985 that the DIA finally assessed downward the plane's range. But there is a postscript—a parting shot, perhaps, taken by the Department of Defense. According to *Soviet Military Power* (1987), the latest edition of the Pentagon's annually revised compendium of the Kremlin's weaponry, Backfire remains a potential strategic threat because it "can be equipped with a probe to permit in-flight refueling so that it can be used against the continental U.S. if sufficient tankers are available."[12] If any words can be said to capture the spirit of interorganizational disputes over the interpretation of technical intelligence, it is these: "can be" and "if."

The interviews with those who had been in the space reconnaissance program, some even before its actual inception, helped to clarify the meaning of disagreements, such as the one involving Backfire, and to place the overall political dimension of the program, much of it never before made public, in perspective. I should add parenthetically that I was acutely aware of the fact that some of those I interviewed were present at the creation by virtue of their considerable ages and that what I was getting from them was not only profoundly important where this relatively unknown aspect of American history is concerned, but that it would sooner or later become irreplaceable. That was a particularly sobering thought.

Finally, there was a handful of individuals, one or two of whom were or had been quite high in the intelligence loop, who provided me with information on condition that their anonymity be respected. I approached these subjects by asserting that it was time for a reasonably comprehensive study of strategic reconnaissance, and particularly the overhead variety, to be made available to the public. I added that the credibility of such a study would necessarily depend on accurate, previously unpublished political details and sufficient technological material to lend credence to the subject matter. This resulted in a series of sessions that were for the most part backgrounders emphasizing the political elements of the space reconnaissance program, supported by recollections of special historical interest. I was told by way of a very short anecdote, for example, that the first real-time imagery came down on the day Jimmy Carter was inaugurated as President and that it was delivered to the White House by E. Henry Knoche, the CIA's acting director. Period. A telephone call to Mr. Knoche, who had by then left the Agency, substantiated the event and the ensuing conversation provided an important, as yet unrecorded, anecdote that serves as the opening to one of the chapters in the study and that has no conceivable security implication.

I was able to use these sources to check the accuracy of material about U.S. reconnaissance satellites that had been in print for years, after persuading them that a reliable study was in the best interest of the people of the United States. Through one of these sources, I was able to authenticate the report in *Aviation Week and Space Technology* that the Titan 34D that exploded right after liftoff at Vandenberg Air Force Base on April 18, 1986 carried a KH-9 (referred to in the article as Big Bird).[13] Indeed, it was the last of the KH-9s, according to my source.

Although I made no effort to learn why these sources saw fit to try to help me, it became clear that they considered themselves patriotic citizens who thought that bringing a project such as mine to fruition was a public service: that within the limits of their more liberal interpretation of national security doctrine, the public's need to know about space reconnaissance and surveillance, particularly where arms control verification is concerned, is overridingly important. Yet in a number of instances, direct questions about specific technologies went unanswered, thereby setting the boundaries of the discussions and reminding me that everyone in the "loop," whatever his political persuasion, had clearly delineated secrets to keep. At one point early in the relationship with one source, he told me that he would explain a particular system only on condition that the information not be printed. This I declined to do since permanently withholding important information moots the reportorial process. Further, had I agreed to such a caveat and then forgotten my promise, I would have simultaneously risked inflicting damage on my country while betraying a valuable and trusting source. I also believe, though I cannot prove it, that my declining to accept material I could not use convinced him that my interest in the subject went beyond what General Keegan has called its "sensational" aspect.

This project was especially interesting to research because it combined investigative reporting with what I hope was some serious scholarship. Ironically, putting together such a mosaic of information mimics the professional intelligence-gathering process itself. That point was made in *The Los Angeles Times's* review: "The book reflects the author's extensive research and an ability to fit together a complex jigsaw puzzle despite many missing pieces that would make him a valued analyst in the CIA." Indeed, to the extent that my research method paralleled the sort done at Langley — that I was practicing what I was investigating — it in itself contributed to my understanding the nature of the subject in a far more intimate way than would have been possible in most other areas.

## NOTES

1. Reconnaissance and surveillance are not synonymous. Where imaging is concerned, the former has to do with the active acquisition of specifically targeted information, while the latter refers to the more passive observation of a place in order to record change. Unless specifically noted, I have used the term reconnaissance to cover both meanings for simplicity's sake.

2. While tactical reconnaissance photos of Soviet ballistic missiles — enroute to Cuba, on Cuban soil, and being withdrawn — were given considerable public exposure for political reasons in October 1962, for example, strategic reconnaissance imagery obtained over the U.S.S.R. by U-2s and Discoverer satellites was withheld from the public.

3. Nicholas M. Short et al., *Mission to Earth: Landsat Views the World* (Washington, D.C.: NASA, 1976), 437 and 439.

4. This was certainly the case when photographs depicting the growing Cuban military presence in Nicaragua were made public at a press briefing at the Department of State on March 9, 1982.

5. D. G. King-Hele et al., *The R.A.E. Table of Earth Satellites* (New York: Facts on File Inc., annually updated).

6. Adm. Stansfield Turner, *Secrecy and Democracy: The CIA in Transition* (Boston: Houghton Mifflin Company, 1985), 65–66.

7. An inquiry to the CIA regarding assistance brought this response from then-Director William J. Casey in a letter dated May 29, 1984: "Unfortunately, for it is an interesting subject, the Agency will not be able to assist you with your project. The offices for the collection of specialized national foreign intelligence belong to the Department of Defense and are classified. I regret I cannot be of assistance in this matter."

8. Side-Looking Airborne Radar and infrared.

9. This is why the book opens with General George J. Keegan, a former head of Air Force intelligence and William E. Colby, a one-time director of the CIA, at odds over what they believe spaceborne intelligence has indicated regarding Soviet strategy. (General Keegan, like General Wagoner, became quite angry during the interview.) Both had access to the same intelligence, yet each placed a differ-

ent interpretation on what he saw based on differing predilections.

10. Letter from Hans Mark to the author, dated May 7, 1985.

11. Letter from Richard Bissell dated March 20, 1984.

12. U.S. Department of Defense, *Soviet Military Power* (Washington, D.C.: Government Printing Office, 1987), 37.

13. "Titan Explosion Cripples U.S. Launch, Surveillance Capability," *Aviation Week and Space Technology* (April 28, 1986): 16–19.

*Jeffrey T. Richelson*

# Commentary

There are three issues I want to comment on regarding both papers. One issue is the military versus civilian angle. Particularly when re- searching or writing about something like Landsat, it seems that the military angle will at some point intrude. Second is the question of users and research and development, and how a difference between the civilian side and the military side exists; and third, the question of secrecy, and the reasons William Burrows gave for why the pro- gram is, or has been, kept secret to such an extent.

I think we can agree that one can write about Earth resources systems without necessarily discussing military capabilities. Military reconnaissance satellite capabilities are substantially better than civil- ian capabilities, at least with respect to black-and-white imagery. There is a significant difference, by several orders of magnitude, be- tween a KH-8, KH-9, or KH-11 photograph and a photograph taken by a civilian system. There are some points, however, at which there is always a military angle. For example, Japan, it turns out, has been using Landsat photography for military intelligence purposes to monitor Soviet Siberia. When the Chinese first requested Landsat pic- tures, the intelligence community convened a variety of panels to study whether the Chinese would, in fact, be getting military intelli- gence out of this information, and they concluded that yes, in fact, there would be a military intelligence payoff to the Chinese.

The second aspect is that one can often infer from the civilian technology the military technology. One rather striking case of this occurred during the trial of Samuel Morrison, a naval intelligence analyst who was put on trial for having passed to *Janes' Defense Weekly* satellite photographs taken of a Soviet aircraft carrier. And, during that trial, John Pike of the Federation of American Scientists started describing how he believed the KH-11 photographic system worked. He said it had a mirror that you flipped back and forth, from side to side, which gave you an extremely wide range of coverage. You could then change the focus of your target from the satellite immediately. While John was going through this discussion, based purely on his reading of the civilian technology, the people behind the prosecution table from the Committee on Imagery Requirements and Exploitation (the intelligence community's committee to decide what satellites photograph and how the exploitation task is divided) suddenly went into something near a panic—getting up from their table, leaving notes near the prosecutor, and talking to the prosecutor. It was quite apparent that John, based simply on reading what the civilian technology was with regard to Landsat, had been able to infer correctly the classified technology. So, in some areas, there is an inevitable military component, relevant to the military perspective.

With regard to the question of users and research and development, there appears to be a sharp contrast among NASA, the Departments of the Interior and Agriculture problem, and the intelligence community situation. In the civilian case, as Pamela Mack explained, a sharp differentiation exists between research and development agencies and user agencies. In the intelligence community, the agencies that develop the satellites are also often the agencies that use the satellites. The CIA has an office in its directorate of science and technology that is responsible for developing what they call advanced collection systems, including reconnaissance satellites. At the same time, the CIA uses that data. And the development people in CIA have produced some of the most significant advances in U.S. reconnaissance capabilities, primarily through contract to industry.

The CIA has an Office of Development and Engineering that works with people at TRW, Lockheed, and elsewhere. And they have been in the forefront of developing advanced capabilities—the KH-11, which was a new step forward in photography, and Rhyolite, which was a new step forward in signals intelligence satellites. Thus, the conflict in the intelligence community arises not from having one agency that does research and development and others that are users, but when three or more agencies (which are both developers and users) develop a system, they are developing it not only for themselves but for the entire intelligence community.

There is a also presumably going to be even greater conflict in the future. Now there are users who are interested in the information produced by these satellites for strategic intelligence purposes and there are those who are interested in it for tactical intelligence purposes. The reason I say the conflict may become even greater among these users is that as systems have developed, like the KH-11, which rather than providing a photograph two weeks or two months after it was taken, can provide the photograph within the space of an hour, or a geosynchronous signal satellite, which instead of taking hours or days to provide information, can beam it down to Europe in a matter of minutes, the information becomes of much more value to tactical military commanders than information arriving weeks later. The military can see a greater use for those satellites than they saw before, and this will create an additional demand. Thus, as we develop these more advanced capabilities, there may be even greater lobbying among the military services and tactical commanders to use that information. Concomitantly, this is a very scarce resource that costs billions of dollars to develop, and clearly a need exists to use that information for strategic long-range intelligence purposes. In the future there will be very bloody battles over this point.

Also relevant is that the intelligence community has developed a bureaucracy to try to deal with these problems. Committees have been organized to look at the requests of all the user agencies — what type of information they want, how often they want coverage — and to establish priorities. From that point, they make a collective decision for the entire intelligence community about what those satellites will photograph, what communications will be intercepted, how often, and so forth. And likewise, another committee in the intelligence community looks at the question of what type of satellites should be built. On this committee the Director of Central Intelligence, a representative of the Defense Department, and other individuals sit, and they again make collective decisions for the entire intelligence community about what type of satellite should be built, and what type of capabilities those satellites should have, and then assign those tasks to specific agencies. One possible reason that bureaucracy has sprung up is because you have the notion of the intelligence community, and what these satellites are producing, whether it's through photographs or signals intercepts, is intelligence, a product required by all elements of the community. On the other hand, officials in Agriculture, the Interior, and other departments may not view the information produced for other departments as meaningful for them.

Another issue I want to discuss is some of the reasons that Burrows gave for secrecy in the space program, often given by various officials. I'd like to add one additional item to the list. In terms of security — protecting the system, making sure it functions — a certain legitimacy to that claim exists. There's also a lot of exaggeration. The Soviets, to a great extent, know our capabilities. They can deduce that a system flying at a 96 degree inclination, 150 miles over the Soviet Union, is not there to pick up Moscow television. It's there to take photographs. Therefore, there is no need to protect that information from anyone because its quite apparent to the Soviets or any other country what that satellite is doing. There may be information about its advanced capabilities that might legitimately be kept secret, but every single fact about it need not be kept secret to protect the system.

One should also keep in mind that the secrecy extends not only over presently operating advanced systems, or even recently retired systems. It's a secrecy that extends to the very beginning of the program, to systems that are no more capable than the SPOT satellite is now. What is being protected is not the system or its capabilities; it is the very concept that reconnaissance itself should not be a subject for public discussion or written about, as Dr. Mark expressed in his letter to Bill Burrows. The Russians and their sensibilities are no longer an issue. The Soviets acknowledge the legitimacy of space reconnaissance when discussing arms control. Once they developed their own systems, they dropped their campaigns against U.S. space reconnaissance, and stopped threatening to shoot reconnaissance vehicles down. It may be a different case if we talk about publishing some of the pictures of their installations, but certainly the fact that the program exists is no longer anything that the Soviets complain about.

With regard to Third World countries, it's clearly becoming apparent that the United States, the Soviet Union, and China are not going to be the only participants in space reconnaissance, particularly photographic reconnaissance. As Burrows mentioned, France has the SPOT satellite. France is also in the process of developing its own military reconnaissance satellite with Italy and Spain; the Germans are talking about their own radar imaging satellite; the Japanese have thought about a reconnaissance satellite. Thus, at some point, with regard at least to all the major- and middle-ranking powers, everyone is going to be overflying everyone else. And at that point, the sensibilities of Third World countries won't even remotely be an issue.

The reason I would add what is called "the line" is that it is an issue that comes up in discussing the question of classification with a variety of officials. The general argument goes that while even the most diehard people in the National Reconnaissance Office realize that there are many details about reconnaissance activities, particularly past reconnaissance activities, that would be quite harmless to make public, they don't want to have to draw a line. What they want to do is cover the entire program with a security blanket, which does a variety of things. One, it makes it harder for anyone interested in penetrating that system, say from a research point of view, from getting to what they consider important information. By making it difficult to get even trivia, it makes it much harder to obtain the information that officials consider important to protect.

I think a second reason for the security blanket is arrogance, to a certain extent. The feeling is "it's our system, it's our information, and you are civilians; you have no business asking us about this. This is a military prerogative, it's a national security prerogative, and therefore, you should go write about something else and not deal with this type of topic." One way to view this attitude is that officials don't know where to draw the line and therefore they are being cautious. Another less flattering way to state it is that they suffer from intellectual laziness. Officials don't want to have to think about the question of what really is security information and what is information that could reasonably be made public, such as the details of systems that have not been operating for the last twenty to twenty-five years. I think this is one of the major reasons for the present degree of secrecy — it is much easier for people on the inside to say, "look, we'll just keep everything secret and not worry about it."